CASK

The Real Story of Britain's Unique Beer Culture

DES DE MOOR

CAMRA
BOOKS

Published by the Campaign for Real Ale Ltd
230 Hatfield Road, St Albans, Hertfordshire AL1 4LW
www.camra.org.uk/books

ISBN 978-1-85249-384-4

A CIP catalogue record for this book is available from the British Library

Printed and bound in the United Kingdom by Short Run Press, Exeter.

Managing Editor: Alan Murphy
Design / Typography: Dale Tomlinson
Sales & Marketing: Toby Langdon
Cover: David Wardle

MIX
Paper from
responsible sources
FSC® C014540
www.fsc.org

Most of the images used in this book were supplied by the author. The Publisher would like to thank those breweries and other establishments who kindly granted permission for their photography to be used. Specific thanks to: Boak & Bailey (p247); Brewery History Society (p173,181,185,186,189,190, 192,197,204,215,236,238,256,267); Bryan Betts (p62); Cask Marque (p75,87,280); Matthew Curtis (p84,88,153,155), Glasgow University Archive (p223,225); Jason Harvey/Ape Creative (p286); The Malt Miller (p101); John Martin at Scottish Brewing Archive Association (p227); Randy Mosher (117); Fran Nowak (p163,166); Nicci Peet at DEYA Brewing Company (p295); SPBW (p148); Track Brewing Co (p271,288).

Contents

Alles draait rond de gisting.

Bumper sticker promoting the Brewing Science Institute (BSI),
Woodland Park, Colorado c.2009.

Introduction

Cask beer is a unique format of live draught beer that, at its best and freshest, delivers a subtlety and complexity of flavour, and an appealingly drinkable texture, unmatched by any other, particularly when applied to well-balanced but straightforward beers of modest strength.

Rarely found in the beer world at large, it has a significant commercial presence only in Britain, where it famously survived efforts by big brewery groups to phase it out in the 1960s and 1970s, provoking a vociferous consumer campaign. Though in its home country it's once again struggling to retain its profile amid a new wave of characterful, quality craft beers in keg, bottle and can, many brewers and drinkers rightly remain fascinated with cask.

But despite all the attention from beer enthusiasts over many decades, cask remains much misunderstood: revered as a supposed inheritor of ancient brewing traditions or lazily dismissed as a warm, flat beverage for old men. While numerous publications recommend great cask beer and places to buy it, and most books on British beer feel obliged to include a brief outline of cask dispense, there is little about how cask evolved, how it is made today, and what makes it so different and special. This book aims to fill that gap, adding to the knowledge of enthusiasts and introducing cask to a new generation, not as the only beer worth drinking but rather as one of the brightest highlights of today's dazzling array of beer styles.

I've drawn on decades of thinking, talking and writing about cask as well as drinking it. I began work on an early version of the text in 2015, but it is largely the fruit of an intense period of research and writing between April 2022 and April 2023. I've visited a range of breweries across Britain, large and small, some ultra-modern with gleaming stainless-steel vessels under precise computer control, others time capsules of an earlier brewing age, with mellowed wood and copper, and relying on machinery installed a century or more ago.

I also visited pub cellars, yeast labs and hop farms; had many conversations, face to face, online and by email, with brewers, licensees, cellar managers, campaigners, marketers, educators and brewing scientists; and spent much time digging into everything from historic brewing texts to the most recent scientific papers and market research reports. The results are by no means the last word on the subject, and I could easily have taken another year or more researching the history alone, but I'm confident the final text addresses at least some of the gaps in our knowledge.

To keep the conversation going, you'll find contact details below.

DES DE MOOR, *London SE14; April 2023*

DRINK CASK BEER

It'll change your life

How this book works

This book is intended to be read in order, with later sections relying on earlier explanations. For example, it is much easier to talk about brewing history once you have explained ingredients and processes, so the history chapters appear later in the text.

I have only used references in the text when relying on a single specific source, avoiding footnotes and endnotes as I suspect many readers, like me, find them irritating. Instead, I have used a simplified version of the 'Harvard' system. For example, 'Bennett (1996:86)' points towards the Bibliography, where you'll find the full reference to 'Bennett, Judith M 1996, *Ale, Beer, and Brewsters in England*', and can track down the reference to page 86 in that book if you wish. Any quotations attributed only by name are from interviews and conversations with people listed under Author's acknowledgements at the back. Everything else should be self-explanatory.

Quantities are given in metric and/or imperial measurements depending on the context. One hectolitre (hl), or 100 litres, is roughly equivalent to 22 gallons or 176 pints (imperial). Many British brewers still measure brew runs in terms of the old brewer's barrel, which holds 36 gallons, 1.64 hl, 164 litres, or 288 pints. An imperial pint (568 ml) is roughly 20% larger than a US pint (473 ml), and a US brewer's barrel holds only 31 US gallons, 1.17 hl, 117 litres, 24.8 imperial gallons, or 198.5 imperial pints. In reverse, a hectolitre is equivalent to around 0.85 US barrels.

Alcoholic strength is quoted throughout in terms of the percentage of alcohol by volume (% ABV).

Sums of money quoted from prior to 1971 use the pre-decimal currency system, with a decimal conversion. One pound (£) used to be divided into 20 shillings (s or /-), each of which was further divided into 12 pennies or pence (d). A guinea was £1 1s (£1.05).

Scientific names are sometimes used to refer to types of yeast or bacteria. These consist of a genus followed by the species. For example, ale yeast is *Saccharomyces cerevisiae*: genus *Saccharomyces* and species *cerevisiae*.

Comments, corrections and suggestions are gratefully received. You can email me at des@desdemoor.com. The home page for the book, with some additional information, is at desdemoor.co.uk/cask. Exclusive supplementary material is available to my Patreon supporters: see patreon.com/ldnbestbeer.

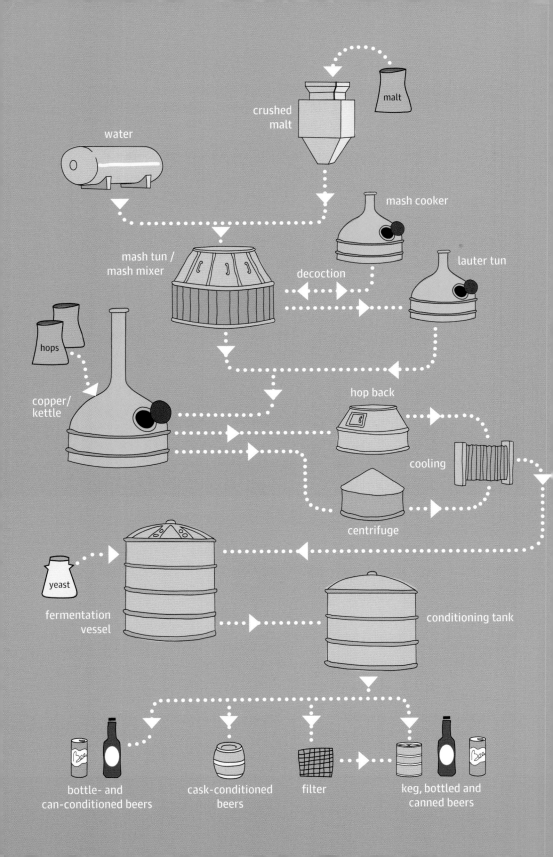

malt

water

crushed malt

mash cooker

mash tun / mash mixer

decoction

lauter tun

hops

copper/ kettle

hop back

cooling

centrifuge

yeast

fermentation vessel

conditioning tank

bottle- and can-conditioned beers

cask-conditioned beers

filter

keg, bottled and canned beers

1 Making Cask

What is beer?

The broadest definition of beer is that it's a fermented, but not distilled, drink prepared primarily using sugars derived from cereals. Fermentation is a natural process involving a microorganism called yeast, which in the right conditions breaks down sugars dissolved in liquids into alcohol and carbon dioxide. The meaning of 'beer' has shifted over the centuries, but today the term is most commonly and usefully employed to designate a family of beverages with a wide range of styles and flavours, encompassing every shade of ale, including pales, browns, porters and stouts, as well as lagers and wild fermentation beers like Belgian lambic.

The source of the dissolved sugars is one of the key factors distinguishing alcoholic drinks. Fruits like grapes, apples and pears contain copious amounts of sugary liquid, as well as wild yeast cells that gather on the skin waiting for a free feed when the fruit starts to rot. So you can make wine, cider or perry by cutting out the wait, crushing the ripe fruit and leaving the yeast to get on with it. This is the way these drinks were made for millennia, and although most commercial examples are now fermented by yeasts cultivated in laboratories in the interests of efficiency, consistency and smoothness of flavour, specialist producers across the world still go about things the old-fashioned way.

In starting with grains rather than fruit, brewers set themselves a harder task. Grains when harvested are dry, hard, and primarily comprised of starch. To obtain a fermentable liquid equivalent to the stuff the wine- or cidermaker extracts through the simple application of pressure, the starch must be converted to dissolved sugar through a succession of additional processes. This is one of the reasons, incidentally, why brewing evolved into one of the earliest large-scale industries while wine- and cidermaking remained essentially agricultural activities.

For reasons explained below, fermentation alone yields only a limited concentration of alcohol, usually no more than 15% alcohol by volume (ABV), often less. 'Spirits' are obtained by applying the further process of distillation, which takes advantage of alcohol evaporating at a cooler temperature than water to separate the two and dispose of as much of the latter as possible, resulting in a liquid much stronger in alcohol. Simply put, whisk(e)y is distilled beer, as is some (in the past, most if not all) gin and vodka, while brandy and Calvados are distilled wine and cider respectively. On this axis, beer belongs with wine and cider as a non-distilled fermented drink.

This broad definition of beer encompasses products that stand outside the European tradition of brewing. Sake (*nihonshu*) and similar drinks from eastern Asia, though often labelled rice 'wines', are technically beers as grains fuel the fermentation. But sake brewers use cultivated moulds to achieve similar outcomes to conventional brewing processes. Famously, the most traditional recipes for chicha, indigenous to the Andes and Amazon basin, involve converting maize starch to sugar by chewing the grains and spitting them out. As neither of these drinks has a significant bearing on our main subject of cask beer, we won't explore them further here.

Our definition inevitably has its grey areas, such as the old-established use of fruit in brewing. Today's fruit beers include many made with flavourings and extracts, but if you add real fruit, its sugars will ferment. In most cases, the fruit contributes only a minority of the final alcohol content so we can still safely regard such drinks as beer. We may reach a similar conclusion on the use of refined sugars and honey to supplement, but not replace, the grains, another practice with a lengthy history.

Beer is also often described in terms of four key ingredients: grains, water, hops and yeast. Two of these aren't exactly defining: water is a key component of all drinks, and yeast is essential to the production of all alcoholic ones. Hops are indeed present in nearly all contemporary beers but are a relative newcomer in terms of the millennia-old history of brewing, and beers can be and are still made without them. That leaves grains which, as we've already seen, are what makes a drink a beer. Today, they're mostly in the form of malted barley – barley grains which have been partially germinated.

Once you've been on a few brewery tours, you'll recognise that one of the remarkable things about the process is its consistency across breweries of all shapes and sizes. From the newbie homebrewer making 10 litres on the kitchen cooker, through the craft brewer dispatching pallet-loads from a railway arch, to the multinational with a global output of thousands of millions of litres a week, pretty much all modern brewing follows the same basic procedures: the major differences are in scale and the extent of automation.

Perhaps even more remarkably, this same process is responsible for everything from the blandest of industrial lagers to the most complex of imperial stouts. And this takes us back to the four ingredients. A skilful wine- or cidermaker can achieve astonishing complexity of flavour, but only has grapes or apples and, possibly, yeast to play with. Using four ingredients, three of them available off the shelf in a dazzling range of varieties, the potential flavours expand exponentially, as each makes a specific and infinitely variable contribution.

This holds for cask beer as it does for other formats: cask brewers often make beer in kegs, bottles and cans too, and though they may tweak the recipes, they go through the same basic steps for each. They can select from the same extensive repertoire of colour, flavour, character and strength. Only in the final stages, after the main fermentation, do the various formats start to diverge, and cask goes down its own route of continuing fermentation and conditioning.

The hot side: mashing and boiling

Grain, malt and sugar

Technically, a cereal grain is a type of fruit produced by various domesticated species of grass, though with a much thinner and dryer outer layer than more familiar fruits. The seed inside is hard and dry, mainly comprised of starch, consisting of sugar molecules arranged in long chains. As the seed germinates, it softens by absorbing water and soil nutrients and begins releasing enzymes, compounds which help break down complex molecules into simpler ones. There are various types of enzymes but the one with greatest interest to the brewer is diastase, which helps break down the starch into sugar, a process known as saccharification. In nature, the young plant uses the sugar to power

Barley harvest

the early stages of growth, until it has sufficient leaves to obtain energy from the sun through photosynthesis.

Malt is produced by allowing the natural germination process to develop the enzymes and soften the grain then halt it in the very early stages of growth.

Barley (*Hordeum vulgare*) is the brewer's grain of choice for several reasons. It's tolerant of a range of climates and conditions and grows so fast that it can be harvested twice a year. In common varieties, the husk, the fibrous protective outer layer of the grain, is so firmly attached that, unlike with wheat for example, it's not removed when the ear is threshed to separate the grains during harvesting. This husk survives through to the brewhouse where it forms a natural filter bed and helps ensure the grains don't become too sticky. The grain is easy to malt, germinating at relatively low temperatures, and rich in enzymes, remarkably efficient at converting starches into sugars. There are numerous barley varieties, and the choice of variety can make a surprising difference to the finished beer, though much of the flavour is developed through the malting process.

Brewers once did their own malting, and a few still do, but this is now the exception rather than the rule in the UK and most other brewing countries where brewers normally buy their grain ready-malted at a specialist facility. Grains are first steeped in tepid water (12–15°C) with plenty of oxygen for around 48 hours, encouraging them to germinate. They're then drained and kept moist and well-ventilated for between four days and a week, as each grain absorbs water and softens, develops enzymes which begin breaking down starches, and grows its first shoots. Germination is then halted by heating the grains, first using a

Floor maltings at Crisp Malt

relatively gentle heat to dry them out and destroy the shoots, then turning up the temperature in a final stage known as curing, which helps develop the flavour and drives off compounds unwelcome in the finished product.

Variations in curing yield different types of malt which contribute varying colours and flavours. Higher temperatures and longer curing times result in a spectrum of colours from gold to amber to brown to black, with a corresponding increase in intensity of flavours from biscuit to bitter roast, like a slice of white toast under a grill. But heat also destroys enzymes, reducing the malt's diastatic power, its ability to convert starches to sugars in the brewery. The backbone of most modern beer is pale malt, or the even paler lager or pilsner malt: these have been dried and cured gently to yield a pale colour and the maximum diastatic power. They're also know as 'base malts' as they're the basis of most beer recipes and can be used on their own. More vigorously heated speciality malts are used alongside pale malts to create darker styles: though these have little or no diastatic power of their own, the enzymes in the pale malt make up for their deficiencies. They include amber, brown, chocolate and black malts, which are roasted to increasing degrees of intensity, and crystal and caramalts, which are partially cooked to caramelise their sugars. Unmalted grains can also be included in the recipe, so long as they're used alongside sufficient pale malt.

Barley malt is now so widely used in brewing that you'll sometimes see it named as a defining ingredient of beer, and the term malt on its own usually means malted barley. But other grains can be used in both malted and unmalted form, each adding its own character, though these days almost invariably alongside rather than instead of malted barley. Wheat (*Triticum aestivum*) is the next most popular brewing grain, though wheat beers are typically 40–60% wheat and almost never 100%. Today, many non-wheat beers contain a dash of wheat as it encourages head formation. Oats (*Avena sativa*) are increasingly popular as they can lend a silky mouthfeel. Rye (*Secale cereale*) adds its distinctive flavour to certain speciality styles. Rice (*Oryza sativa*) and maize (*Zea mays*) are best known as unmalted additions to light lagers, adding additional fermentable material while maintaining a light body and flavour.

The dry grains, or grist as brewers call them, are crushed in a mill to expose their starches ready for brewing, not to a fine flour but to a mix of granules of various sizes. Bigger breweries and some smaller ones have their own mills, but many buy ready-milled grain from the maltster.

Small additions of various kinds of refined sugar serve similar purposes as rice and maize: though sugar is regarded as anathema in some brewing traditions, it's by no means unknown in British breweries. Honey is essentially a form of refined sugar and can be used to supplement grains in beer, though drinks which derive most of their sugar from honey are known as mead and form a third category alongside beer and wine/cider/perry. Added sugars don't make a beer sweeter as they're nearly all consumed during fermentation, though dark sugars and honey will likely add other flavour characteristics. The exception is lactose, an unfermentable sugar derived from milk that, if used, survives into the finished beer, adding sweet and creamy notes: it's traditionally associated with milk stouts but increasingly finds its way into other styles too.

Sources of fermentable sugar other than malted grains, whether unmalted grains or refined sugars, are termed adjuncts by brewers.

Water

Fruit, as used by wine- and cidermakers, already contains water, but brewers must add their own. Water in nature is never entirely pure: a wide variety of other compounds like mineral salts are dissolved in it, varying according to the source and the local geology. Its precise composition affects the chemical changes that take place during brewing and fermentation and helps determine the characteristics of the finished beer.

Brewing requires a lot of water, and historically brewers had their own water sources like springs and wells, influencing the style of beers they brewed: for example, chalky London water proved an excellent match for the roasted malts of porters and stouts while the more sulphurous Burton water was better suited to hoppy pale ale. Today, most brewers take water from the public supply and

Harvey's brewery

treat it with small additions of salts and other ingredients to suit the beer style they're brewing, sometimes filtering and purifying it first so they can build its profile from scratch. But some brewers, including many traditional cask producers, retain their own supplies, regarding them as an important contributor to their beer's distinctive character.

Somewhat confusingly, the traditional term for water as a brewing ingredient is liquor. After treatment, cold water is stored in the cold liquor tank (CLT), which will either be kept in a cool environment or have an integral cooling system if needed. Water is heated, ready for brewing in the hot liquor tank (HLT). Brewers refer to the water used for many other important ancillary purposes, like cleaning, cooling or steam heating, simply as 'water'.

Mashing and lautering

Water and grist finally come together in the process known as mashing, which takes place in a tank called a mash tun. Mashing procedures vary, but nearly all the beers discussed in this book are made using the one traditionally favoured by English brewers, the single infusion mash. Water is heated to around 75–80°C in the hot liquor tank, but by the time it's mixed with the grains in the mash tun, the temperature drops to around 65–68°C, at which point it's held for around an hour or perhaps a little more. Heat activates the enzymes that convert the starches to sugars, resulting in a liquid known as wort, which is then run off from the grist, a process known as lautering. As the wort drains, the mash is sparged by spraying more hot water onto it, helping rinse out the sugars. The spent grains left behind are sold off as cattle feed or biofuel: they can also be used as a baking ingredient.

Copper mash tun at Greene King

Sparging

Hops and flavourings

Hops have become the most recognised ingredient in beer, rather ironically as they're the only non-essential one of the four. As we'll see later, unhopped beers have been familiar throughout most of brewing history, though today they're rare indeed, and the characteristic flavours and aromas of hops are a component of all the most familiar modern styles.

Hops are the fruiting part of the hop bine *Humulus lupulus*, a species of perennial herbaceous climbing plant in the hemp family (*Cannabacae*), which also includes the cannabis plant. As with cannabis, hops are dioecious, with male and female reproductive parts usually developing on separate plants, and the female plant produces the active ingredients. These are found in hop cones, technically known as strobiles, largely in a sticky resin known as lupulin secreted where the individual petal-like leaves of the cone join the central stalk. Besides their bitter flavour and distinctive resinous aroma, hops possess anti-bacterial and stabilising properties that make brewing easier to manage and extend the shelf life of the results.

Freshly harvested hop cones, known as green or wet hops, are sometimes used for seasonal specialities, but hops are mostly used in dried form, either as whole leaf hops which are simply dried cones pressed into bales, or longer-lasting and more compact pellets which are pulverised cones pressed through a die, sometimes combined with freezing techniques to concentrate the active ingredients. Some brewers also used processed hop extracts.

At least 300 hop varieties are commercially available today, with new ones appearing all the time. Traditional European varieties like the English stalwarts Fuggle and Golding, and German and Czech so-called 'noble' hops like Hallertauer Mittelfrüh and Žatec (Saaz), tend to have a rounded and restrained aroma and character, perhaps subtly floral or grassy with an earthy bitterness. 'New world' hops from the USA, and to some extent Australia and New Zealand, tend to be more vivid and expressive, with powerful citrus, pine and tropical fruit notes and assertive peppery bitterness. They've proved popular in more contemporary styles, and several of them are now grown in Europe, though don't develop quite the same intensity here. Meanwhile, European growers have been busy developing new varieties, or reviving old ones, that suit local growing conditions while providing a similar character to new world imports.

Before hops became ubiquitous, other flavouring and preservative ingredients often found their way into beer. Such options remain open to today's brewers, though almost always alongside rather than instead of hops. Coriander and dried orange peel are perhaps the most familiar through their continuing use in certain

Sacks of coriander and dried orange peel

traditional European wheat beer styles, though a wide range of other spices find their way into modern specialities. Fruit also has an ancient history as a beer ingredient and the growth in craft brewing has witnessed a revival of interest, particularly among brewers of 'sours'.

Boiling and cooling

Hops are introduced into brewing during the second major stage of the process, when the wort is boiled vigorously, typically for around an hour or a little more, in a vessel known as a copper or kettle. In their natural state, bitter hop acids are insoluble in water, but sufficient heat changes their chemistry, allowing them to pass into the wort. Boiling also kills off microorganisms, destroys any enzymes left over from mashing, removes undesirable aromas, precipitates unwanted solids which can be separated and discarded, and concentrates the wort a little through evaporation, increasing its potential strength.

Boiling is rough on aroma and flavour, as the volatile essential oils that provide these readily evaporate, so brewers typically make several hop additions, adding hops at the start of the boil for their bitterness and preservative qualities and towards the end for their aroma, perhaps using different varieties at different times. With the increasing focus on hop character, some brewers have experimented with alternatives to boiling, such as infusing hops separately at perhaps 75–80°C before adding the resulting hop tea to the wort, or making 'raw beer' at temperatures short of boiling point.

Additional hops can be added for aroma immediately after the boil when the hopped wort is separated out, either in a vessel called a hop back, where the spent hops themselves provide a natural filter, or in a whirlpool which uses centripetal force to separate solids from liquids. Spent hops can be used as cattle feed, along with spent grain, or composted as fertiliser. The wort is cooled by passing through a device called a heat exchanger or paraflow, often with the addition of oxygen. At last, the brewer has a liquid suitable for fermentation.

Miles Jenner with vintage copper at Harvey's

Gravity

All other things being equal, the more grain in the mash in proportion to water, the greater proportion of sugar in the wort and the more alcohol in the finished beer. Sugar is heavier than water, so a sweet wort will weigh more than the equivalent volume of water. Brewers express this in a measure known as **specific gravity** (SG). Water is considered to have an SG of 1°, so a wort that's 5% sugar by weight will have an SG of 1.05°. By convention, SGs are written as four digits and in the UK often without the decimal point, so 1° becomes 1.000°, or simply 1000°, and 1.05° becomes 1.050° or 1050°, usually pronounced 'ten-fifty'.

The specific gravity of wort just before fermentation is termed **original gravity** (OG) and was once used to calculate the duty on beer. Alcohol is lighter than water, so as sugar is converted to alcohol during fermentation, the beer attenuates towards its **final gravity** (FG). This varies according to the style and the amount of sweetness and body the brewer intends, but for most British styles is typically around 1.004–1.010°. The FG of cask beers is slightly higher when they're packaged so there's sufficient sugar to fuel a continuing fermentation, as explained below.

The international measure for the alcohol content of the finished product, now also used for duty calculations, is the percentage of **alcohol by volume** (ABV), or the proportion of alcohol making up the overall volume of the product. If you took a litre of 5% ABV beer and removed everything else, you should be left with 50 ml of pure alcohol. Because alcohol is lighter than water, you get a lower result if you measure **alcohol by weight** (ABW) which was once used in some jurisdictions: for example a 5% ABV beer is only 3.95% ABW, meaning that if you took a kilo and removed everything else, you'd end up with 39.5 g of alcohol.

Broadly speaking, a 1.050° wort yields a beer of around 5% ABV, though this varies a little according to the amount of attenuation during fermentation. If it's above 5%, the beer will be notably dry, with little residual sugar; if below 5%, it will likely taste sweeter and fuller on the palate.

The brewer is the unwilling keeper of wild animals.
FRANK LOTT (1895:180)

The cold side: fermentation and conditioning

Yeast

Scientifically, the term fermentation covers several different processes used by microorganisms to extract energy from carbohydrates, with varying degrees of relevance to brewing. But in the alcohol industry, the term used on its own almost always refers to just one process, more precisely named alcoholic fermentation. This is carried out by yeast, a single-celled organism of a type known as a eukaryote, belonging to the kingdom of fungi. At least 1,500 different species have been identified, not all of which produce alcohol, and there are multiple variants within individual species, known as strains. An individual brewer's yeast cell is, typically, almost spherical and around 5–10 μm (0.005–0.01 mm) in diameter: it takes around a million cells to create a visible colony. Yeast mainly reproduces by a process known as budding, where a new cell grows from the membrane of its parent.

Yeast cells budding: note bud scars

In common with other fungi but unlike plants, yeast doesn't use sunlight to grow, instead deriving its energy from carbohydrates. In this respect, yeasts are more like animals, including ourselves, as they're capable of aerobic respiration, a metabolic process in which sugars are broken down in the presence of oxygen, releasing energy and leaving behind two by-products: water and carbon dioxide (CO_2). But some yeasts can use an alternative metabolic process that enables them to survive in environments where free oxygen is scarce. This is anaerobic respiration, in which the yeast obtains oxygen directly from the sugar itself. It's this process that results in alcoholic fermentation. Although one of the by-products, CO_2, is the same, the other is alcohol rather than water. It's a much less efficient process, utilising no more than 6% of the energy yielded by the aerobic alternative, but its evolutionary advantages are obvious.

Certain species of yeast will ferment even when oxygen is plentiful, so long as the concentration of sugar is sufficiently high, as in wort. Chemically, there are many different types of sugars, described as simple or complex according to the complexity of their molecules, and wort contains a mix of them. Brewer's yeasts can only metabolise the simpler ones, leaving behind more complex carbohydrates known as dextrins. The extent to which the yeast converts sugar to alcohol is known as attenuation. As the alcohol concentration increases, it adversely affects the cell, which doesn't die but instead becomes dormant, a phenomenon rather delightfully referred to as going to sleep.

This is why drinks produced by fermentation alone, like beer, wine and cider, have a limited alcoholic strength, rarely rising above 15% ABV. Some strains can produce stronger results: Champagne yeasts, for example, are noted for their tolerance of higher concentrations of alcohol. Yeast can be 'roused' into fermenting a little more by physically agitating it, but when pushed too hard it becomes stressed and protests by releasing unwanted flavour compounds.

Yeast is used in two basic forms, wet and dry. Wet yeast is the slurry-like barm that can be cropped from a previous fermentation, though it can also be bought from yeast suppliers. A cheaper and more convenient alternative is dried yeast in the form of small granules, like the sort used for home baking. Some breweries add dried yeast directly to the wort, though others turn it into a wet yeast first by propagating it. Yeast's other uses besides baking include as a food supplement naturally rich in vitamins B1, B2 and iron, while yeast residues from brewing are used to make savoury spreads like Marmite and Vegemite.

Alice Batham, now the head brewer at her family's Bathams brewery in the West Midlands, says her parents gave her a daily teaspoon of yeast residue from the brewery as a tonic when she was growing up, and she tastes it regularly today. She invited me to try: I was expecting a fruity, estery flavour, but was taken aback by the intense

Dried yeast

bitterness, not from the hop compounds absorbed during fermen-tation but from the yeast itself. This recedes in the finished beer, but yeast bite, as it's called, was in the past a well-known off-flavour resulting from a poorly controlled fermentation.

Though yeast itself contributes almost nothing to the final flavour of a well-brewed beer, besides alcohol and CO_2, it produces small quantities of up to 500 different compounds that can have a major impact on flavour and aroma, for better or worse. These include esters, associated with fruity and, in higher concentrations, solvent-like aromas and flavours: banana, pear, apple, aniseed and perhaps roses and honey. They can sometimes suggest rising dough or fresh

A thick barm forms on the top of the fermenting liquid

bread, as they're also produced during breadmaking. Some yeasts also produce significant quantities of phenols, giving spicy, smoky, clove-like and, in high concentrations, medicinal flavours and aromas.

Some by-products such as buttery diacetyl, acetaldehyde with its green apple tang, and sulphur compounds like cabbage-tinged dimethyl sulphoxide (DMS) and eggy sulphur dioxide are largely reabsorbed or released in the later stages of a well-managed fermentation, though modest amounts may remain and contribute to character when appropriate. More complex alcohols, known as fusel alcohols, are also produced in small quantities: these can add hot, rough flavours which will break down over time. Unwelcome compounds, or inappropriately high concentrations of otherwise welcome ones, are usually termed off-flavours. I've considered these in more detail in Chapter 4.

Yeast species

Though a vast diversity of wild yeast flourishes in the wider environment, nearly all brewers use strains deliberately cultivated for the purpose, which almost always belong to one of two different species. Crucial differences in the behaviour of these distinguish the two great families of beer styles: ales and lagers.

Ale yeasts ferment at relatively high temperatures of 16–22°C, with some strains getting even warmer. They work fast, typically taking around three to four days to complete the main fermentation, but also produce significant amounts of flavour by-products. Beers made with ale yeasts usually have a signature 'yeasty' note, with at least a hint of estery fruit and sometimes spice.

Such beers are known as ales. The ale family includes bitter, mild, the various pale and golden ales, brown ale, and, with a few minor exceptions, porter and stout: nearly all the beers that end up in cask are ales. Many important styles originating outside the UK are ales too, including traditional Belgian and Bavarian wheat beers and numerous other styles associated with Belgium like Trappist and abbey ales, many of these using yeasts that produce clove-like phenols as well as fruity esters. Around 200 strains are available commercially, with varying tendencies to produce additional flavour compounds.

One aspect of yeast behaviour of great interest to brewers is known as flocculation, the tendency of cells to stick together and form a distinguishable mass, which varies between species and strains. In a simple open fermentation vessel a high proportion of ale yeast cells collect on the surface of the liquid where they form a thick, creamy, bubbly head known as barm, which can be cropped for reuse in the next brew, known as repitching. For this reason, ale yeasts are also termed top-fermenting or top-cropping yeasts, though a more accurate term is warm-fermenting (as this behaviour isn't invariable). Scientifically, they're members of the species *Saccharomyces cerevisiae*, which roughly translates as 'beer sugar fungus'.

The yeasts responsible for fermenting most of the world's beer, though, belong to a different species, lager yeast. Compared to ale yeast, they prefer lower temperatures and ferment more slowly, taking perhaps a week to 10 days to complete the main fermentation at around 9–12°C. This more considered pace yields fewer additional flavour compounds, a quality which is then enhanced by chilling the beer for an additional period, during which the liquid clears and the remaining unwanted by-products break down, resulting in a more stable drink with a simpler flavour profile. Brewers describe this as clean-tasting, meaning there's little or no trace of fermentation by-products.

Such beers are known as lagers, and it's the extended cold storage, or lagering. that gives them their name, from German *lagern*, 'to store'. As these yeasts are more prone to sinking to the bottom of a vessel, they're often called bottom-fermenting or bottom-cropping yeasts, but cold-fermenting is a more accurate term. Their scientific name is *Saccharomyces pastorianus*, after microbiologist Louis Pasteur.

Although the most familiar examples in English-speaking countries today are unassertively flavoured golden beers of 4–5% ABV, lager denotes a whole family rather than a specific style. They can range in colour from pale straw to black, and from below 0.5% to above 10% in strength, and present a correspondingly wide range of flavours, though lacking the characteristic yeasty signature of their cousins.

There are various hybrids: beers fermented with ale yeast then lagered at lower temperatures, like Kölsch from Cologne (Köln), or with lager yeast at ale-like temperatures, like the historic California common style particularly associated with Anchor Steam Beer. And even though we tend to place the words 'cask' and 'ale' together, beer fermented with lager yeast can be, and sometimes is, conditioned in a cask.

Other yeasts play a small but significant role. Kveik was previously known only to a few farmhouse brewers in western Norway but very recently has been adopted by some craft brewers as a 'miracle yeast'. It can ferment extremely quickly at very high temperatures, up to 30°C or more, without producing unpleasant flavours, though it does lend a characteristic fruitiness. It's usually placed with the ale yeasts, but appears to form 'a group of genetically distinct and domesticated beer yeasts…with possible mixed ancestry', likely a cross between *S. cerevisiae* and a wild strain (Preiss and others 2018).

The best-known wild yeasts are members of the genus *Brettanomyces*, or Brett as it's often known (the name means 'British fungus' for reasons that will become clear later). Compared to *Saccharomyces*, Brett yeasts are active over a wider range of temperatures, from 10°C to as high as 37°C, though they're happiest at around 22°C. They're known as 'super-attenuating' as they ferment more slowly but more thoroughly, tackling dextrins and other complex sugars, and they're more active in the presence of oxygen. They yield a distinctive flavour profile often described as 'funky' or 'spicy' and can produce slightly sour notes too.

Brett yeasts that are naturally present in the brewery environment and in brewing vessels play a major role in wild fermentation (as discussed below), and brewers seeking their distinctive character also use lab-propagated strains. But more often they're regarded as spoilage organisms: unwanted Brett in a beer may be hard to detect when it leaves the brewery but will flourish in the weeks and months that follow, creating potentially explosive additional carbonation and flavours that are highly intrusive if they haven't been designed in.

House yeast

Every yeast culture yields its own complex blend of additional flavour compounds, leaving the sensory equivalent of a fingerprint on the finished beer. Until relatively recently, most breweries fermented all their beers with their own live cultures of house yeast, which, through constant selective cropping and repitching, adapted to the conditions of the host brewery and acquired their own flavour signature in the process. If, after multiple generations, the performance of the yeast began to deteriorate, it would be refreshed with a donation from another brewery. This inevitably meant detectable changes in flavour profile and yeast behaviour, but the new yeast would eventually also adapt to the environment of its new home, becoming distinct from its ancestor.

Many newer craft brewers choose yeast from commercial suppliers according to the recipe, like grains and hops. But plenty of breweries retain a house yeast and jealously guard it as integral to their brand. Many of these cultures are very old and complex, often consisting of several cohabiting strains. A mix of two strains is relatively common, as at Adnams: one strain consumes too many sugars and stays in suspension too long, while the other consumes too few and stops working too early, but so long as the brewers keep them in balance, they work together to achieve excellent results. Few are as genetically rich as the Black Sheep yeast which consists of a staggering 27 different strains naturally coalescing into three separate cultures.

I've tasted plenty of great beers from brewers who adopt the shopping list approach, but convenience comes at the cost of local character and distinctiveness. At the Chiltern brewery, they talk about the slightly nutty character of the yeast used since production started in 1980 as the 'Chiltern stamp'. At Marble, the house yeast is seen as part of the brewery's 'thumbprint'. They're not quite sure where it came from: 'My best guess is that it was originally from Gales,' says head of production Joseph Ince, 'but it's adapted, and when I last had it typed it wasn't quite like anything else. It's ours. It's quite estery, it ferments incredibly well, and it has the highest flocculation I've ever seen.'

Will Bott, head brewer at Titanic, noticed a 'staggering flavour difference' when forced to use dried yeast rather than the live house culture during the Covid-19 lockdowns, particularly on the subtly flavoured Steerage best bitter. Tiny Rebel, founded in 2012, initially acquired a house yeast partly because it was more economical than buying packet yeast for every brew, but also recognised its potential contribution to character. 'We trialled quite a few yeasts from different labs, with multiple 20-litre buckets on the go,' explained brewing director Gazz Williams, 'and eventually found an English ale yeast that gave a roundedness to the beer and left a little bit of sweetness, so we went with that.'

When hundreds of old-established British breweries succumbed to the tide of 'merger mania' that began sweeping the industry in the 1950s, many now-redundant house yeasts ended up as freeze-dried or cryogenically frozen samples at the National Collection of Yeast Cultures (NCYC), established in 1948 and now based in Norwich. This also now provides a confidential safe deposit service where active breweries can keep reference samples, but the astonishing repository of biological heritage in its 'open collection' of around 4,000 strains has proved a valuable resource for various more recently established brewers looking to adopt a house yeast. When Robert Wicks began setting up Westerham brewery in Kent in 2003, he was determined to honour the heritage of the previous Westerham Black Eagle brewery, opened as a satellite site by a London porter brewer in 1841. It ended up as part of Allied, which closed it in 1965, but samples of the yeast, doubtless evolved to suit the soft local water from the Greensand Ridge, had been deposited at NCYC in the 1950s. Robert retrieved these and secured the rights to the strain from Carlsberg.

Fermentation vessels

The simplest fermentation vessels (FVs) are open tanks, sometimes covered with a lid to protect from dust but without an airtight seal. They're essentially an enlarged version of the homebrewer's plastic bucket with a clean tea towel draped over it, though usually with added conveniences like cooling coils or jackets and devices for harvesting yeast. They're known as rounds or squares, depending on their shape. The material of choice was originally wood, but as this is near-impossible to sanitise thoroughly, they're more usually stainless steel, and the remaining wooden ones have usually been retrofitted with more hygienic polypropylene linings.

Closed FVs are vessels with an airtight seal. The most familiar is the cylindro-conical vessel (CCV) or unitank, a tall tank with, as its name suggests, a main cylindrical-shaped body section tapering to a cone at the bottom. Even supposedly top-fermenting ale yeast tends to compact in the cone, from where it can be cropped through a valve supplied for the purpose. An integral jacket provides temperature control, while various other valves and attachments allow for sampling, venting excess carbon dioxide, known as spunding, and racking or emptying out the finished beer.

While most brewers across the world have been convinced by the hygiene, efficiency and precise control offered by CCVs, a few, particularly cask producers, still insist on old-school open vessels. This isn't just sentimental adherence to tradition – there's some very complex science around the way yeast behaviour in different environments affects flavour and character. 'Regardless of what you do,' says Fergus Fitzgerald of Adnams, 'if the vessel is a different shape or size or height, you get different flavours.' The brewery replaced its motley collection of heritage vessels in the early 2000s with a new facility, but rather than CCVs opted for a uniform set of flat-bottomed, unpressurised stainless steel squares, most of them around 50,000 l capacity, 'built around our house yeast,' says Fergus. Fyne Ales upgraded to closed vessels when it expanded in 2014 but chose models with shallow cones so the geometry was closer to the original open tanks. Theakston uses exclusively open tanks, while the Granite brewpub in Toronto proudly describes its cask beers as 'open-fermented' in publicity.

That doesn't mean that you can't make great cask beer in CCVs – plenty of brewers do, including Moor in Bristol and Rooster's in Harrogate, as well as larger players like Fuller's in London. RedWillow in Macclesfield began with simple open tanks but now uses closed vessels with spunding valves. Minimising the dissolved oxygen when the cask beer is racked, says co-founder Toby McKenzie, 'makes the beer just that little bit fresher, crisper and more refined.' But it does mean that the choice of vessel can profoundly affect flavour and character, and the recipes must

CCVs at Brewster's Brewing Co

be devised with that in mind. When Fuller's moved from open 'double drop' fermenters (see below) to CCVs in the late 1970s, the brewers found they needed to tweak the house yeast to retain the desired quality and flavour profile, removing one of its three strains. The venerable ale yeast soon took to settling neatly in the cones.

Today, most breweries use a single tank for the entire process, but a few heritage fermentation systems still in small-scale use recall the days when fermentation was managed in two distinct stages. The initial, most vigorous stage, lasting around two days, took place in a tank, whereupon the liquid was transferred to other vessels, often unbunged casks, for cleansing, or separating beer from excess yeast. Double dropping was a 19th-century improvement to the process, with the initial fermentation in the uppermost of two square vessels, after which the beer was simply dropped into the vessel beneath, leaving much of the initial yeast sediment behind. The system was retained into the 21st century at the old Brakspear brewery in Henley-on-Thames. When this closed, the vessels were transferred to the Wychwood brewery in the Oxfordshire town of the same name, where they're still used to make Brakspear brands, though now under the ownership of Carlsberg.

The two best-known heritage cleansing systems are Burton unions and Yorkshire squares. In the former, fermentation begins in an open tank, then the beer is transferred to a union set, a battery of large wooden casks interconnected with pipes and troughs. Yeast works up into swan neck pipes protruding from the top of each cask, leaving most of the beer behind, then flows through the troughs where the sediment is further separated and the liquid returned to the casks. As its name suggests, this system was once preferred in the prominent English brewing town of Burton upon Trent, but today only Marston's, now also a subsidiary of Carlsberg, retains a working union set, used for only one beer brand, Pedigree, plus the occasional special.

Yorkshire squares achieve the cleansing process in a single square vessel, traditionally constructed of sandstone or slate, divided into two sections by a flat deck not far from the top. The beer is placed in the main chamber below, and the yeast works into the upper chamber through a large circular hole in the deck, surrounded by a lip which traps the sediment while the liquid flows back into the

Yorkshire squares at Samuel Smith

lower chamber. Samuel Smith in Tadcaster is the only significant remaining user of historic vessels like these. Black Sheep, not far away in Masham, adopted the system when it opened in 1992, though it's since exchanged slate squares for unique custom-made stainless-steel versions which the brewers call, in an apparent contradiction, Yorkshire round squares. Despite their circular shape, they preserve the vital deck that separates the yeast. 'It's a point of difference for us,' head brewer Dan Scott-Paul told me. 'It imparts character, a dry, slightly astringent yeast bite.'

Wort into beer

Adding yeast to wort is known as pitching, though the action itself is rather gentler than its name suggests. Achieving the right pitching rate helps ensure the fermentation will get off to a good start, not too fast nor too slow. The ideal count varies according to the volume of wort, its gravity, the beer style and the yeast strain, but a typical rate for ales is 2–2.5 million cells per millilitre (cells/ml) for every 0.010° of original gravity.

That's an awful lot of cells. Consider a small commercial brewery making a 1,000-litre batch of a 4% ABV best bitter, with an OG of around 1.040°. That would require 4 × 2.5 million cells/ml, or 10 million cells – 1,000 litres is a million millilitres, so that's 10 million million cells. And once you start thinking of mega-breweries working in batches of hundreds of thousands of litres, the numbers rapidly stretch beyond astronomical into unimaginable.

Fermentation doesn't begin immediately: first, there's a period called the lag phase, lasting perhaps 12 hours, with no visible activity but much going on at the microbiological level as the yeast cells prepare to ferment. Activity rapidly becomes more vigorous and visible as the yeast enters the exponential or logarithmic phase when most of the alcohol in the finished beer is created, usually taking around two to three days for a typical session ale. These phases together are often termed primary fermentation.

The yeast begins hungrily consuming sugar, energetically budding to produce more cells and starting to make alcohol and carbon dioxide. It soon scours up all the oxygen in the wort and starts fermenting in earnest. The temperature increases rapidly and the acidity of the liquid increases. Most brewers now apply a gentle brake by cooling the vessels, typically limiting the temperature to 20–22°C, or slightly cooler, with higher temperatures yielding more esters and other flavour components.

In a closed vessel, all this activity is hidden from view, except that, as yeast specialist Chris White describes it (1999), 'airlocks bubble like crazy', as CO_2 escapes though the layer of water that prevents air from getting back in. If things get too vigorous, the brewers may connect the valve to a hose dipped into a bucket of water, which bubbles like a witch's cauldron. It's a reminder of the origin of the term 'fermentation' itself, from the Latin *fevere*, 'to boil'. CO_2 is itself a useful product, for brewing and other purposes, and the biggest brewers capture it for later use. Until recently, equipment for doing this was bulky and costly, and most of the gas produced by microbreweries is still vented to the air, but a few are now investing in small-scale capture systems.

Yeast makes even more of a visual impression in an open vessel, as large numbers of cells attach themselves to each other and to rising bubbles of carbon dioxide, soon creating a thick barm. The emerging CO_2, which is heavier than air, tends to sink back towards the surface. Together with the increased acidity, the yeast head and its cushion of gas form a natural barrier to contamination, one of the reasons why, even in the days before modern hygiene techniques, brewers were still able to achieve some degree of quality and consistency in open vessels.

The yeast head goes through a succession of changes in appearance, eloquently described in the mid-19th century by brewing scientist and instrument maker John Levesque:

> The first visible signs of fermentation are in a delicate white line all round the gyle-tun [fermentation vessel], which increases gradually, until the whole surface is covered with a thin cream, which rises very gradually; it then breaks out into a fine cauliflower head, increasing in size and depth until it again resolves into the spiral or rocky head: the next change is into a head with a smooth surface…[which] grows thicker and heavier towards the cleansing point; when skimming or separation is necessary for the discharge of the yeast (1854:55).

To the fermentation enthusiast, this evolving appearance is a joy to behold, particularly if you're aware that yeast produces most of the crucial flavour compounds during this stage. The cauliflower head, as its name suggests, has a dense pattern of bubbles separated by darker-coloured striations. The rocky head is the most spectacular, resembling whipped cream or a meringue pie topping. It reminded German brewers of thick curly hair, thus the term *Kräusen* (pronounced 'kroyzen'), from *kraus*, 'crinkly' or 'frizzy'. Today some English-speaking brewers refer to this stage as high kräusen (German *Hochkräusen*).

Brewers obtain more accurate measurements of the progress of fermentation by using simple but ingenious instruments called saccharometers, a type of hydrometer: the more alcohol in the liquid, the lower the device sinks, indicating the gravity on a scale. The object is almost never to use up all the sugar, leaving a little for sweetness and body and, with cask, to provide for a continuing fermentation, as we'll shortly see. Unfermentable dextrins also remain: these don't taste particularly sweet but contribute to texture and body. Of the fermented sugar, 48% becomes alcohol and 46% carbon dioxide. Most of the remaining 6% ends up in new yeast cells. The quantity of yeast increases visibly and dramatically by a factor of around four or five, so for every kilogram pitched, the brewer can expect to crop 4–5 kg.

Cropping

Cropping yeast for repitching is normally accomplished just as the head starts to decline: what John Levesque calls the 'cleansing point'. Yeast can be cropped manually from open FVs with an appropriate utensil like a spatula or scoop – Burton Bridge uses a dustpan and in one small brewery I spotted a large, slotted kitchen skimmer bound to a broom handle. Vessels at bigger traditional places like Bathams, Harvey's and Hook Norton are equipped with a parachute, a Victorian invention like a funnel which does indeed resemble a parachute and is lowered to just under the surface of the head. Some breweries, like Woodforde's, have FVs fitted with suction pumps, but there's room for improvisation here: at Castle Rock in Nottingham I saw a brewer happily cropping from the top of a large FV using a modified vacuum cleaner. In a closed tank like a CCV, as the yeast reaches the end of primary fermentation, the temperature is dropped to around 6–8°C. Any remaining activity subsides and the yeast cells in suspension begin to

Bathams parachute

flocculate and sink into the cone, from where they're cropped using a valve installed for the purpose.

Live yeast is kept in a cold, dark place, ideally at 1–2°C, to keep it inactive and contaminant free, and used within two weeks of cropping at most. When the Covid lockdowns of 2020–21 disrupted production schedules, breweries who normally rely on a regular yeast cycle faced a particular challenge, and some even ended up brewing small runs just to keep the yeast going then dumping most of the resulting beer. 'You can't furlough yeast,' a struggling brewer told me.

Repitching is commonly limited to a certain number of generations, perhaps 10 or 12, or a certain period: in the breweries I visited, this varied from two to 18 months. After this, brewers propagate afresh from a reference sample. But some yeast cultures are remarkably ageless, like the one at Harvey's of Lewes. The brewery was last obliged to seek a fresh source when its existing supplier, the British Pure Yeast Company, ceased trading in 1956. The supplier advised that recent deliveries had been procured from Truman's Black Eagle brewery in London, but when head brewer Anthony Jenner approached Truman's directly, he was disappointed to find its yeast 'in no way resembled previous consignments,' as his son Miles, the current head brewer, recounts.

Following a 'frantic search… in October 1957, he approached John Smith's Tadcaster Brewery Company. 30 pounds [13.6 kg] of Back Yeast [cropped from the fermenters] were despatched by passenger train from York on the Monday morning and arrived in Lewes at noon the following day.' (Jenner 2019.) The yeast behaved well, and the brewers have been repitching it ever since, now for well over 3,000 generations. Though specimens are kept for security, it's not yet been repropagated, and still yields world-class beer. Timothy Taylor's yeast has been repitched continuously for a mere 36 years. The house yeast at Theakston still has some catching up to do: brewer Mark Slater explained that they'd taken a decision not to repropagate unless absolutely necessary, and when I visited in October 2022 they'd reached generation 195.

Conditioning

After around perhaps three or four days of vigour, yeast activity declines rapidly as the supply of fermentable sugars approaches exhaustion and the environment becomes more alcoholic. The temperature starts to fall and the cells begin to sink slowly but surely to the bottom of the vessel. Fermentation has now entered the stationary phase. Some yeast activity is still ongoing, but no longer obvious. The liquid is now alcoholic, so no longer wort, but is still some way from being fit to drink. Brewers term it green beer.

The stationary phase is more commonly referred to as conditioning, but that's a tricky term. Condition can also refer to the concentration of carbon dioxide in the beer when it's served, and with cask 'conditioned' beer, the process only completes in the pub cellar. Conditioning at the brewery does help develop carbonation, but there's much more going on besides. Diacetyl and acetaldehyde produced during fermentation are now useful to the yeast, which begins to reabsorb them, handily removing their intrusive flavours. Unwelcome aromas from sulphur compounds like DMS mainly bubble off with the CO_2. No doubt other subtle reactions are taking place which help create a rounded and integrated flavour.

Conditioning also helps clarify the beer as the remaining yeast cells fall. Sinking along with them are further unwanted solids like proteins. Brewers normally reduce the temperature during this phase, typically to under $10°C$, which encourages the yeast to absorb diacetyl more readily and settle more quickly as well as discouraging unwanted microorganisms, sometimes followed by a crash cool to $5°C$ or less to drop out the last of the yeast. The beer is said to drop bright, something that, until very recently, nearly all beer was expected to do before being considered saleable. The process typically takes three days, perhaps a little more. There's an ancient tradition of ensuring every brew spends a Sunday in the vessels so it's 'blessed by the Sabbath', and even in these secular times many still implement a seven-day fermentation and conditioning cycle.

Dry hopping

Dry hopping, more correctly termed cold side hopping, is the addition of hops after the wort has been cooled to fermentation temperatures or below. This is the surest way of imparting the maximum amount of aroma, and therefore perceived flavour, while contributing almost nothing in the way of bitterness or preservative and stabilising qualities. The practice has a lengthy history but has never been so popular as today, when it's become the most common way of achieving the intensely hoppy character of most (but not all) contemporary pale ales. Hops are typically added during conditioning, by hand into an open FV, using a special attachment on a CCV, or with high-tech gadgets with names like hop rocket, hop gun and hop cannon. It's also possible to dry hop directly into casks, as we'll see in Chapter 2.

While fermentation and conditioning are thought of primarily in terms of the interaction between yeast and malt sugars, yeast can also interact with hop derivatives in subtle and complex ways that impact on flavour and character, a process known as hop compound biotransformation. For example, yeast enzymes can break down flavour compounds called terpenes, releasing intensely aromatic esters, and change odourless substances into aromatic ones.

Hop plugs at Adnams

Scientific awareness of these phenomena goes back at least to the early 2000s, but it's still something of a frontier of knowledge. Beer writer Claire Bullen (2019b) spoke to brewers who'd noted classic citric, piny West Coast hops ultimately yielding flavours closer to perfumed lemon zest and lavender. Cloudwater in Manchester experimented with dry hopping one batch of a double IPA while the yeast was still notably active and another batch of the same beer after crash cooling. Tasters subjectively noted a marked difference: the normal method yielded the expected woody, mango and onion aromas while the 'active yeast' batch exploded with the scents of 'a verdant Californian orchard'.

Other unexpected interactions arise from dry hopping. Hops themselves contain enzymes capable of breaking down unfermentable dextrins into fermentable sugars, potentially prompting unplanned additional fermentation, excessive carbonation and unwanted yeast flavours. This phenomenon, known as hop creep, was investigated by brewing scientists as far back as 1893, but remained a minor concern until the current era of hop profligacy. Low temperatures and careful separation of hop solids can help, but some brewers now include hop creep in their calculations when planning fermentation regimes.

Other fermentation methods

Lager fermentation

Both ales and lagers undergo the same basic processes of fermentation and conditioning but with differences in the yeast species, temperature and time. As already discussed, lagers are fermented with *Saccharomyces pastorianus*, which works more slowly at lower temperatures than ale yeast and creates fewer flavour compounds. Crucially, lagers are also conditioned at lower temperatures and for longer than ales. Traditional lager styles also differ from their ale counterparts in choice of ingredients and wort preparation, using decoction mashing in which the temperature is progressively increased by removing and boiling portions of the mash and returning them to the mash tun. But these aren't the essential differences. Many UK brewers make wort with domestic malts in a single infusion mash and then ferment it using lager yeasts and methods, resulting in beer which is clearly lager rather than ale.

Lager tanks at Moor brewery

Yeast is pitched at around 5–8°C, at a higher rate than with ale, with around 3.75 cells/ml for every 0.010° of original gravity, helping to get this more sluggish yeast off to a good start. The lag phase lasts around 16–24 hours and the exponential phase takes five to seven days, with the temperature typically pegged at 9–12°C.

Now the characteristic cold conditioning known as lagering begins, with the temperature dropped to between –2 and 3°C, and kept there for an extended period. These days this is often achieved simply by cooling a CCV, but the more traditional lager brewers prefer to transfer the beer to dedicated lagering tanks kept in cold cellars. Lagering times vary by brewery and style, but should at least be measured in weeks: perhaps four weeks for a lighter beer, six to eight weeks for a quality pale lager, and three or four months for stronger and hoppier styles, often a little less overall for darker beers.

Even in such chilly conditions, fermentation continues at a slow rate as the yeast continues to feed on residual sugars, producing carbon dioxide which is trapped within the sealed vessel and dissolves readily into the cold beer. When the pressure becomes too great, a spunding valve is used to vent some of it, achieving the ideal level of natural sparkle with no need to add extra gas during packaging. Solids precipitate out and unwanted flavour compounds produced earlier in fermentation break down even more thoroughly, though the method isn't quite so effective at ridding the beer of diacetyl and sulphur compounds like DMS: indeed, in modest quantities, these substances are considered part of the flavour profile of many classic lagers.

Unsurprisingly, the big brewers have found ways to circumvent such time-consuming practices. These include: using high proportions of unmalted grains and syrups to achieve 'smoother' but less characterful flavours further down the line; raising the temperature to hurry the yeast then crash-cooling to stop fermentation on schedule whether or not it's complete; high-gravity brewing, or making high-strength beer which is then diluted before packaging; compressing lagering times to a bare minimum; blending to average out deficiencies in multiple batches; filtering to remove solids which didn't get a chance to drop out naturally; tweaking with a variety of additives and extracts; pasteurising and force carbonating to achieve the stability and condition the beer would otherwise have reached in its own time; and finally recommending the beer is served 'extra-cold' at 2–4°C so that the drinker's nose and tongue are sufficiently anaesthetised not to detect the inevitable unpleasant flavour artefacts that result. It's easy to be overcritical of such products, which are after all enjoyed by millions of people every day, but whether they are lagers in the original sense of the term is highly debatable.

Wild and mixed fermentation

While ale and lager fermentation have much in common, wild fermentation differs not only in certain crucial technical respects but in the flavour profiles of the beers that result. Though much beloved of connoisseurs and adventurous brewers, these are very much a minority speciality in terms of volume.

A true wild fermentation omits any active pitching of yeast, relying instead on the indigenous microorganisms of the brewery environment. The best-known examples are the lambic beers of Brussels and the Pajottenland in central Belgium, where the technique is known as spontaneous fermentation. As with lager, there are differences with ingredients and mashing and boiling practices, and though they're not the crucial distinguishing factor, they result in a wort well suited to the treatment that follows. It contains plenty of dextrins alongside fermentable sugars, thanks to a proportion of unmalted wheat and a complex mash at multiple temperatures, while hops are aged for a year or more to reduce their bitterness while retaining their preservative properties.

The hot wort is exposed to the resident population of wild yeasts and bacteria by being left overnight in a large, shallow, rectangular vessel called a coolship (Dutch *koelschip*) placed in a well-ventilated area. Coolships, incidentally, were once a common method of cooling wort in conventional brewing, and there are disused examples at some historic British breweries such as Hook Norton; at Elgoods they revived theirs to make wild fermentation beers. The next day, the wort is transferred to wooden vessels, typically big ex-wine casks or large oak vats,

Coolship in use at Elgood's

and left largely to its own devices for periods from eight or nine months up to three years or more, during which time it undergoes a complex series of fermentations induced by up to 200 different microorganisms which either entered in the coolship, or, more significantly, are resident in the wood. Brewers rely on the climate to help regulate the process, retaining the traditional seasonal pattern of brewing only in the cooler months, then leaving the beer to mature over at least one summer.

The process involves not only yeast but also different kinds of bacteria. The most important are members of the genii *Lactobacillus* and *Pediococcus*, capable of lactic fermentation, another anaerobic process which is also used in making yogurt and various pickled and fermented foods. One of its products is lactic acid, which lends a clean, lemony sourness. As air creeps in over time, it encourages the growth of *Acetobacter* bacteria, which produce acetic acid, the substance that gives a pungent sourness to vinegar, through an aerobic type of acetic fermentation.

Alcoholic fermentation is carried out by various species of wild yeast, including some more normally associated with winemaking. Several months in, various *Brettanomyces* species begin digesting the more complex sugars and dextrins, adding distinctive spicy and animal-like flavours. Given further time, some of the more intrusive flavour compounds break down, and the beer's overall profile becomes ever more complex. Beers from multiple casks at several different ages are then blended to make oude g(u)euze, or macerated on fruit like sour kriek cherries.

An alternative, slightly more controllable method is mixed fermentation, where the wort first undergoes a conventional fermentation with cultivated brewer's yeast, then is treated to encourage the activity of other microorganisms, by ageing in wood and/or by deliberately adding a second 'mixed culture' of wild yeasts and acid bacteria. Once again there's a Belgian model, in beers variously

Barrel ageing at Fyne Ales

termed Flemish oude bruin (old brown), sour brown or red ale. Numerous craft breweries have adopted wood ageing in recent years, in many cases because they're also interested in the flavours imparted by the wood itself, and the drinks it previously contained, like wine or whisk(e)y, as well as the distinctively spicy, funky and sour notes obtained through complex fermentations.

Wild and mixed fermentation beers can be served from cask too, though the traditional examples generally aren't. But the main reason I've dwelt on this approach is because it informs the historical context against which modern cask beer evolved. A late 18th-century professional English brewer transported through time into the present day would find himself in more familiar surroundings in a Belgian mixed fermentation brewery than a British cask one, as I'll explain in Chapter 6.

There are other ways of boosting acidity. Many contemporary sour beers are kettle sours, produced by inducing a brief lactic fermentation between mashing and boiling. The latter process kills off the bacteria and fixes the level of acidity in the wort before it's fermented in the conventional way with brewer's yeast. The results are cleaner and more predictable but considerably less complex.

Hygiene

There's an old industry adage that brewing is 90% cleaning. It may not be the most romantic subject for the interested beer drinker, nor the factor that most often tempts people into the industry, but keeping things clean is just as much an essential part of the successful brewer's skill set as managing mashing or fermentation procedures. A 1950s study identified 27 species of wild yeast plus various moulds present in breweries in places where they shouldn't have been, to say nothing of bacteria (Wiles 1953:282). Hygiene practices have improved since then, but constant vigilance remains essential.

Modern breweries are designed to make cleaning as easy as possible, with smooth, waterproof and well-drained floors so not only unintended spillages but cleaning water can be dealt with easily and potential havens for germs are minimised. Brewing equipment is often plumbed into a cleaning in place (CIP) system which automatically applies a cycle of caustic (caustic soda, usually sodium or potassium hydroxide) washes and multiple hot water rinses, but you'll still often see staff climbing into vessels to scrub them out manually, either as an alternative or a supplement to CIP. The requirement for impeccable hygiene continues beyond the brewery gates and all the way along the supply chain until the beer reaches the appreciative drinker's lips. This is particularly true of cask beer, and we'll return to this point in some detail later.

2 Cask from tank to glass

So far, practically all beer has followed a similar journey, from the rarest small batch craft ale to the most ubiquitous industrial lager. Even the most *outré* wild fermentation brew has still undergone the same basic process of mashing, boiling, cooling, fermentation and conditioning. It's only as the beer heads towards the packaging line that the formats begin clearly to diverge, with cask beer emerging as a distinctive product, a draught beer that's still fermenting in the container it's dispensed from – fresh, naturally carbonated, and, to some extent, with a distinctive flavour development.

Casks

Cask making

Today the term 'barrel' is used generically in everyday English for a variety of cylindrical containers with bulging waists, and even some straight-sided ones, but originally it meant a container of a specific size. It still does in the brewing and pub trade. The older generic term is 'cask', which originally referred to a wood container made of interlocking staves bound with hoops.

Such vessels and the skills and technology needed to make them, known as coopering, have a long history. There are depictions of open wooden tubs made from staves bound with hoops, the likely predecessors of closed casks, in Egyptian tomb illustrations from 1900 BCE. Several Classical writers note the widespread use of wooden casks among the tribal Celtic people of Gaul, which then encompassed modern-day France and several surrounding territories, and Roman naturalist Pliny the Elder, around 77 CE, mentions the habit of keeping wine in wooden vessels 'around the Alps' (1906:Ch 27:132).

In the two centuries following these remarks, casks largely replaced ceramic amphorae as the vessel of choice for European and Mediterranean trade, and they remained the most widely used bulk containers for nearly two millennia, reaching the Americas at the earliest opportunity in the hold of Christopher Columbus's ships when they landed in the Bahamas in 1492. Casks were largely replaced in the 20th century by packaging made from other materials – aluminium, steel, cardboard, textiles, plastic – and in other shapes, like drums, sacks, boxes, pallets and shipping containers.

The characteristic bulging profile, with a protruding belly or bilge, is a geometrical solution to the problem of assembling separate staves with sufficient tightness to create a closed and, if required, watertight container. The design uses the same engineering principle as the architectural arch and the result is exceptionally strong and robust, with the added advantage of a shape that can be moved easily by rolling. The lip, or chime, that protrudes beyond the rim of each head facilitates manual handling by providing a gripping point.

Besides liquids, it was once common to store dry and solid goods in casks – everything from flour and smoked fish to nails and ammunition. But wet casks used for liquids, including alcoholic ones, were the most sophisticated and expensive versions. Building a resilient waterproof vessel out of a porous material like wood, particularly one strong enough to withstand the pressure of carbon dioxide from fermentation, was the ultimate test of the cooper's skill.

Very few people possess that skill today, and the term cooper has become just a family name of opaque origin. 'When I'm out for a drink and people ask me what I do and I say I'm a cooper,' says Euan Findlay of the Theakston brewery, 'they say, "what's one of them?"' Euan fell into the job by coincidence and is now likely the only full-time fully qualified craft cooper employed by a UK brewery.

Most of Euan's working day is spent repairing and maintaining existing casks, mainly by cannibalising staves from defunct ones acquired from the wine and whisky industries. These are cleaned by charring the inside over a fire then planing the surface down. But Euan also showed me how he makes new casks, starting with staves cut from straight planks of oak, usually Bavarian oak which is less prone to warping. These are tapered at each end into a cigar shape, with bevelled sides that will eventually lock together and perpendicular grooves near both ends.

The staves are gathered at one end and held in place with an iron truss hoop – some of the hoops in Euan's cooperage are over a century old. The wood is then softened with steam so the staves can be bent into the desired shape using a windlass, a band placed around the assembly and progressively tightened. As the edges lock together, the truss hoops are replaced by permanent hoops, four in all, and the cask is dried into its final shape by setting a fire of wood shavings inside it, charring the inner surfaces. Two flat, circular head pieces made from further planks are slotted into the appropriate grooves, and the cask is completed by cutting and lining two bungholes. Working at full speed, Euan can make four nine-gallon (41 l) firkins in a day.

The Flowers brewery in Stratford-upon-Avon briefly experimented with stainless steel casks in 1934 but it wasn't until the late 1950s, when steel became more affordable, that the industry began to adopt them more generally. Aluminium alloys of the sort used in aircraft were introduced as a more lightweight

Euan Findlay at Theakston cooperage

alternative in the early 1960s but are rarely seen nowadays. Making a sufficiently sturdy aluminium cask is complex and expensive and the metal itself is even more attractive to professional thieves than steel.

Steel is lighter, stronger and more durable than wood, needs less maintenance, and is easier to clean and sanitise effectively. You can't use caustic with wood as it gets absorbed and is impossible to rinse out thoroughly, so cleaning is limited to water and steam. A wooden firkin weighs around 6 kg more than a steel one. Its only practical advantage is that it provides moderately better insulation, helping keep the beer at an even temperature.

Some beer is now packaged in casks made from recyclable high-density polythene plastic (HDPE), which are much cheaper and notably lighter than their steel cousins: a plastic firkin tips the scales at around 8 kg less. They can be produced in bright and attractive colours and are good for branding. They're not quite as strong and resilient, and may not be quite so easy to sanitise as plastic is prone to scratching, but their advantages are sufficient that, according to one manufacturer, they now account for 25% of the UK's cask population.

Making a steel cask once required multiple welds, but today each one is constructed from two discs of sheet steel, each of which is then shaped to form half of the main body. A chime is welded to each half and the two are then welded together, requiring only three welds in total. The only other components are the bushes – the housings for the two bungs. Plastic casks are even simpler: they're made in a single piece by a process called 'blow moulding', in which a cylinder of heated, softened plastic is placed in a mould and blown into shape, a technique also used for everything from small drinks bottles to giant storage drums.

The transition from wood to steel was resisted in some quarters, much as some traditionally minded licensees are resistant to plastic casks today, though partly because it coincided with the increasing promotion of pressurised keg beers which were also packaged in steel. But the argument was ultimately lost on practical and economic grounds. Today, only two breweries still regularly package a significant amount of beer in wooden casks – Theakston and fellow Yorkshire brewer Samuel Smith – though a growing number experiment on an occasional basis. I'll consider whether wooden casks make a difference to flavour in Chapter 4.

Anatomy of a cask

Why do modern steel and plastic casks still so strongly resemble their wooden predecessors in size and shape, given they are no longer constructed from separate staves? One good reason is compatibility: sticking to the old design as far as possible minimised the need for new equipment and working practices at the time the change was made, though you'd normally expect this influence to lessen over the decades. The more compelling reason why even the garishly coloured plastic objects seen in today's cellars would still be familiar to 1950s brewers and publicans is because there are features of the traditional design that particularly suit the management of cask beer.

One of these is the bulging bilge. As a fermenting liquid, cask beer contains solids in suspension which will eventually sink, and when the cask is placed on its side, its curvaceous midriff provides a convenient place for the sediment to collect. The two circular ridges around the circumference recall the hoops of a wooden cask, though they are provided as rolling rings to facilitate movement.

The two bungholes are arranged to take best advantage of the shape. The largest one, around 60 mm in diameter and right in the centre of the bilge, takes a bung called a shive with a thinner circular centre, the tut. The cask is filled through this hole, which later plays a role in controlling condition and facilitating dispense. The second hole is in the head, close to the chime, on the opposite side from the shive hole and at right angles to it. This protrudes from the cask as a short neck with an opening that's typically 37.5 mm at the front, tapering slightly inside to 35 mm, and takes a bung called a keystone.

The beer is dispensed through this hole which, if the cask is placed on its side with the keystone closest to the floor and the shive facing directly up at the ceiling, provides access to clear liquid from above the sediment. The bungs were traditionally made of limewood but today are almost always plastic as it's more hygienic and resilient, and easier to colour-code.

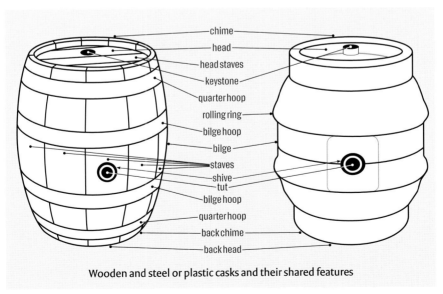

Wooden and steel or plastic casks and their shared features

The naming of casks

Tradition is also followed in the names and sizes of standard beer casks, as listed in the table below. The figures are for imperial gallons and pints, and the metric equivalents are rounded to two decimal places. The measures refer to the capacity of the cask and therefore the volume of beer inside when it's filled to the brim. A licensee wouldn't expect to get 72 saleable pints out of a firkin, however: allowing for sediment and wastage, 68 is a more typical yield. Regulations allow some tolerance, though in practice most casks hold a little more than their declared capacity.

NAME	GALLONS	LITRES	PINTS
Pin	4½	20.46	36
Firkin	9	40.91	72
Kilderkin (kil)	18	81.83	144
Barrel	36	163.66	288
Hogshead	54	245.49	432
Butt	108	490.98	864
Tun	252	1145.62	2,016

Some of the names are derived from Dutch. While the origin of pin in this sense remains obscure, firkin means 'little quarter' (Dutch *vierdeken*), as a firkin has a quarter of the capacity of a barrel. A kilderkin, often shortened to 'kil', was a 'little hundred' in an older system of measurements (Dutch *kinderken*, from Old French *quintal* meaning five twenties). Hogshead is an English term with an obvious literal meaning, although how a large cask came to be associated with a head of a pig is now anyone's guess. Butt originally meant a goal or target (French *but*), and its application here perhaps follows from an association between an archery target and the head of a large cask. Tun is a very old term for a large cask which likely has Celtic origins and is related to the word 'ton' as a unit of weight. Brewers and cellar staff often refer to the sizes in regular use by their capacity in gallons, talking about 'nines', 'eighteens' and 'thirty-sixes', though a pin is always a pin, not a 'four-and-a-half'.

Today, by far the most common casks in circulation are nine-gallon (41 l) firkins, and some breweries only supply in this size. Kilderkins are much rarer, only used for best-selling beers in high turnover pubs, though several more traditional breweries maintain populations of them. Many are reluctant to supply pins, except perhaps for occasional strong specials, but changing market conditions have inspired some to reconsider them, as discussed in Chapter 8.

Barrels are more familiar to today's brewers as a measurement rather than an actual, physical cask. I've spoken to many brewers who've never seen one, and I hadn't myself until I visited the Sarah Hughes brewery at the Beacon Hotel in the West Midlands, where they're still used for the best-selling Sedgley Surprise best bitter. I've subsequently found a few other traditional breweries using small numbers for the most popular lines at the busiest pubs, and they're standard for the bitter at Bathams, not far from Sarah Hughes, as each of the brewery's 12 pubs still manages to empty one a day on average. Hogsheads are even rarer, though Bathams has a couple for its brewery tap. Butts and tuns have long been exceptional and are now extinct, though I've included them in the table for historical completeness.

The decline of the larger sizes is testimony not only to falling consumption but to increased concern for health and safety in the workplace. When full, a steel firkin weighs 50 kg. By contemporary standards, such a weight requires two people to lift safely. When I tackled one unaided using the best technique, my spine complained for the rest of the day. There are correspondingly greater issues for larger casks, which pose a safety hazard in themselves if inadvertently dropped or allowed to roll out of control. The cellar manager at the Beacon relies on a mechanical winch and considerable care and practice to do her job. While the masculinity of old-school draymen may have been measured by their ability to toss full barrels around single-handed, nobody with any concern for workplace welfare would advocate a return to the days when workers were routinely expected to put their personal safety and musculoskeletal health on the line for the sake of a few gallons of beer.

Nonetheless, some brewers and cellar managers lament the decreasing use of the larger sizes, not just as an indicator of reduced sales but because they believe bigger casks produce better results in terms of the flavour and condition of the finished product. There's a rationale for this. With cask beer, the casks themselves are more than simple containers for liquid: they also function as fermentation vessels, and, as in the brewery, their geometry and fluid dynamics affect yeast behaviour to some extent. Yeasts that work smoothly in larger casks can get over-excited in smaller ones, something that brewers are increasingly confronting with the renewed interest in pins. Both Adrienne Heslin at West Kerry and Alice Batham told me they'd experienced the most explosive results from the smallest casks.

Casks in circulation

Another traditional characteristic that casks retain is that they're returnable, refillable vessels. Even in the disposable decades of the 1960s and 1970s, breweries stuck with reusable containers, and it wasn't until the 2010s that single-use recyclable vessels like membrane kegs gained a significant presence in the industry.

A new steel firkin costs around £100, with a discount for buying in bulk. It's usually guaranteed for at least seven years, but if properly treated will last for many decades. When, late in 2021, CAMRA launched a social media hunt to find the oldest cask still in circulation, the Tarn Hows brewery in Cumbria reported they were still using one made in 1951. I raised the subject more recently in a social media group for brewing professionals and heard from several respondents still filling casks made in the 1960s and 1970s. At a relatively busy brewery the average cask gets refilled every six to eight weeks, so one made in 1961 might well have been reused over 400 times and counting. A few get too badly dented and can even break if they're particularly roughly treated, but overall, they're more likely to get stolen before they succumb to wear and tear.

Plastic casks are considerably cheaper, but as they've only been widely used for a relatively short time, their long-term resilience is untested. Ultraviolet light cumulatively degrades plastic left out in the sun, and it's possible for the inner surface to become so scratched that it harbours persistent infections. Even so, some have been in reliable circulation for more than a decade.

The downside to this otherwise efficient and sustainable arrangement is that it requires emptied casks to be collected and repatriated. Before the 1990s, when nearly every British pub was tied to a particular brewery, this was a simple matter: only one brewery made deliveries, and its draymen picked up all the empties at the same time. Today, the trade is more fragmented: a single pub may deal with

Everards' dray, early 20th century

multiple suppliers and order only a handful of casks from each, which means more breweries making more calls to pick up fewer casks.

There are various ways of identifying the owner and tracking the container. Each cask is stamped with a serial number and a brewery name, and a barcoded label is attached each time it's refilled. Most casks also carry colour coding. The British Beer and Pub Association (BBPA) and SIBA (Society of Independent Brewers) jointly manage a voluntary registration scheme for these. For example, Harvey's casks have an upper light blue band (nearest the head) and a lower light green band (nearest the back head), while Harviestoun casks have three bands: yellow, black, then another yellow.

If tracking containers becomes too difficult and time-consuming, as it may for smaller breweries, particularly when sending beer further afield, there's the option of cask (and keg) hire. Companies like Close Brothers, who trade under the Ecask and Ekeg brands, and Kegstar offer a 'fill and forget' service where breweries rent clean containers from a common pool, fill and deliver them, then leave it to the owning company to collect, clean and reuse them.

Whichever system is used, the customer is, legally, buying the contents of the cask but only borrowing the cask itself. This remains the property of someone else, as normally made clear in a statement printed on it. Despite this, casks are far more likely to go astray than get broken, either through deliberate theft or ignorant misappropriation. One reason some brewers are reluctant to use pins is that these cute little objects are particularly likely to drop out of circulation, ending up as flowerpots or bar decorations. When hospitality venues go out of business, the people who clear the site may have no idea what to do with the empties and sometimes dump them indiscriminately.

The big hire companies are in a stronger position to keep track of their casks, but smaller breweries sometimes face an uphill struggle. An industry body called Keg Watch provides a central contact point for information about stray or stolen casks, kegs and pub gas cylinders, and works with various partners, including the police, to recover them. In the six months between March and October 2022, it recovered over 100,000 casks and kegs with a replacement value of over £8 million (2022).

Cask cleaning

Before a cask can be filled with fresh beer, it must be thoroughly cleaned and sanitised. As casks are reused multiple times, filling a brand-new one is a rare event, but even these must be properly prepared. Most empty casks in a typical brewery have recently returned complete with dregs and encrusted solids, with an accompanying menagerie of microorganisms. In smaller breweries, they're cleaned by hand using high pressure hoses, while bigger operators have an automated line.

The exact procedure varies from place to place but the following regime is typical. First, any remaining bungs are knocked out and the outside washed thoroughly, with old labels scraped off. An initial high-pressure hot water rinse disposes of any remaining beer and debris and shifts much of the encrusted matter. Next, the cask is filled with a hot detergent solution such as caustic (sodium or potassium hydroxide) or an alternative, which usually shifts the remaining residues. The detergent is thoroughly rinsed out with more hot water, then the interior is sanitised, either with superheated steam or a weak acid solution or both. The results are carefully inspected, both visually with a torch and by sniffing for unwanted odours. If necessary, the cask is cleaned further, perhaps by manual scrubbing.

Automated cask cleaning lines are one of the more visually intriguing features of a larger brewery. The one at St Austell has nine stages, with a sensor prior to the first stage to check that the shive hole is pointing downwards so it can engage with the cleaning heads, and some clever mechanics to reposition the cask if not. Staff check that the line is working properly using a special 'sight cask' with a transparent head. I followed the progress of this as it was loaded, rotated into place, and subjected to numerous applications of hot water, caustic and steam before rolling out squeaky clean. Such machines are increasingly designed to use water and energy with maximum efficiency: this one recycles the 'dirty' water from the final rinse, which by this stage is hardly dirty at all, and uses it for the initial rinse of the next cask entering the line.

A fresh keystone bung is hammered into place immediately after cleaning and the cask is now ready for filling. In bigger, more automated breweries, the cleaning line leads directly to the racking (filling) line, but smaller breweries often have to do both jobs separately. If the casks need to be kept aside for a while, the shive hole is bunged too, but only loosely, to protect against dust and other potential nuisances. Freshly cleaned casks are considered good for only 48 hours, after which they'll need to be cleaned again.

*Cask cleaning is as important as any other job in the brewery.
There's no point in making a great beer and putting it in a dirty cask.*
BRUCE ASH, Woodforde's Brewery

Into the cask

Ensuring a continuing fermentation

It's time now to consider one of the essential features of cask beer, the continuing fermentation, or cask conditioning as it's often called, in the cask itself, and how this is facilitated. By now, the bulk of the alcohol has already been made, so we don't want a vigorous exponential fermentation of the sort that took place earlier in the brewery tanks. Instead, a gentler level of activity is required, enough to carbonate the beer, help protect it from oxidation and contamination, and perhaps complete a few complex processes that subtly contribute to flavour.

Fermentation requires active yeast cells and enough fermentable sugars and other nutrients to feed them. The simplest and, according to my research, most common method of ensuring this is to interrupt the conditioning process at the right point, when just enough sugar and yeast remain to ensure the desired result. This can be done by cooling, typically when the beer is still at least 0.002° higher than the intended final gravity (FG). So, if the brewer is aiming for an FG of 1.008° for a typical session beer, they will likely slow the fermentation and package the beer when it's still at 1.010° or above.

Far fewer yeast cells are needed than for pitching, with ideal counts usually in the region of 0.5–1.5 million cells per millilitre. Most of the yeast will have settled out by this stage, but with a well-designed recipe, a reliable and healthy yeast, and a well-managed brewing and fermentation process, there are normally enough active cells in suspension to finish the job. 'Still the best yeast count,' says James Clarke at Hook Norton, 'is the finger test. You take a pint glass sample, hold it up to the window, and if you can see your finger relatively clearly then we know we've got the yeast count a bit right. Of course, we check with a haemocytometer [an instrument that accurately counts yeast cells] to make sure.'

Given that yeast activity has largely subsided, what reawakens it sufficiently to ensure activity in the cask? The most important factor is likely the increase in temperature. A beer racked at, say, 6–8°C is now warmed to at least a cellar temperature of 10–12°C, which also releases carbon dioxide evolved during the main fermentation and dissolved in the cooler circumstances of conditioning. The physical process of transferring the beer also rouses the yeast, agitating previously settled cells back into suspension, and introduces oxygen through contact with air. In other types of packaging, this would be a problem, but with a still-fermenting beer, the yeast scavenges it in short order, putting it to good use in budding new cells.

Some of the bigger producers, like Fuller's and Greene King, centrifuge the beer while it still contains sufficient residual sugar. This removes practically all the yeast from the initial fermentation, which is then replaced with carefully measured doses of fresh yeast, a process known as reseeding. Greene King has a sophisticated automated system for reseeding quickly and reliably. In theory, a different yeast strain could be introduced at this point, but the brewers I spoke to found the main fermentation culture performed well enough in cask that there was no need to bother with a second yeast.

Rather than centrifuging, beer is occasionally cold filtered before reseeding. I know of one quite prominent producer who has used this method in the last decade, though they were circumspect about it as some keen cask drinkers insist on drinking only unfiltered products. But centrifuging is functionally equivalent to filtering, if arguably slightly kinder to the beer. And a beer that has been filtered at the brewery then undergone cask conditioning with live yeast before being served without any further filtration is practically indistinguishable from one that's been put in a cask straight from a tank.

Another, rather more common way of helping things along is priming: allowing the beer to attenuate to its final gravity and then adding a carefully measured dose of extra sugar, usually in the form of a highly fermentable glucose syrup at a rate of perhaps 1.5–3 grams per litre. Even brewers who normally rely on slightly under-attenuating the beer occasionally prime if they find their calculations haven't quite worked out. An occasional alternative is to use unfermented wort or partly fermented wort, the latter known as kräusening.

The extent to which cask fermentation contributes to carbonation levels varies. Gazz Williams at Tiny Rebel noticed when the brewery expanded and moved from open to closed fermentation vessels that beer intended for cask was already relatively well carbonated from its initial fermentation so changed the process to reduce the fermentation in the cask itself, dropping practices like priming.

Even if both yeast and sugar content are tweaked slightly at racking, what follows is essentially the completion of the fermentation begun in the brewery, using the same yeast, and the cask is effectively an extension of the brewery fermentation vessel. The term secondary fermentation is often used to describe what happens in the cask, but I've avoided it here because it's potentially confusing, particularly from a historical perspective, as I'll explain in Chapter 6.

Fining

The association between clarity, or brightness as brewers call it, and quality is deep-seated in beer culture, and there's a rational basis for it. Yeast, one of the main potential sources of turbidity, tends to settle out once it can no longer ferment, so clarity can be a guarantee that the beer is finished and ready to drink. Haze, on the other hand, may indicate the beer is still green, retaining off-flavours and undesirable yeast bite; or that it's become contaminated with wild yeast and an unintentional fermentation is stirring things up; or most likely that it's the last dregs of the cask, drawn from too close to the sediment.

The objective truth is more complex, as not all reasons for haze are bad ones. Certain speciality styles are intended to be hazy precisely because the crucial factors that cause the haze – protein-rich ingredients and yeast in suspension in wheat beers, hop haze in hazy, juicy pale ales and IPAs – are style-defining characteristics. Nonetheless, generations of brewers have pursued the goal of creating a 'pin bright' beer, a near-transparent liquid that you can 'read a newspaper through', showing off colour and carbonation to best advantage. Most drinkers have expected their beer to look like this, at least until very recently.

Cask beer contains active yeast that initially remains in suspension, particularly as the cask is rolled between warehouse, dray and pub. Once in place in the cellar, nearly all casks will eventually drop bright of their own accord. However, that process may take days or weeks unaided, an impractical luxury in a busy pub with limited space, so it's normally helped along by additives known as finings. Traditionally, these are made of isinglass, sometimes known as white finings, a collagen, or protein-based body tissue derived from the swim bladders of fish. Its rather curious name is another Dutch derivation, from the obsolete term *huisenblas*, 'sturgeon bladder'.

Finings in solution at
St Austell brewery

Beluga sturgeon, a species also sought after for caviar, was once considered to yield the best isinglass, but today's sources are more commonly various tropical fish from the South China Sea or Nile perch from Lake Victoria, all of which are also fished for food. The swim bladders are removed and sun-dried to produce rather curious objects known as whole leaf, as they slightly resemble large leaves, though they're thick, tough and translucent beige or pale yellow in colour. Far more common today are flakes, powders and pastes that can be diluted and macerated in weak food-grade acid, or ready-made solutions in concentrated form.

Finings work electrostatically: yeast particles stay in suspension because they each carry a negative charge, which repels them from each other and inhibits them from flocculating. The collagen particles in the finings carry a positive charge which neutralises the charge on the yeast cells, so they start to clump together until the mass sinks under its own weight. As with many aspects of brewing, the quantity must be finely judged – too little won't clear the beer sufficiently, while too much will knock the yeast into the sediment before it's had a chance to complete its task.

At a time when more people are adopting vegetarian and vegan diets, brewers' use of isinglass has attracted critical attention, with clickbait headlines about beer made with 'fish guts'. Many non-carnivorous cask drinkers, including me, are pragmatic about isinglass, reasoning that the substance itself isn't supposed to be consumed. If the cask is properly managed, practically all of it sinks into the sediment to be discarded: one study found an average of 1.8 mg per litre remaining in the samples tested (Baxter and others 2007:133) and, in territories where beer ingredient labelling is mandatory, it's not normally required to be listed. But I understand why some drinkers choose to avoid it for ethical, health or allergenic reasons.

Some brewers now use vegan-friendly alternatives derived from sources including mineral silica and proteins extracted from pulses or fungi. Brewers report mixed experiences with these: some say they're not quite as effective as traditional isinglass, or that their efficacy is shorter-lived. But one I spoke to was so delighted with a brand he initially tried for a vegan special that he's since rolled it out across his range. Rooster's has switched entirely to vegan finings, and brewer Ol Fozard observes that though they work more slowly, the results are just as bright.

An even simpler alternative is to leave the beer unfined, an approach increasingly common in a market more tolerant of haze. More yeast cells in suspension will encourage a more active fermentation over a longer period, and there will be much more yeast in every mouthful, with inevitable impacts on behaviour and flavour. As discussed in Chapter 4, some proponents of unfined beer argue that these are for the better, while others insist that bright is best, particularly for traditional styles that have evolved to be poured this way.

A different type, auxiliary finings, are intended to remove protein solids rather than yeast. These work the opposite way round to regular finings, comprising negatively charged particles that attract positively charged proteins. If required, they're usually added in the fermentation tank about 24 hours before the beer is racked and left to complete their task before isinglass or an alternative is introduced, otherwise the two cancel each other out. There are no dietary concerns about auxiliary finings as they're made from vegetable sources, usually seaweeds like carageen or kelp.

Racking

The term racking can refer to any transfer of beer from one vessel to another but is commonly used for putting it into bulk containers like casks and kegs for dispatch. Racking cask beer, at its simplest, involves connecting a hose to the fermentation vessel using a valve that draws from above the sediment, attaching a right-angled tubular steel racking arm to the other end of the hose, which fits neatly into the shive hole of a freshly cleaned cask, then letting the beer flow, either by gravity or aided by a pump. So long as the flow is well-regulated, the beer isn't too lively, and a cool temperature encourages carbon dioxide to dissolve, you'll end up with a nice full cask, without excessive foaming, in around 30 seconds. Finings and priming sugar, if used, are added as the cask is filled. Some brewers use an intermediate tank called a racking tank which might drive a more sophisticated filling head, or perhaps more than one so several casks can be filled at once.

Casks are usually labelled immediately before they're filled. As well as the beer brand, the label should include a best before date, the date and time of filling, a batch code, and, often, a unique barcode. This not only helps manage distribution and stock control but enables the brewery to track down the source of any subsequently reported problems more easily and to check other casks in the same batch.

Racking lines at bigger breweries are almost as much fun to watch as cleaning lines. The line at Adnams can fill 300 casks per hour. At St Austell empty casks are automatically positioned below multiple filler heads. An operator guides each head into the shive manually then presses two buttons simultaneously to commence filling, which stops automatically when complete. When they invited me to try, I found guiding the head took more coordination than expected, but eventually managed to fill a firkin with flagship Tribute.

Racking is also the point at which beer can be dry hopped in cask, using a plug-shaped pellet of compressed whole leaf hops that is simply dropped in

Cask racking at
Thornbridge

through the shive hole before the cask is filled, typically using a 1-oz (27 g) plug
for a firkin or a thicker 2-oz (57 g) for a kilderkin. This once-common practice has
dwindled, partly because the results can be unpredictable for the same reasons
discussed when I considered dry hopping in brewery tanks, with the added
disadvantage that any unexpected effects won't show themselves until after the
beer has left the brewery. But it adds a distinctive dimension to the hop character
of a small handful of beers, including at Adnams, Bathams and Theakston.

The final task is to seal the filled cask with a shive, normally done by hand with
the aid of a mallet. A practiced operator can drive home a shive with one well-
judged whack and move onto the next with a machine-like rhythmic precision.
When I tried at St Austell it took me a good five blows before the cask was bunged
securely enough to be whisked away on the conveyor and into the distribution
chain.

Storage and distribution

Brewers usually get the continuing fermentation off to a good start by storing casks for at least a couple of days after filling, ideally at the intended cellar-cooled serving temperature of 10–12°. Knowing that once the beer reaches the pub, the typical licensee will want it on sale quickly, some insist on keeping it longer – two to three weeks in the case of one particularly fastidious brewer I spoke to – but this must be balanced against the practicalities of storage space and cash flow. A week is more typical: it's the preferred period, for example, at Brewster's in Grantham. 'Sometimes we have a run on things and have to ship casks more quickly,' says founder and head brewer Sara Barton, 'so we put a sticker on them asking the landlord to keep them for a week.'

The ideal is to ensure that, once filled, casks stay at cellar temperature until the beer is poured. High temperatures provoke inappropriately vigorous fermentations, producing off-flavours and excessive pressure so that the liquid explodes out of the casks when tapped and perhaps even pops the bungs of its own accord. Extreme heat, such as the 30°C+ heatwaves that are becoming increasingly common in the UK, can kill yeast, resulting in an incomplete conditioning and yet more off-flavours. At the other end of the scale, keeping a cask too cool slows conditioning, and at 2°C or below produces a chill haze as tannins from grain husks and hops start to bond together. The haze dissipates as the beer warms again, but the shelf life is irrecoverably reduced. Temperature affects finings as well as yeast behaviour: suppliers recommend keeping fined casks at 10–14°C and warn that the additive may not work outside this range.

In practice, beer is robust enough to tolerate a little variation, and unbroken 'cold chain' distribution is rare. This is usually fine when a brewery makes its own deliveries to local outlets, but selling beer further afield through a distributor can be more challenging. 'I drove past our distributor's yard during the summer and saw our casks stacked up outdoors in the sun,' recalled one regretful brewer. 'I drove past again two weeks later and they were still there. We found a new distributor after that.' This is undoubtedly one of the reasons why drinkers report that cask tastes better in outlets geographically closer to the brewery, leading some to conclude that it doesn't travel. The truth is that live conditioning equips it to travel well, but only if it's scrupulously looked after at every stage of its journey.

The term dray for a vehicle used to deliver beer is, incidentally, Germanic in origin, related etymologically to 'drag' and 'draw', and once meant a low, horse-drawn cart without fixed sides used to transport any heavy load. When internal combustion engines replaced horses, the word lost its general application, but brewers simply transferred it to newer vehicles used for the same purpose.

Horse-drawn drays are rarely seen nowadays but the term 'dray' is still used

Currently only three UK breweries keep their own horses and use them commercially for very local deliveries: Hook Norton, Samuel Smith and Wadworth. A few others hire horse-drawn drays for show purposes. But most still refer to their diesel lorries, and sometimes even their transit vans, as drays.

Shelf life

Beer carries a best before date rather than a use-by date. The former is advisory, whereas the latter is obligatory where there's a food safety risk. Though beer is unlikely to become unsafe to drink, its flavour tends to deteriorate over time: aromatic and bitter compounds break down, the texture thins out, oxygen imparts staleness and dead yeast produces savoury 'umami' flavours. Certain beers, particularly stronger or robustly flavoured styles like barley wine, imperial stout and sour mixed fermentation brews, can benefit from long ageing, but most beer is best drunk fresh and young, and cask is usually no exception.

Cask probably has the fastest average turnaround of any commercial beer. It typically takes around a week to brew, ferment and condition a session ale, plus another day in the packaging process. Allowing for at least a couple of days of cask conditioning, customers might then be enjoying it at the brewery's own taproom, or at a local pub, within 10 days of mashing in. Brewers may prefer at least some of their beer to spend a little longer in cask, depending on style and the behaviour of the house yeast, but likely no longer than a couple of weeks.

Best before dates vary but are typically set to between six weeks and three months after racking, so long as the cask is kept sealed. Cooler temperatures help, as Eddie Gadd at the Ramsgate brewery discovered during the Covid-19 lockdowns in 2020: casks kept in the taproom cold room at 10°C stayed good for around a month longer than those in the brewery's warehouse, where the regular 12°C temperature matches most pub cellars. In practice, most casks are used long before their expiry date as licensees are keen to sell them quickly. Once the cask is opened and the beer starts to flow, it's very much on the clock, as we'll shortly see.

Some cask beer turns out to have unexpected ageing potential, particularly when brewed to a stronger recipe. I've sampled excellent strong bitter that was more than two years old, and several brewers have told me of casks forgotten in a quiet corner then rediscovered a few years later, still in excellent form. Oakham brewery even has a flourishing sideline in beer that's deliberately cask-aged, including a core brand, Green Devil IPA (6%), and numerous specials. Rather than being primed with sugar, these beers are kräusened with part-fermented wort and kept at least six weeks – and up to two years for the strongest examples – with occasional venting if the pressure builds excessively, before fining and shipping. It's a similar approach to barrel ageing, as explained in Chapter 1, but in a clean stainless-steel cask with no additional wild fermentation or influence from wood. Particularly with stronger beers, the result is a more mellowed, rounded flavour, with a fine carbonation and no alcohol burn.

I can make your beer taste like shit… but what you've got here is beer that's well looked after.

ROBBIE DOUGLAS, general and cellar manager,
Crosse Keys, London EC3 (quoted in Betts 2017)

Cellaring and dispense

The cellar is the final staging point before a draught beer reaches the drinker, and if that beer is still fermenting, it's a particularly crucial link in the chain: 'In the cellar,' says Greene King quality manager Susan Chisholm, 'you're finishing off the brewing process.' As pub manager Robbie Douglas makes bluntly clear in the quote above, how this happens determines the quality of the beer placed in front of the drinker, for better or worse. Yet, while most beer connoisseurs have visited a brewery or two, to most of us the cellar remains a mystery. It's the place into which the bar staff annoyingly disappear when you're in a hurry to enjoy a last pint, muttering something about 'changing the barrel'. I know of only two or three pubs in London that actively invite the public into their cellars. Of course, some have health and safety issues that preclude this, but others simply haven't thought of it.

Cellars

The word cellar suggests an underground room, and this was indeed once the preferred location, benefitting from natural cooling in the days before artificial temperature control. Today, there are plenty of cellars at the same level as, or even above, the bar. Irrespective of its location, the cellar should be dry, well-drained and easy to clean, much like a brewery, and kept at a cool and even temperature, protected from draughts and sudden shifts of heat and cold.

Cellar temperature is one of the watchwords of cask beer, though there's some debate about the exact range it covers. In the past it was often quoted as 12–14°C, but many people, including nearly all the brewers I spoke to, prefer the cooler side of that range and downwards to 10°C or even a shade below. Andrew Ford, manager of the Hand in Hand in Wimbledon, London, one of the tiny number of publicans who invite the public into the cellar, aims for 11° in winter and 10° in

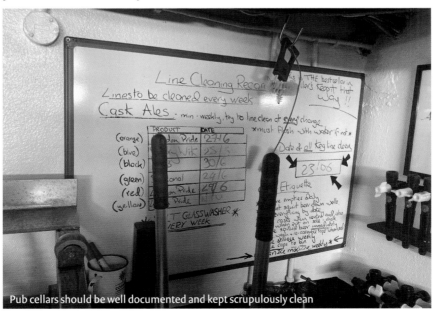

Pub cellars should be well documented and kept scrupulously clean

summer, arguing that while beer will readily warm up in the customer's hands – 'and people do have a tendency to clasp it to their chests,' he says – it can't be cooled down easily once poured.

'I prefer my cask to be a bit cold,' says Mark Hyson at Stewart Brewing. 'It's always going to warm up.' Perhaps it's the influence of drinking even cooler keg, bottled and canned beer, but I tend to agree, despite growing up in southern England where, according to many northern brewers I spoke to, cellars are too warm, perhaps due to the milder climate. Whatever the exact temperature, it shouldn't be warm in any meaningful sense, as the popular stereotype has it – just not quite so cool as keg beer.

The ideal cellar is of a size proportionate to the pub's turnover, with sufficient elbow room to manage it efficiently. Based on a weekly delivery pattern, Greene King (2018:5) advises that a cellar 'should be large enough to take the equivalent of 10 days stock', otherwise deliveries must be arranged more frequently. Cask beer places an additional demand on cellar space as it needs to rest undisturbed before tapping.

As beer is legally classed as a food, cellars and dispense equipment are subject to food safety legislation, and cask is a particularly delicate and vulnerable product. A good cellar is scrupulously clean, tidy and well-lit, with no rubbish or other unwanted clutter. A thermometer displayed in a prominent position provides an instant temperature check, with the cooling equipment easily accessible and kept free of obstructions that can inhibit its performance. A chart on the wall shows when the cellar was last cleaned and when it's due another brush-up. All the tools and paraphernalia for managing the beer, as well as cleaning equipment and materials, are well-organised and easily to hand. There's a system for arranging the stock, according to date and perhaps with best sellers in one place and changing guests and less popular beers in another.

Staff need to keep track not only of when a cask was delivered but when it should be tapped and vented as described below, when its contents should go on sale and when any remaining beer should be discarded, all of which can vary from beer to beer. I know cellar managers who keep all this information in their heads, but woe betide their colleagues if they're off sick or on leave. Most keep obvious written records: chalk marks on the casks themselves, whiteboards, and clipboards on the walls. Once again, there are parallels with brewery practice, where fermentation schedules are meticulously documented, and, as in a brewery, sampling is a crucial arbiter of a beer's progress towards perfection.

All this should sound obvious, but any travelling cellar assessor has their share of horror stories: pubs that turn off the cooling to save on bills then lose much more money with excessively foaming or spoilt beer; cellars that reek of blocked drains, or, at the other extreme, of inappropriately smelly disinfectants that can affect beer flavour; the chef's boxes of browning lettuces stacked in one corner in flagrant disregard of hygiene regulations forbidding food in cellars; the floor still sticky from the beer spilt yesterday when tapping a particularly vigorous cask. Such cellars are doubtless in a minority, but one significant enough to cause significant concern for overall cask quality, as discussed in Chapter 8.

Lines

While some pubs and bars still retain the old practice of filling a customer's glass straight from the cask, beer is more conveniently dispensed from taps on the bar, connected to the cellar by tubes known as lines. These are a particular quality trouble spot as stale beer can collect in them, potentially causing off-flavours and excessive foaming, and harbouring infections. Live beers like cask, and some contemporary craft kegs, also contain yeast solids and sometimes residues from dry hopping, which multiply such problems if they become lodged in the lines.

Amazingly, lines made from lead, a toxic metal, remained in use until well into the second half of the 20th century. Today, the material of choice is invariably plastic, either polythene or PVC. Cask lines were once typically 13 mm (½ inch) in diameter, but many pubs have replaced these with narrower 9.5 mm lines to reduce wastage. Multiple lines are commonly gathered into a python, a thick, well-insulated plastic outer sleeve with integral cooling.

Lines should be as short as possible, both to reduce the need to cool beer on its way to the bar and the capacity of the lines themselves. This is a good reason for keeping cellars close to bars, but the practicalities of building layout aren't always favourable. Ten metres of 9.5 mm tubing contains over 700 ml of liquid,

Well-organised cask cellar showing lines and self-tilting stillages

or around 1¼ pints, and many pubs have longer runs than this – I know of some where the lines hold four pints or more. All that beer sits around going stale when the bar is closed or if there are long gaps in the use of a particular tap. Python cooling helps, but won't entirely avoid the need for stale beer to be pulled through and discarded at the start of a session.

Line cleaning is one of the keystones of bar hygiene. 'Without question it is wise to make this an absolutely fixed ritual,' writes Patrick O'Neill in CAMRA's definitive guide to cellar management, 'to avoid any temptation to just leave it until tomorrow.' (2020:94.) It's very much like cleaning brewery equipment: first the line is thoroughly flushed with fresh water, then a specialised line-cleaning solution, usually based on caustic, is pumped in and left to soak for 10–20 minutes before being discarded. A second dose of line cleaner follows, after which the line is rinsed with water until no trace of the cleaner remains. If you see someone behind a bar pulling repeatedly on a handpump that only seems to be dispensing water, this is likely what they're doing. Like bigger breweries, some bigger pubs have automatic CIP (cleaning in place) systems.

Industry guidance insists on cleaning every line at least weekly, and the gold standard is to clean them between every change of cask. It sounds onerous, but to conscientious licensees it's not an unattainable goal. 'We always clean the lines between each cask,' one of them told me, 'unless we're really busy, and even then we at least flush thoroughly with clean water before connecting another cask.' But even licensees with harder noses should appreciate the economic arguments. An infected line causes excessive foaming, or fobbing as it's known, rendering the beer impossible to pour without wastage. Based on Greene King's calculations (2018:15) and the average price of beer in late 2022, one drip tray full of foam per day in a pub with 10 taps (cask and keg) equates to over £20,000 down the drain every year.

Inside the cask

When Alice Batham took her MSc in brewing science and practice at Nottingham University, she was irritated to find there were 'absolutely no scientific papers on cask: from the 1950s it's all keg products that are researched. I do understand it as cask processing is simpler, but more needs to go into research and education to improve the quality of cask.' As a member of the sixth generation of the family owning the historic Bathams brewery in the Black Country, where she's since become head brewer, Alice grew up immersed in traditional cask practice. She decided to begin to plug the gap by making it the subject of her master's dissertation. 'The research did show all the things we wanted to happen were happening,' she told me, but she's still surprised that 'brewers assumed they did without anyone actually looking to check.'

The things brewers want to happen are characteristic of any alcoholic fermentation. The yeast readily scavenges any oxygen that got in during racking, helping keep the beer fresh while the cask remains sealed, and buds to multiply itself: it consumes the remaining fermentable sugars conveniently left in by the brewer, producing alcohol and carbon dioxide. The additional alcohol is modest, typically around 0.2% ABV according to Fyne Ales technical brewer Yvonne Wernlein, but enough that brewers allow for it in their duty calculations. So long as the beer is cellar cool, the CO_2 smoothly dissolves into it.

We can also assume that other fermentation-related processes take place, as they did back at the brewery: esters and other flavour-active substances develop; green flavours like acetaldehyde are reduced; diacetyl is created then largely re-absorbed; sulphur compounds emerge but are then dispersed once the cask is vented, as described below. All these processes and more may contribute to the evolution of flavour and character, their impact increasing the longer the beer is kept before it's sold. But this is where we start to reach the frontier of scientific knowledge and enter the realms of speculation and subjectivity. What is clear is that the development of beer in the cask goes far beyond the simple carbonation suggested by the brewer's term 'conditioning'.

Exactly where and when do all these interesting things happen, in terms of the cask's location at the time? The common belief is that casks undergo conditioning in the pub cellar, but while that might once have been the case, most brewers today tend only to dispatch casks once they're almost ready. As beer continues to develop in transit, some brewers release casks earlier if they're destined to spend a week or so in distribution, and later if they're just going round the corner to a busy pub.

'It's my job to make things as easy for pub staff as possible,' was typical of the sentiments brewers expressed to me. 'I've run pubs and I know what it's like,' says Joseph Ince of Marble Beers. 'I don't want our beer venting on a stillage for five days before you can put it on. We have all the gear, we can make it easy for pubs to serve it the day after delivery, and the quicker we can put money into the pubs' hands, hopefully the quicker they can put money into ours.' Some of the old-established family brewers with small estates of pubs have closer relationships with licensees who retain traditional skill sets, making it easier to ship beer earlier, passing on more responsibility for managing the final stages of fermentation. But brewers supplying larger estates or mainly selling to the free trade aim to minimise the need for intervention at the pub.

The brewery that's arguably gone furthest in trying to make cask quick and easy is Marston's, one of the UK's largest producers, now owned by Carlsberg. In 2010 it launched Fast Cask, devised by brewing director Richard Westwood. The yeast used for fermentation is centrifuged out and replaced with a yeast that's been processed to form 'beads'. These act like tiny sponges, soaking up sugars that are then fermented. The advantages of a live fermentation are partially retained, but because the beads are much bigger and heavier than single yeast cells, they rapidly sink, allowing the beer to drop bright very quickly without being fined. The casks are allowed to precondition before shipping so they can be put on sale within hours of delivery.

On its launch, Fast Cask was inevitably criticised by traditionalists and others who debated whether it could achieve the same complexities of flavour as the established method. Over a decade later, it's still in use for a few Marston's brands, like Jennings Cumberland Ale and Wychwood Hobgoblin, but has otherwise failed to revolutionise the industry in the way some commentators predicted.

Even Fast Cask couldn't hope to make the format completely idiot-proof, nor imbue it with the ability to provide truly instant gratification. Live fermentation ensures there's always an element of unpredictability and inevitable variation between one cask and the next, and a need for patience and understanding in dealing with it. Cellar managers soon learn this from experience. Casks from one brewer may arrive in a sluggish mood and require coaxing into sufficiently sparkling condition. Another brewer may send beer bursting to get out, which then needs time to calm down.

Experienced cellar keepers regularly cite Timothy Taylor as a noted source of lively casks, and the brewery's chief executive Tim Dewey is unapologetic:

> We don't make life easy if it detracts from the beer. We let the yeast flow in and add priming sugar, and we don't say to outlets that the beer will be ready in hours: it'll take at least 48 hours, and we encourage them to give it a week in the cellar. The secondary fermentation is not an academic box ticking exercise, it adds a whole other layer of complexity to the beer, and we don't want to short-change that even though it's problematic.

Cask management

Venting

In storage at the brewery and during distribution, casks are invariably kept upright to save space, but moved by rolling on their sides. It's in this manner that a cask typically arrives in the pub cellar. If the manager holds lots of stock or prefers to age beer, the cask may end up stacked on its chime again for a while.

Stillage at the Hand in Hand pub, Wimbledon

There's even a way to draw beer from this position using the 'vertical extraction' system explained below. But the most traditional, and most widespread, method of positioning a cask for dispense is on stillage, on its side, securely supported at a slight angle, with the shive on top and the keystone at the lowest point.

The simplest method is to use three wedge-shaped wooden chocks on a flat surface, preferably raised at least slightly above the floor. With a chock on each side at the front and a third in the middle at the back, the cask is lifted clear of the surface and tilted slightly downward: the angle can be increased as the cask empties by moving the rear chock closer to the bilge. More common are permanent purpose-built stillages supporting multiple casks, often with ingenious self-tilting devices that hold the cask level when it's full and gradually tilt it to around 12° as it empties.

For the beer to complete its conditioning properly, it needs first to be thoroughly mixed up, with yeast, finings and dry hops, if used, dispersed throughout the liquid. This will likely already have been achieved in transit, but most sources recommend rolling a cask before placing it on stillage. Some cellar keepers exercise judgement here depending on the source. If it's fresh from the brewery down the road, particularly if it's been sitting on its end for a while, a good shake may be in order. But casks that have travelled a long way via a distributor may need to be treated more gently as they've already been disturbed several times, thus tiring the finings.

What does cask beer taste like immediately after delivery? This varies greatly depending on the cask and the circumstances, but it certainly won't be at its best. Depending on the weather and other conditions when in transit, it could be at a range of temperatures, though probably not the right one. It will certainly be hazy with unsettled solids that make an undesirable contribution not only to appearance but to flavour. The carbonation will vary depending on the beer itself and how long it's been in the cask: it could be so fizzy it refuses to settle in the glass, or unpalatably flat as the yeast hasn't yet had time to generate sufficient carbon dioxide. It may have noticeable off-flavours like green apple and sulphur, or it may be palatable but nowhere near its peak. As Susan Chisholm points out, 'just because a beer has dropped bright doesn't mean it's ready'.

Before anything else can happen, the beer needs to acquire the ambient temperature of the cellar. Depending on the starting temperature, this may take several hours. A cask that's been in the cellar for a while awaiting a position on the stillage already ticks this box, but once moved should be left undisturbed to settle and acclimatise for anything up to 24 hours.

After cleaning and sanitising the shive and keystone and their housings, the cask is vented by knocking a fresh, clean, tapered peg known as a hard spile through the tut, the indentation in the middle of the shive, with a short, sharp tap from a blunt, heavy object. Hard spiles are around 60 mm long and made from a hard wood like beechwood, or tough plastic, so they can form an airtight seal. Many cellar keepers now prefer the plastic version: 'If you take one thing

Spiles can be made of wood or plastic. Note yeast working through soft spile on right-hand cask

away from this interview, it should be this,' said veteran cellar manager Mark Dorber as he pressed one into my hand.

The resulting pressure change releases carbon dioxide, and along with it most of the unwanted sulphur compounds. It also facilitates correct conditioning, as veteran brewer Mark Tetlow, who has worked for several major cask breweries and is now at Oakham, explains. 'Until the gas is off,' he says, 'the finings and the yeast don't drop as the CO_2 holds them in suspension like little water wings.'

It's important to vent at cellar temperature: venting a warm cask will likely unleash a mass escape of gas that takes some of the liquid contents with it. This not only results in waste, mess and an unwanted yeast facepack, it can also cause injury from a high velocity spile. And some of the CO_2 may be lost for good, resulting in flat beer. Even at room temperature, the amount of excess gas released on venting varies. Many modern beers, observes Patrick O'Neill, 'do not evolve much gas and do not give any indication of continuing to "work" [ferment] after venting.' He wryly adds: 'More's the pity, some might think.' (2020:37.)

If little gas emerges, the hard spile is pushed home to retain what remains and any that subsequently evolves. For livelier beers, it's replaced by a soft spile. These are shorter, around 40 mm, and made of porous wood so gas can escape in a controlled manner: the best ones are bamboo, though there are cheaper functional alternatives. The cask now needs to be checked regularly and the spile replaced with a clean one every few hours. If the beer is actively fermenting, gas bubbles and visible yeast residue emerge. Once yeast activity subsides, the cask is hard spiled to retain the carbonation. Ed Razzall (2014) advises that, if there's no visible activity around a soft spile for three seconds, you should wait another three seconds and, if there's still nothing, replace it with a hard spile.

By manipulating the spiles in response to yeast behaviour, the skilled cellar keeper can precisely attain the required level of carbonation. What should this be? Alongside the popular stereotype of warm cask beer is the equally prevalent and incorrect one of flat cask beer. The truth is that cask should have a noticeable, even pronounced carbonation, but at a gentler level than a typical keg, canned or bottled beer, sparkling wine or fizzy soft drink.

The laws of physics dictate that gases dissolve more readily into liquids as temp-erature decreases and pressure increases. Cool cellar temperatures encourage CO_2 to dissolve into the beer, while the build-up of pressure inside the cask as more gas is produced by fermentation also encourages it to dissolve. Venting the cask and dropping the pressure immediately releases the excess gas that's unable to dissolve, but the reduced pressure also means some of the dissolved gas can no longer stay in solution, so starts to emerge as characteristic bubbles until a new equilibrium is achieved. Further gas will bubble out as the temperature starts to rise, as when the beer is poured and served. One consequence is that cellar temperature affects the level of carbonation: beer emerges fizzier from a cooler cellar than a warmer one.

One way of expressing the level of dissolved carbon dioxide scientifically is by volume. At normal atmospheric pressure and 12°C, beer will absorb about 1.1 volumes of CO_2. What this means is that if all the CO_2 were extracted from a litre of the beer, it would expand to occupy 1.1 litres of space. Another way of looking at this is in terms of grams of CO_2 per litre: 1.1 volumes is roughly equivalent to 2 g/l, which is widely considered an ideal figure for cask. The beer will form a good head when poured, and although it may look relatively still in the glass, will still effervesce on the tongue without bloating the stomach. In contrast, typical keg or canned beers have around 2.5 volumes of CO_2, or around 5 g/l, more for some styles, fuelling a more assertive sparkle and continuous bubbling in the glass.

Pub staff can't usually measure carbonation accurately, but so long as a well-made beer is vented then hard spiled as soon as gas stops emerging, it should be close to the ideal level, with the cellar keeper's own taste the final arbiter. In my view, too much cask beer is served under-carbonated. Leading brewing scientist and educator Keith Thomas found the average CO_2 content of 39 beers on sale at a UK beer festival was 1.73 g/l, 'not quite enough to give a strong tingle on the tongue', and some had only 1.2 g/l, 'definitely low enough to be a dull pint' (2017:33).

Anecdotally, it's an issue in many pubs too, with staff over-venting and soft spiling inappropriately, perhaps because they're following a set procedure rather than using their judgement based on the current condition of the beer. Some licensees undoubtedly prefer flatter beer as it's easier to pour accurately with less wastage, without considering that they'll likely end up pouring it less frequently as fewer customers will want to drink it. In fact, it's better to err on the side of the hard rather than the soft spile, as it's much easier to vent CO_2 than to add it back in. This was the point Mark Dorber was making with his parting gift.

Another factor that may give rise to over-venting is the relatively widespread but mistaken belief that cask beer needs oxygen. 'The beer should be allowed to breathe,' is an expression I've heard from several publicans and cask enthusiasts. But at this stage of its life cycle, yeast is perfectly capable of completing its task without additional oxygen. Indeed, this gas is now unwelcome, as it will produce stale off-flavours and nourish potential infections. Its ingress is in any case limited while the yeast protects itself with a blanket of CO_2. The only possible grain of truth behind the belief is that some drinkers appear to prefer the flavour of certain beers once they begin to show very early signs of oxidation – John Keeling, former brewing director at Fuller's, says certain dedicated London Pride drinkers won't touch it until at least its second day on the bar.

Venting disturbs the sediment once again, so the cask must settle, and perhaps develop further condition and flavour before it's served. Once resealed with a hard spile, it can be safely kept on a stillage at cellar temperature for several days, perhaps more.

Tapping

To pour the contents, the cask is tapped through the keystone hole. Today's taps are almost invariably plastic, of a simple but robust design with a cone valve that opens on a quarter turn. They have one or two threaded outlets for attaching lines at the front and a tapering rear section that fits into the cask, capped with a hop filter that looks a little like a miniature plastic laundry basket. On the cheapest and most common versions, the outlet sticks straight out at the front, but there are alternatives with an outlet pointing down, or both, or outlets protruding from each side so two lines can be connected at once. They take a little getting used to, as you'll find when you try to use one for the first time.

A sanitised tap is knocked firmly into the keystone, pushing the bung inside the cask. A closed tap is an effective seal so the cask can be kept unused for a while after tapping. There are different schools of thought about when to tap: some say it's best not to do it before venting as the pressure of carbonation will make it difficult to achieve without significant spillage, but many cellar managers tap immediately afterwards so long as there are clean taps available. Disturbing sediment isn't an issue at that point and the beer is now available for sampling. Greene King advise either tapping 24 hours before venting or at least 24 hours before use (2018:9).

Taps in place at Butcombe brewery

Once the beer is ready and required at the bar, a clean line is connected to the tap outlet, often through another small hop filter, and the tap opened. Immediately before the first pint is poured, the hard spile is either replaced by a loosely inserted soft one, or partially removed. This enables air to fill the space the beer vacates, otherwise a vacuum will develop, halting the flow, and releasing it will disturb the sediment. The fact that it's dispensed under normal atmospheric pressure is one of the reasons why cask pours smoothly at a slightly warmer temperature compared to beers which need additional gas pressure to force them from the keg.

A race ventilator

Some cellar keepers swear by clever plastic gadgets known as automatic spiles or race ventilators, with two valves controlled by ball bearings. Applied immediately after venting, these function as both hard and soft spiles. They let out carbon dioxide when the pressure inside the cask rises and let in air as it falls when the beer is drawn out, so once in place don't need to be changed.

Atmospheric pressure is a double-edged sword as the air will eventually spoil the beer. The liquid is protected to a point by the blanket of CO_2 generated by yeast, and hard spiling the cask again when the bar is closed will also help. Oxidation results when oxygen reacts with compounds in the beer to produce the stale taste of damp cardboard. Unlike CO_2, oxygen enables the growth of *Acetobacter* bacteria which convert alcohol to vinegary acetic acid. Air carries dust particles which convey other troublesome microbes, including wild yeasts and other bacteria which can produce unpleasant flavours, and the open airway offers a route in the other direction, dissipating the carbonation so the beer starts to flatten. The deterioration is gradual and progressive, and a skilled cellar manager should be able to taste its early signs: 'The cask starts to taste tired before it tastes sour,' explains Thornbridge brewer Dominic Driscoll.

When I asked brewers how long they recommend a cask remains on sale once the first pint is poured, they almost invariably answered 'three days'. Several then paused before qualifying this with something like, 'Well, you might stretch it to four or five, depending on the beer, and if everything else is done properly, but it might not be at its best.' Patrick O'Neill is more cautious, recommending only two days for 'ordinary milds and bitters'. Stronger, more robustly flavoured styles fare better. 'Strong bitters can stand three,' continues O'Neill, 'and barley wines or strong old ales will normally last nearly a week. High temperatures, bad hygiene and over-venting will reduce these times, while scrupulous cellar work... will extend them.' (2020:27.) So, pubs should only attempt to stock cask in

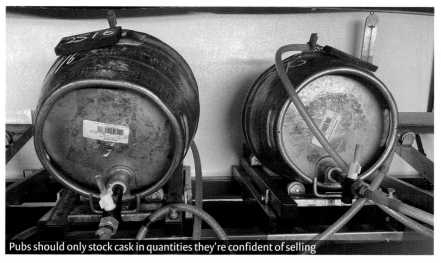

Pubs should only stock cask in quantities they're confident of selling

quantities they're confident will sell while still in optimum condition and be prepared to discard beer that's past its best rather than continuing to serve it.

Even with the best-kept cask and the healthiest turnover, not every drop can be sold. Eventually you reach the sediment, or trub, a mix of yeast debris, finings and other solids suspended in what remains of the beer. This and other waste caused by spillages, sampling, loss in lines, glasses overflowing when pouring and so on is known as ullage and pubs normally receive an allowance for at least some of it. At this point, the cask is removed from the line, which is ideally then cleaned as mentioned above. The courteous cellar keeper re-bungs the cask to stop the sediment – which soon becomes unpleasantly smelly – getting out and debris and wildlife getting in, before stacking it for collection. If all goes to plan, it's soon on its way back to the brewery, to be cleaned and refilled so the whole process can start again.

Quality time

As should be evident from the above, the timeline of an individual cask in the cellar can vary hugely. Except in the rare case of Fast Cask, it will typically require around a day to settle and acclimatise before venting, and perhaps another one or two days before it's fit to drink, with some beers taking much more.

When asked why his Fremlins' Mild was so locally renowned, Bob Harvey, licensee of the Woodmans Arms in Bodsham, Kent, explained he always followed the advice of a retired publican friend, who had told him: 'The secret of keeping beer and ale, my lad, is to order it in advance so it can lay for two weeks before you tap it.' (Tubbs 1966:22.) Writer and blogger Paul Bailey, whose post on cellarmanship (2013) first alerted me to this pearl of wisdom, observes that 'less time for publicans to wait before the beer can be served, unfortunately often means less time for characteristic signature flavours to develop, and this may well be the reason that many once classic beers are now mere shadows of their former selves.'

Though the trend today is towards making cask as 'plug and play' as possible, as Sara Barton puts it, many experts agree that patience has its rewards. 'I've run pubs,' says brewer Eddie Gadd, 'and I really believe that casks benefit from being left undisturbed, ideally five days on stillage before you pour from them. Not all pubs can do that but if you can, you'll end up with much better beer over time.' The Castle Rock brewers told me one of the pubs in their small estate preferred to stillage casks for five days to positive effect, though the beer is decent enough if drunk earlier.

Mark Tetlow says:

> The cask that you get to two weeks after venting and hard spiling you can guarantee will be the best beer in the cellar. Once the yeast is on the bottom producing a little extra gas, all the flavours are starting to mature, the hop character is softening, and the sediment gets really compact which gives you a better yield. And always, always sample the beer before you connect it to the beer line. If you go to one pub where the beer is absolutely fine, and to another where it's nectar, the second pub has done the best conditioning.

Time is unarguably a factor with those few remaining beers that are dry hopped in cask. The fluid dynamics of a busily working beer break up the compressed plug and the hop fragments are dispersed through the liquid, releasing their essential oils. Bitter alpha acids won't dissolve at this low temperature, but depending on how long the beer is kept, other factors can increase the suggestion of bitterness, such as the release of tannins. To some, the beer is no longer at its best once this happens, but others appreciate the flavour changes. And then there's the much-underexplored field of biotransformation, mentioned in Chapter 2.

Mark Dorber began his career in the industry with a summer job at the White Horse in Parsons Green, West London, in 1981, eventually managing the cellar and helping turn the pub into the noted specialist beer outlet it remains today. Its flagship cask bitter was Draught Bass, which was originally dry hopped, but Bass ended the practice because of fears about hop creep and hop solids causing dispense problems. Mark thought the change was for the worse, so secured a supply of hop plugs and began adding them himself. He also experimented with ageing the beer in the cellar. 'We would sell a young Bass at 10 days and a three- or four-week-old Bass side by side,' he recalls. 'We taught the customers what was going on and to understand the difference. We'd do comparative tastings every day, and overall, they preferred the older version.'

Today, Mark leases Adnams' pub the Anchor in Walberswick, Suffolk, a regular stockist of Adnams Southwold Bitter, one of the few remaining traditional brews that's still dry hopped in cask, using Fuggle. He remains fascinated with the technique and aims to mature each cask for several weeks before it goes on the bar. 'If you start putting vegetal matter in a cask of beer, it's going to do things to the yeast,' he observes. At the brewery in nearby Southwold, I tasted a fresh sample alongside an aged one and certainly noted the difference in complexity: the developing hop tannins had given the older beer a tantalisingly spicy bitter quality that reminded me of lemon tea.

Another former Adnams cellar manager, and now independent brewer, who advocates promoting flavour development through ageing is Ed Razzall. In a 2014 blog he describes the effect of keeping a cask of the brewery's Ghost Ship for two months before serving. 'The difference is remarkable, I promise you. Gone are the spiky, prickly hop notes, and the beer is mellowed, malty, spritzingly carbonated [and] glacially clear. Any funky off notes from the yeast will have gone, and it will be a joy to drink.'

Vertical extraction

It's also possible to tap beer from upright casks. Known as vertical extraction, this is a little trickier to manage successfully, requires more cleaning and makes sampling more difficult. Some claim it yields more ullage as the back head provides less surface area for sediment than the bilge. Stuart Bateman is one brewer who believes a beer's condition develops better on a conventional stillage, but others argue that, if done properly, it can produce better quality results than the traditional method and is in any case a useful option when cellar space is short. It's particularly common in Scottish pubs where cellars are typically small, and is spreading elsewhere as newer, smaller venues like micropubs and specialist bars proliferate.

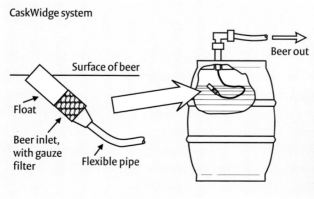

CaskWidge system

Surface of beer

Float

Beer inlet, with gauze filter

Flexible pipe

Beer out

The method requires working entirely through the keystone: the shive is left sealed and ignored. A special extractor housing known as a shank is knocked in and the cask is vented, either with an integral valve or through a housing that accepts hard and soft spiles. The beer can be sampled by siphoning.

There are two methods for conveying it to the bar. The first is to insert a hollow steel extractor rod through the shank until its inlet is just above the sediment. A clean line is connected to the other end of the extractor. The second, more recently developed and highly praised by the users I've spoken to, is the proprietary CaskWidge system. This replaces the rod with a flexible tube incorporating an inlet mounted on a float that automatically positions itself just below the surface as the cask empties.

Cellar trainer and former licensee Annabel Smith is an advocate for this float-based system. Both the horizontal and the steel extractor methods, she points out, draw beer from the lower part of the cask, just above the sediment, so there's often a sudden plunge in quality as the layer of liquid that's been sitting at the top, nearest the air, finally reaches the bottom. But CaskWidge continuously draws from the upper layer while it's at its freshest.

While it's impossible to pour beer straight from the cask using these methods, they work with handpumps and other dispense systems. All other considerations remain the same, including the demands of venting and conditioning and the need to empty casks promptly.

Cask breathers

First introduced in the late 1970s as a way of extending the shelf life of a cask without excess gas, cask breathers or aspirators aid an active beer's natural protection by supplementing its blanket of carbon dioxide. The cask is vented and spiled in the usual way, but after the first pint is drawn, the spile is immediately replaced by a connection to a demand valve of the sort found in

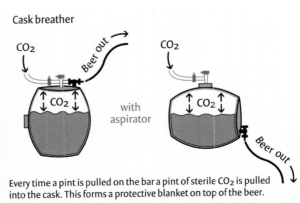

Cask breather

with aspirator

Every time a pint is pulled on the bar a pint of sterile CO_2 is pulled into the cask. This forms a protective blanket on top of the beer.

divers' breathing apparatus. This includes an airtight diaphragm which is pushed outwards if excess pressure builds up in the cask, opening a valve to vent it like an automatic spile. But if the pressure starts to drop as the cask empties, the diaphragm is sucked inwards, opening another valve to let in sterile gas.

The medium used is usually CO_2, though nitrogen or a mixture can be used. Once normal atmospheric pressure is restored, the diaphragm relaxes and the valve closes again. Some people assume that because the beer encounters extraneous CO_2 it must surely absorb some and become excessively carbonated. But the laws of physics still apply, and if pressure and temperature remain constant, there will be no further uptake.

By using a breather correctly it's possible to keep a cask on sale for up to six days without any noticeable deterioration in quality. Some manufacturers claim this can be extended to 20 days, though cellar experts are less convinced. The system will protect the beer from oxidation and other airborne damage throughout, though other problems might arise from the prolongation of natural processes beyond what the brewer intended. Still, even a few more days is a boon to venues that still want to offer cask but have too low or too erratic a turnover to work within the normal timescales. I've known breathers used in small country pubs and in brewery taprooms and other venues that don't open daily, where the only alternatives would be excessive and expensive waste or no cask at all.

There is absolutely no advantage to using the system where turnover is sufficient not to require it, as it simply adds extra complications for cellar staff, encumbering them with more equipment that must be cleaned and maintained. Trainer and cellar assessor Nigel Sadler points to the experience of one big brewing group who issued breathers to all its pubs in the interests of shelf life, but failed to explain how they were best used: he found numerous examples of incorrect and unhygienic use with high turnover beers that would have been sold in time anyway.

Cask breathers provoked many decades of bitter controversy among cask campaigners, thanks in part to a failure to understand the science. Despite the recommendation of CAMRA's expert Technical Committee, the campaign's 1982 annual general meeting (AGM) voted down a motion to accept their use, blocking pubs which adopted them from appearing in the *Good Beer Guide*, as members 'thought that the system could be the thin end of the wedge' (CAMRA 1982:1). Numerous blind taste trails, such as one in eastern England that concluded 'even experienced beer-tasters could not tell the difference' (CAMRA 1999), failed to shift opinions and the ban was upheld at subsequent AGMs. Finally, in 2018, CAMRA adopted a 'neutral position', which it still retains (CAMRA 2022a), though this hasn't stopped certain branches continuing to disapprove.

Dispense methods

Gravity

The simplest and most time-honoured method of pouring cask beer is directly from the tap in the keystone, known as gravity dispense. Although now rare in old-established pubs, it remains a popular method at beer festivals and among the new wave of micropubs. The method has long had its enthusiasts. A manual for bar staff first written in the mid-60s remarks that 'experienced bitter drinkers will persistently aver that beer drawn straight from the cask is superior to any drawn through pumps,' but concludes that the opinion 'probably stems merely from the fact that they can *see* it being served.' (Coombs 1982:20.)

Some drinkers believe beer dispensed this way is flatter, as it often has a more modest head, but so long as the cask is kept cool the reverse should be the case: the liquid has the shortest distance to travel and the maximum carbonation is retained in the glass. So long as it's been well-managed, the resulting pint should have a healthy sparkle and a reasonable head, though not as dense as when poured through a beer engine, particularly with a sparkler, as explained below.

Despite its advantages of simplicity and cheapness, the method poses some challenges. A bar is too warm a place to keep a cask and you might not want stillages occupying otherwise valuable retail space. The historic solution was to take glasses into the cellar or fetch beer to the bar as often as necessary in large jugs, which inevitably dissipated carbonation. The Star Inn, a heritage pub in Bath, still recalls this practice by serving its Draught Bass from glass jugs for those who like it that way.

Alternatively, there are ways of cooling casks in the public area. The low-tech method is to use evaporation by draping them in wet cloth, surprisingly effective but ugly, messy, unpleasant to manage and requiring constant attention so usually reserved only for emergencies. In-cask systems which introduced a water-cooled

Gravity dispense is a popular method at some micropubs

Handpulls at Vat and Fiddle pub, Nottingham

probe through the shive, coupled with an insulating jacket around the cask, were once popular and are still occasionally seen, though they can make managing condition more difficult and are yet another item to keep clean. Most beer festivals now use insulated cooling jackets wrapped snugly around the outside of the cask, incorporating tubes that circulate chilled water. Micropubs and similar venues often have a cold room or cellar as close to the bar or serving area as possible, providing the additional opportunity to create a visual feature using a picture window.

Beer engines

The simple manual pump known as the beer engine, or more familiarly as the handpump or handpull, has become the emblem of cask beer. The distinctive pump handles on the bar, and the theatre of operating them, lend the format an attractive and easily recognisable visual feature, perhaps misleadingly as beer engines are neither a defining feature of cask nor the only practical method for dispensing it.

Below the bar is a simple mechanical pump based on a piston. When the handle is upright, the piston is closed, but starts to rise as the operator pulls the handle towards them, creating a vacuum which pulls beer into the cylinder. When the handle is pushed back, a valve opens which allows beer to remain in the cylinder. Another pull forces the beer out of the cylinder and through an outlet, while simultaneously pulling in more beer behind it ready for the next pull. The pump is normally set up so a single smooth pull yields either a quarter- or half-pint. The extra pressure and agitation as the beer works its way through the system helps encourage a good head but dissipates some carbonation.

Beer engines were originally mounted on the back bar, and some still are, particularly in countries like the US where keg taps usually emerge there too. In Britain nearly all of them migrated to their current position on the bar itself in the late 19th century. In the classic design the outlet is a simple tap that emerges a short distance below the handle, so the glass is filled below the bar. But more recent designs incorporate swan necks, which both increase the sense of theatre, as the customer can easily see the beer flowing, and help agitate it to produce a more copious head.

Air pressure and other rarities

A few decades ago one of several clear dividing lines between the beer cultures of England and Scotland was the presence in Scottish pubs of sturdy but elegant bar mounts, often of gleaming brass, known as tall founts (pronounced, and sometimes spelt, 'font'). These were the customer-facing end of an air pressure cask dispense system introduced in the 1870s, the ancestor of today's familiar pressurised gas dispense for keg, which ultimately supplanted it in most other countries. Air pressure continued in use in Scotland well into the 1980s, and a tiny handful of historic installations remain in service.

One of them is in the Bow Bar, a delightful place in Edinburgh's Old Town refitted in 1987 as a reconstruction of a traditional one-room alehouse, where all the cask is dispensed this way. The founts here are known as Aitkens, perhaps the best-known design, introduced in the 1960s. Assistant manager Lloyd Thomas is too young to harbour nostalgia for them, but his enthusiasm is undisguised. 'Once you get the hang of them,' he told me, 'they're a brilliant piece of kit and it's a shame you can't get them anymore. The control over how good a pint you can pour is excellent and the beer is smoother, more knitted together. I've worked in bars with handpulls and I don't like them, the beer just seems to come out flat and won't hold a head for more than 30 seconds.' As the equipment is no longer made nor supported, Lloyd and the pub's general manager, Mike Smith, apply considerable time and initiative to keep it going, tracking down second-hand spare parts and improvising when necessary.

Originally, the pressure was created by a hydraulic system known as a water engine that forced water into a sealed tank, compressing the air above it. On today's legacy systems, it's supplied by electric compressors like the one chugging away in a corner just outside the Bow Bar's immaculate cellar. It's used in conjunction with a variant of the vertical extraction system, with pressure supplied via a hose connected to a valve in a steel housing clamped onto the keystone, incorporating a spear to extract the beer.

Turning the tap handle on the fount opens another valve, allowing beer to flow out of the cask under pressure. The control so valued by Lloyd is provided by a simple air hole just under the tap. If it's left open, additional air is sucked into the beer just before it emerges, creating a denser head, but it can be closed with

Aitken founts at Bow Bar, Edinburgh

Recapture trays

the thumb while pouring, enabling the operator to vary its effect by partially closing or 'feathering' it, as Lloyd puts it, like a skilled recorder or penny whistle player manipulating the pitch of notes.

Beer poured this way is particularly lively in the glass as the additional pressure prevents the release of carbon dioxide, so is more likely to fob and overflow. To reduce wastage, the system was often used in conjunction with recapture trays, and the Bow Bar has these too. Under every tap is an individual drip tray: turning the tap halfway disconnects the airhole and starts drawing 30% of the beer from the tray rather than the cask. To facilitate this, there's another valve below the level of the bar which must be turned before the beer will flow. If it's not turned off once a pint is poured, fresh beer slowly works its way into the tray, which eventually overflows if left unchecked, something that catches out new staff unused to the system.

This all sounds a little like the bad old pub habit of emptying the contents of drip trays back into casks, and new installations are frowned upon, though any spilt beer is fed back straight into the tap from its own tray and should be reused very quickly. It still requires trays and glasses, as well as all other parts of the system, to be kept scrupulously clean, and staff must pour carefully so beer doesn't drip over their hands. A similar system is sometimes used alongside sparklers in the north of England, as explained below. Otherwise, casks behave as they do under ambient pressure: the additional weight of air doesn't hasten oxidation and the beer remains drinkable for the same period as with ordinary spiling. The Bow Bar is one of my favourite cask pubs, and I've admired and appreciated every pint I've had there over the years. This visit was no exception: beers from the founts were all beautifully fresh and spritzy, with a lasting head and a focused aroma.

How did such a successful system, and one that embodied a distinctive national tradition, fall so comprehensively out of use? Some of the blame must, sadly, lay at the feet of CAMRA. In 1977 London brewer Truman, part of the then much-reviled Watney group, launched a new cask product dispensed by a variant of the air pressure system. CAMRA's National Executive promptly banned this, and all other beer served in a similar way, from being classed as real ale, unthinkingly removing the eligibility of all but a tiny handful of Scottish pubs for the *Good Beer Guide*. Following much heated debate and a threat by Scottish members to split the campaign, the dispute was resolved by devolving approval of the system to local branches. The fuss undoubtedly harmed both the reputation of CAMRA and of the founts themselves. The fact that they were more difficult to distinguish from keg taps didn't help, and they were progressively superseded by the more distinctive and symbolic handpumps.

Another once relatively common but now rare method of dispensing cask is with a powered pump, replacing the muscle power of the bar staff. Metered electric pumps appeared in numerous pubs, particularly in parts of the English Midlands and northwards, in the 1960s: a classic design, made by Mills Brothers of Sheffield, incorporated a glass half-pint cylinder into the bar mount, visibly emptied by a moving diaphragm when the pump was activated. Like founts, they were considered easily confused with keg taps and have almost entirely disappeared, though a few working installations remain in northeast England.

A more modern variant is the flojet pump powered by compressed gas, not in contact with the liquid but used to operate a diaphragm that pulls it to the bar. The system is particularly useful with long lines or where the bar is a long way above the cellar, and both types of pump allow cask taps to be mounted on the back bar alongside keg taps, as in some contemporary craft beer pubs.

Glassware

Anyone familiar with the Belgian beer scene will know how seriously the country's brewers, pub staff and drinkers take the subject of glassware. Though there's an element of marketing hyperbole in the insistence that every beer, or at least every brewery, must have its own glass, the belief that glass design affects the appreciation of beer has a firm scientific basis. In the simple words of US beer writer and tasting expert Randy Mosher, 'the geometry of the glass affects the way the beer looks, smells and tastes' (2009:104). The shape of the vessel profoundly influences head formation and the extent to which carbon dioxide escapes, which help determine carbonation, mouthfeel, aroma and palate.

A glass that tapers towards the rim helps emphasise aroma, as with a wine-glass or brandy snifter. Goblet-style glasses, like those used for Belgian Trappist ales, give plenty of room for the much-prized head, but also provide extra surface area, dissipating carbonation more rapidly. Then there's the ergonomic question of how easy and comfortable the glass is to drink from, which will affect your experience of the beer. This has a consequence for temperature – you can hold a stemmed glass without your body heat unduly affecting it, or you can cup it to warm the beer. Without a stem you don't have that choice, particularly if, like those drinkers Andrew Ford mentions, you clasp the glass to your chest.

UK beer culture could learn from the Belgians here, as most glasses currently in common use do little to flatter their contents. Sadly, some drinkers' concern for glasses doesn't seem to stretch much beyond how full they are. UK law stipulates that draught beer must be served only in measures of one-third of a pint (189.5 ml, historically called a nip), two-thirds (379 ml, sometimes called a schooner),

TYPES OF GLASSWARE

Shaker
Used for ales, particularly in the USA.
Originally devised as part of the kit for
'shaking' and serving cocktails.

Tulip
Used for ales, particularly in the UK.
A shapely, more aesthetically pleasing version
of the straight 'sleeve' pint glass.

Nonic
Used for ales, particularly in the UK. The bulge
is intended to prevent the rims chipping in
the glass washer (hence 'no nick').

Weissbier Glass
Used for German-style wheat beers.
The extended height and tapering shape allow
the thick foam to be captured at the top.

Chalice or Goblet
Used for strong ales, particularly in Belgium.
The shape and name echo the religious origins
of Trappist and Abbey beers.

Pilsner Glass
Used for true pilsner lagers,
particularly in Germany. The tapered shape
allows deep foam to collect at the top.

Stemmed Tulip
Used for strong ales, particularly in Belgium.
The curved shape both retains foam and allows
aromas to be accentuated.

Seidel
Used for helles and other lagers,
particularly in Germany. The thick glass and
handle help to keep the beer cold.

or multiples of a half-pint (284 ml). In practice, most cask is sold in pints (568 ml) and halves, in glasses designed to hold the full measure when filled to the brim.

Local authorities permit bar staff to underfill by up to 5%, leaving only minimal room for a head and none for aroma. And drinkers are also entitled to insist that glasses are filled completely with liquid beer. Oversized lined glasses, with an etched or printed line to indicate the correct measure, leave a little space for a more flattering pour, but are rarely seen outside a few specialist pubs and beer festivals. Customers unused to them sometimes complain they're being sold short, but pint glasses that are also lined for halves and thirds provide a simple way of getting more aroma room.

Cask glasses in common use are split into two broad types. Straight glasses are tumblers with no handle that taper slightly outwards towards the top. The simplest straight-sided conical designs, known as shakers in the US, have been around since the early days of mass-produced glassware in the mid-19th century. They're typically made of quite thick glass to withstand the rigours of pub life, which makes them a little uncomfortable to drink from. More iconic is the Nonik, with its distinctive bulge about 25 mm from the top. This is intended to help prevent damage to the rim when glasses knock against each other, allowing for thinner glass and providing a handy grip for the drinker. Based on a US design originally intended for soft drinks, it was introduced to the UK in 1948. Variants include tulip shapes with a more elegant, rounded outward taper.

Glasses with handles are known as mugs, or sometimes jugs, mimicking the shape of the opaque mugs and tankards they replaced. The best-known is the dimple mug, with three bands of interlocking hexagonal dimples wrapped

around a slightly barrel-shaped body. Beer historian Martyn Cornell (2015) observes that the resulting multifaceted effect 'seems particularly suited to reflecting and refracting the colour of amber beers' like traditional English bitters. Introduced in the 1960s, the dimple was once ubiquitous, particularly in more upmarket pubs, then fell out of fashion before undergoing an ironic rehabilitation as a retro icon in the early 21st century. The chunkiness helps a little to retain the temperature but makes the glasses heavy and awkward. They feel intrusive on the lips and are so uncomfortable to hold by the handle that most drinkers grip them around the body.

Of course, there's nothing wrong with wanting simply to drink a straightforward pint and choosing a straightforward glass from which to drink it. But deeper appreciation of beer flavour demands something better – ideally a stemmed glass that's oversized for the intended measure, with a shape that tapers inwards, comfortable to hold and with no colours or large logos obstructing the view.

In recent years, several new glass designs have emerged to cater for the tendency to drink newer craft beers in smaller measures, like the Teku, a classic Italian design by brewer Teo Musso, of veteran craft brewery Baladin, and beer writer and expert Lorenzo Dabove, which first appeared in 2006. It's rather like a stemmed wineglass but with angles rather than curves, tapering inward to an outward-tilting lip. Several UK breweries use more traditional stemmed glasses for serving halves and two-thirds measures which work almost as well. Simpler but still elegant, and perhaps more robust in pub use, is the Mencia tumbler. This is stemless but has an inward angle that focuses aroma and head and is very comfortable in the hand.

Teku glasses

One important requirement is a smooth inner surface, ruling out nucleated glasses which are etched inside. These are fine for more carbonated beers, like the pale lagers whose branding they often carry, where the irregularities help create steady streams of bubbles. The effect doesn't work so well with the lower carbonation of cask and will just make the beer go flat more quickly.

The glass is the very last link in the chain and still has the potential to spoil the experience. Grease interferes with head formation, while scratches provide unwelcome nucleation sites. Glasses inadequately rinsed or washed with too much or the wrong sort of detergent cause similar problems as well as retaining unwelcome odours. They should be kept inverted to avoid dust and other intruders, but well-ventilated so they dry properly and don't get musty. A good pub has plastic matting on the glass shelves to create airspace beneath, and never stacks glasses on each other. There are hygiene considerations too: glasses can transmit saliva-borne infections, which is why pubs today always provide a fresh glass when you return for a refill rather than risk your dirty glass contaminating the beer tap. And well-trained bar staff know that while the bottom half of the glass is fine to touch, the top half is only for the customer.

Pouring and sparklers

There's more to pouring beer than simply getting liquid into the glass. The head, a crucial component of visual appeal and a contributor to mouthfeel and aroma, is formed during the pour. And this is the last opportunity for carbon dioxide to escape before the beer is handed to the drinker.

The head results from bubbles forming in the liquid and dragging proteins behind them to the surface. Some of it comprises air trapped by turbulence when the beer is poured, while some is formed by carbon dioxide escaping from the beer itself. These CO_2 bubbles also drag some of the flavour components with them, particularly bittering compounds and aromatic oils. A good head often leaves lacing, the traces of foam that cling to the inside of the glass as it's emptied.

A good head isn't necessarily an indicator of good carbonation, as significant gas may have escaped while forming it. In countries like Germany and the Czech Republic, lager is typically poured much more vigorously than in the UK, almost straight down into an oversized wide-brimmed glass, often with a nucleated bottom, then left to settle if necessary and topped up. This creates the desired thick head, but also dissipates CO_2. Justin Hawke of Moor Beer, an aficionado of good lager as well as cask ale, demonstrated this to me with his own excellent helles in a comparative tasting at the brewery taproom. The crash pour, as Justin called it, yielded a beer with notably more modest carbonation, much closer to the cask beers we sampled alongside it.

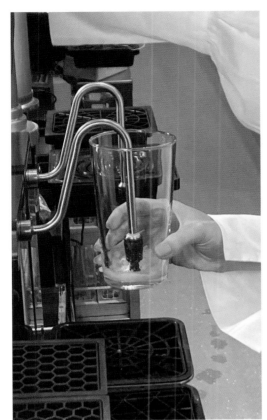

Sparkler

Pouring through a beer engine with a swan neck and sparkler

This sort of treatment is fine with highly carbonated beer from a pressurised keg, but risks knocking cask beer flat. Cask is best poured in as smooth and steady a movement as possible, one of the reasons why air pressure works so well. With a handpump, a few steady pulls should be enough to fill a pint glass. Some pumps have a shorter spout: with these, the glass is held at a 45° angle with the nozzle just inside the rim but not touching it, then gradually brought upright as it fills. The straighter the angle, the more turbulence and the more head. Other hand-pump fittings have a longer swan neck spout that reaches right into the glass to fill it from the bottom up. Pouring from one of these usually requires leaving the beer to settle before topping up, losing a little more CO_2 in the process. Finally, advise the manuals, the beer should be placed 'on a drip mat, bar towel or counter tray with the branding facing toward the customer' (St Austell 2022:13.5).

Which brings us to the sparkler, a tiny plastic object that's provoked disproportionate sound and fury. Sparklers are nozzles that fit over the spout of a beer tap, forcing the beer through a ring of small holes, rather like a shower head, which both aerates the beer and encourages CO_2 to escape. The width of the holes varies, with narrower 0.6 mm 'tight' examples producing a more intense effect than the wider 1 mm versions. The beer normally needs to settle for a few seconds before it's topped up, resulting in about 10 mm of dense, creamy head atop a slightly less carbonated liquid. The head will persist for some time as the beer is drunk, often leaving plenty of lacing.

Sparklers strip some of the bitterness and essential oils from the beer and transport them into the head with the CO_2, altering the balance of flavour and aroma: taste the head itself with a finger or teaspoon and you'll find it's sharply bitter, much more so than the beer beneath. Some argue that sparklers help to round out and integrate the flavour.

Cask beer poured without a sparkler should still produce at least some head, even on gravity dispense, thanks to natural carbonation and aeration during pouring. But the result is typically not as dense, persistent or lacy. Instead, there's a loose head with larger bubbles that are less stable so tend to dwindle more quickly. But more CO_2 and flavour will be retained in the liquid itself. If there's no visible head at all, something's likely wrong: the beer is underconditioned or stale, or the glass is dirty.

Sparklers have been around for a while – beer historian Gary Gillman (2017) traces early brass versions to 1885. Historically, they were more favoured in the West Midlands and the north of England, and weren't common in Scotland, where the air pressure system produced a similarly textured result. They've since been more widely adopted north of the border as air pressure has declined. Some commentators suggest their popularity in the north was because beers tended to be less hoppy where hops weren't grown commercially, so the sparkler made the best of this by emphasising the hop character on first impression.

Whatever the truth, the geographical division still holds, and the tendency of some of the big pub groups to recommend sparklers globally has generated much of the controversy. 'We're on the sparkler boundary here,' says Mark Tetlow at Oakham in Peterborough, while Sara Barton at Brewster's Brewery in Grantham, a 20-minute train ride further north, considers herself firmly in sparkler territory. While drinkers to the south of Bristol prefer unsparkled beer, some pubs to the north, towards the Midlands, favour the gadget, so Butcombe Brewing recommends serving its beers either without or with a looser 1-mm model.

One outlying sparkler-friendly brewery is St Austell in the Cornish town of the same name, thanks to the Yorkshire influence of the late and much-respected Leodian Roger Ryman, appointed head brewer in 1999. Despite describing herself as 'a good old southerner', Roger's successor, George Young, continues to recommend the practice. 'The beers look great,' she says, 'and they were designed with more hops in them so the loss through condition is taken into account.'

Since they produce foamier beer, sparklers are sometimes coupled with another controversial device, the autovac. Any overflow falls into a tray and is recycled back through the handpump. As with the sparkler itself, the additional agitation contributes to a creamy head but knocks out carbonation. It also increases the hygiene risk by further exposing beer to air and adding still more passages and surfaces where infections may lurk. As with recapture trays used with air pressure systems, hygienic use of an autovac requires thorough and frequent cleaning, a fresh and spotless glass for every pour and staff capable of keeping their hands out of the way of the flow.

Some drinkers have entrenched views on sparklers, but the question of whether a beer is better with or without them is surely down to the beer and the drinker's taste. As George Young suggests, brewers who know their beer is likely to be dispensed via sparklers develop their recipes accordingly. With very hoppy beers, the effect can tip the balance. Tom Fozard's brewery Rooster's in Harrogate, is deep in sparkler territory, and his brother, head brewer Ol, even has a sparkler tattoo. But Tom admits that he's undecided as to whether he prefers their hoppiest regular cask beer, a West Coast IPA, on gravity dispense. Staff understanding helps. Toby McKenzie of RedWillow, also in sparkler country, points out that if beer from a fresh cask is very lively, so that 'you can feel the handpull shuddering', it becomes extremely difficult to fill a glass through a sparkler and the simplest solution is to take it off.

Drinkers aren't obliged to follow brewers' advice if they have strong preferences of their own: 'It's the drinker who is paying for the beer, it's their choice whether the beer is poured with or without,' says Annabel Smith (2022). What's really needed is more awareness among drinkers, and more opportunities to try sparkled and sparkle-free pours side by side.

Sociable cask

One final requirement of great cask beer is a great pub in which to enjoy it, or some comparable venue like a bar, taproom or club. This isn't just sentiment. In terms of carbonation levels and flavour, there's little to distinguish keg beer drunk in a pub from canned beer chilled in a domestic fridge, except perhaps that the draught product is likely to be fresher. But it's near impossible to reproduce the complexities of cask from a can or bottle. It *is* possible, as we'll discover in Chapter 3, to achieve something very close to cask in smaller vessels such as minikegs, but these are invariably a sideline for breweries that rely primarily on cask sales to survive.

If you have a suitably cool place for a stillage, an aptitude for mastering cellar skills and sufficient friends, or sufficient disregard for your health, to get through at least a 36-pint pin in three days, you can conceivably enjoy pub-style cask beer from the comfort of your own armchair. This might work as an occasional treat: Theakston, for example, sells properly cask conditioned Old Peculier direct to the public in returnable wooden pins at Christmas, with detailed instructions on how to manage them. But for most of us the opportunity to drink cask depends on outlets with sufficient demand to justify buying it in bulk quantities and installing the infrastructure to manage it. Without communal spaces in which to drink it, cask as a format could not survive.

When I asked brewers what they thought were the most positive aspects of cask, many of them responded that it was the ultimate social beer. Exploring the topic further brought us first to the point above: cask depends on social drinking. It's also evolved to *suit* social drinking, favouring styles that are relatively low in alcohol and benefit in terms of flavour and drinkability from lower carbonation and milder serving temperatures. Beer has the widest repertoire of any alcoholic drink, up to and including specialities with complex and intense flavours that approach the strength of wine, but it is near-unique in its capacity to deliver flavour and character at low strengths in large volumes. Cask does this best of all, making it the ideal drink for sharing quality time with friends in a social space then walking safely home.

Cask beer needs that delightful balance as it's primarily a social lubricant. There should be just enough hops to cut the sweetness but not so much that it distracts people from socialising.

Simon Theakston, joint managing director, T&R Theakston 2022

3 Cask compared

What makes cask cask?

There are a multitude of ways of packaging and serving beer, and cask isn't the only one worth considering. Arguably, not all styles are well-suited to cask, just as classic cask styles don't always fare well when treated in other ways. But even so, there's something particularly special about cask, which, when done well and with the right type of beer, achieves an apparently unique quality and complexity. What precisely is that special something, and are there other ways to achieve it, using different types of vessels and other methods?

When the 1970s activists who founded the Campaign for Real Ale (CAMRA) grappled with defining the beers they were trying to protect, they came up with a definition of real ale as beer that, to summarise, was live and still fermenting, packaged in casks and dispensed without extraneous carbon dioxide pressure (CAMRA 1972:3). Such beers were easy to distinguish from other British commercial beers of the time, which were largely filtered, pasteurised, and, if served on draught, dispensed under gas pressure. Campaigners then realised that a small and shrinking number of bottled beers were also packaged with live yeast, so 'real ale in a bottle' became an approved format too. In the 21st century, things got complicated, with a proliferation of non-cask beers that were unfiltered, unpasteurised, and sometimes even underwent additional fermentation in kegs, cans and novel vessels not foreseen by the policymakers of decades before.

Finally, in 2020 CAMRA replaced its definition of real ale with a more general one for live beer. This applies to any beer 'that when first put into its final container contains at least 0.1 million cells of live yeast per millilitre, plus enough fermentable sugar to produce a measurable reduction in its gravity while in that container, whatever it may be.' (CAMRA 2022b.) This is a relatively modest yeast requirement, considerably less than the 1 million or so cells cask brewers consider sufficient for a healthy continued fermentation, as it's intended to encompass many non-cask beers too. But it's supplemented by a definition of cask-conditioned beer as 'live beer that continues to mature and condition in its cask, any excess of carbon dioxide being vented such that it is served at atmospheric pressure'.

Though it's possible to quibble that this once again brings the eligibility of air pressure into question, it otherwise does a good job of capturing what to me are the four crucial features of cask beer:

1. **Continuing fermentation** contributes to freshness and complexity of flavour and allows and requires the intervention of skilled cellar managers in shaping the result.
2. **Casks** provide a container of a size and shape that influences the way fermentation proceeds, and tailor the beer for consumption in social spaces.
3. **Venting**, perhaps the most overlooked feature of cask, enables the beer to be served with slightly lower carbonation at a slightly warmer temperature.
4. **No pressurised gas** as this will undermine the qualities achieved through venting.

With these features in mind, let's take a quick tour around the other main methods of packaging and dispensing beer, and see how they compare to cask.

Brewery conditioning

The things that excite creative cellar keepers about cask are precisely the things that disturb brewers keen to create robust, reliable, long-lasting products with consistent quality, flavour and character, resistant to the possibly ill-informed and uncaring ministrations of distributors, retailers and drinkers. In response, they've developed methods of fixing the character of their beer while it's still under their control at the brewery and minimising the extent to which it subsequently changes.

Brewery conditioned beers complete their fermentation at the brewery and are then packaged with the intended level of carbonation already fixed. The simplest way to achieve this is to attenuate the beer fully, chill it so as many yeast cells as possible sink to the bottom of the tank, then rack from above the sediment. Modern pressurised fermenting vessels allow precise venting to achieve the desired carbonation.

This is the method used to make the most traditional unfiltered German and Czech lagers, and beers inspired by them but made elsewhere, as well as many modern keg, bottled and canned 'craft' beers. Some yeast inevitably remains in the beer, which is often at least a little hazy. Many beers made this way qualify as 'live' by the CAMRA definition, though the potential for further fermentation is minimal.

There are more thorough methods. I've already mentioned centrifuging as it's employed by some bigger cask brewers to remove the yeast from the initial fermentation. With cask, this is replaced by fresh yeast, but centrifuged beer can be packaged in keg, bottle or can without further yeast addition.

The older mechanical technique for extracting yeast is filtration, using fine-grained materials like diatomaceous earth (Kieselguhr), a naturally occurring porous calcified rock, or artificial polymers. The beer is usually chilled to encourage protein particles to clump together beforehand, a technique known as cold filtration. The results depend on the fineness of the filter and how it's applied: fine filters can block flavour

A cylindroconical vessel (CCV) can be used to adjust carbonation at the brewery without additional fermentation after packaging

molecules, so some brewers apply only a light filter, enough to remove most of the yeast and ensure a bright result which is possibly still 'live'. At the other extreme is sterile filtration which will reduce cell counts to around 0.01 per ml.

A sure way of producing a biologically stable product is pasteurisation. The principle is simple: sufficient heat is applied for a sufficient time to kill off as many microorganisms as possible. Though, as we'll see in Chapter 6, Louis Pasteur first suggested the process, he didn't advocate pasteurising beer, as its 'delicacy of flavour is altered' (1928:18 fn1). Even though the process has been considerably refined since and is widely applied to the more industrial, commercial beers, many beer connoisuers eschew it for its negative impact on flavour, which can result in a rather cooked, oxidised, dull-tasting beer. Pasteurisation doesn't remove haze-causing solids, so pasteurised beer is usually filtered first.

Additional processing like filtering and pasteurisation tends to drive off carbon dioxide, which won't be replaced as the beer is no longer fermenting, so more must be added to retain sufficient sparkle, a process called force carbonation. Though, as mentioned in Chapter 1, it's possible to capture CO_2 during fermentation and return it to the beer later, many breweries still rely on bottled gas for this.

Force carb, as brewers call it, is another topic provoking strong views, with real ale campaigners traditionally rejecting beers with added gas, recaptured or otherwise. Other commentators ridicule attempts to distinguish 'good' from 'bad' CO_2, pointing out that the gas is chemically identical whether it's been released from a fermenting yeast cell or squirted from a tank. But the complex environment of the beer does affect gas behaviour, and some, including Annabel Smith, argue that natural conditioning produces smaller, better-dispersed bubbles that feel softer in the mouth and don't produce so much sharp and metallic-tasting carbonic acid in contact with water.

Robert Wicks of Westerham brewery compares the difference between natural and force carbonation in beer to the difference between the traditional method of making Champagne and similar products, where the wine is refermented in the bottle and the yeast sediment subsequently removed, and the pressurised 'Charmat' method used for cheaper sparkling wines like prosecco. 'It affects the character of the carbonation, producing tiny bubbles with a much softer mouthfeel,' he says. I suspect that much of the perceived difference is due to the amount of CO_2. Force carbonation is typically used for beers that are intended to be relatively fizzy, with at least 5 g/l, compared to the more modest 2 g/l of a well-managed cask.

Interestingly, the latest CAMRA definitions make no mention of carbon dioxide added at the brewery, so a force carbed beer can still count as live.

Gas dispense

As we've seen, one of the factors limiting the useful life of cask beer is the ingress of staling, contaminant-laden air. Sterile gases like carbon dioxide and nitrogen (N_2) provide a more inert environment, and given sufficient pressure, a method for dispensing a more consistently sparkling product. As we'll see in Chapter 7, the increasing prevalence of gas dispense in pubs was one of the key concerns that provoked the first flowering of the modern beer consumer movement in the 1960s.

Using gas to push beer to the bar requires applying what's known as top pressure, considerably beyond the atmospheric level maintained by a cask breather. In these conditions, some of the added CO_2 dissolves into the beer, increasing its carbonation, so it needs to be cooled to 8°C or below before it pours without excessive fobbing (foaming).

Pressuring cask in this way results in carbonation levels far beyond the design specification, and a beer that won't pour properly at normal cellar temperature. It became a widespread practice in the 1960s and 1970s and was correctly disparaged in the early days of CAMRA. Thankfully, the industry has since moved on and top pressure dispense is now normally reserved for beers that were designed for it, including other forms of live beer.

Mixed gas dispense was first introduced by Guinness for its nitrogenated nitrokeg draught stout to create a distinctive texture and appearance using nitrogen (N_2) forced into the beer at the brewery. This forms smaller bubbles than CO_2, resulting in a creamier mouthfeel and a more stable head. The keg is then pressurised with a mix of gases, typically 70% N_2 and 30% CO_2, and poured through a tap with a sparkler-like nozzle, creating the characteristic cascading appearance as the gases are released.

Nitrogen is now commonly applied to non-nitrogenated keg beers too, in lower proportions, typically 40% N_2 to 60% CO_2. In these circumstances, nitrogen doesn't dissolve so won't add additional sparkle. It's also much more readily and cheaply available than CO_2 as it makes up 78% of the air we breathe and can easily be extracted and purified, so pubs that invest in suitable equipment have a free and limitless supply.

Powered pumps like the flojets mentioned above are also often used for keg. The beer is kept under sufficient pressure to carbonate it properly but requires no extra gas to transport it to the bar.

Cellar at the Bow Bar, Edinburgh: Casks on vertical extraction in foreground, kegs coupled with two separate lines for beer and gas

Other containers

Casks but not cask

It's long been common practice, particularly among cask-focused microbreweries, to sell bright beer in casks for parties and similar events. The organisers are unlikely to have the skill, time and facilities to manage a proper cask beer, so the brewery fills the cask with a beer that's already fully conditioned, either in another cask or a tank, leaving as much live yeast as possible behind. The beer should already be optimally carbonated, clear and bright (thus the term), so it can be tapped, vented and its contents drunk almost straight away once it reaches the venue, perhaps after a judicious rest to let the gas settle. But it won't generate its own carbon dioxide, so will go flat and become vulnerable to oxidation and souring within hours, not usually a problem at a busy event where the contents are quickly consumed.

Serving barrel-aged mixed-fermentation beer, as described in Chapter 1, directly from the barrel it's aged in isn't unknown, but by the time it's ready, there's likely to be little residual sugar left, so like bright beer it's vulnerable to deterioration, a particular problem with a specialist beer that might be a slow seller. Some brewers have found ways round this using gas blankets. A barrel-aged beer can also be transferred to a normal cask for further conditioning, likely with a little priming, but is more likely to end up in a can, bottle or keg.

Kegs

Once metal replaced wood as the material of choice for draught beer, there was no need to retain the traditional barrel shape for beer with no sediment. Thus the development of the keg, a cylindrical container usually made of stainless steel, although plastic versions are becoming more commonplace. The most common keg size is 50 l, with 30 l and 20 l kegs also in wide circulation.

A keg is designed to stand upright, with a single access point in the centre of the head to receive a gadget called a coupler. This has connectors for both beer and gas lines, with no need for bar staff to get involved with bungs, taps and spiles. Attached to the coupler is a valve to let the gas in and a tubular steel extraction spear reaching down to just above the bottom. The keg is kept pressurised, first by its carbonated contents and then by the introduction of pressurised gas – either carbon dioxide or mixed gas as explained above – as it empties. Typically, the pressure of gas pushes out the beer, but a pump may also be used.

Empties at Moor Beer,
Bristol; keg at the front

Most big brand keg beers dispensed under gas pressure are pasteurised, so keg was long regarded in the UK as the antithesis of cask. But kegs can also contain unfiltered, unpasteurised products that could even qualify as live beer. Many of the keg beers produced by modern craft brewers fall into this category. Some, like Moor Beer in Bristol, condition in keg, using a process analogous to cask conditioning. But kegs can't be vented and are designed for use with gas pressure so produce more carbonated beer that needs to be served cooler: emptying them in other ways is difficult, as beer festival staff attempting this have found. Once on the bar, keg beer lasts longer than cask as it's protected from air, but not by much: trade quality manuals recommend no more than five days. And like cask, keg is also vulnerable to issues like inappropriate cellar temperature and dirty lines.

Membrane kegs

Often referred to by their best-known brand name, KeyKeg, membrane kegs are a high-tech version of bag-in-box containers (below). The beer is sealed into a sterile flexible bag, the membrane, housed inside a rigid outer cylinder typically made of translucent PET, like a large plastic bottle but with an additional sturdy base and lid. There's a coupler on top, like a standard keg, but the gas inlet feeds into the space between the bag and the outer layer, so pressurised gas or even compressed air can be used literally to squeeze the contents out. Kegs of this type come in 30, 20 and 10 l sizes, the smaller ones ideal for low-turnover specialities like strong and mixed fermentation beers.

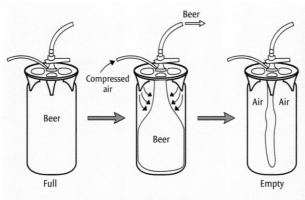

Membrane kegs: photo right shows new kegs waiting to be filled.

KeyKegs began as simpler plastic cylinders marketed as lightweight, non-returnable and recyclable, ideal for sending beer and other drinks further afield with no need to collect empties. But it was the addition of the inner bag that caught the attention of brewers and some beer connoisseurs as a way of dispensing keg without contact between beer and gas, with no opportunity for it to become fizzier than intended. There's an ongoing debate about the sustainability claim – in practice, many membrane kegs have ended up in landfill in the UK, though there are now networks of third-party businesses who will collect and recycle them. There are several competing designs, including some, like Ecofass, with disposable inner bags inside reusable outer shells.

Like standard kegs, membrane kegs can contain unfiltered live beer, but the facility to empty them without extraneous gas has made them particularly appealing. Stuart Bateman, for example, considers them as a useful alternative to conventional cask, with a longer shelf life: those from Batemans contain still-fermenting beer and the brewery labels them 'keycasks'. CAMRA approved membrane kegs in 2015 and they soon started to appear at local festivals, making their debut at the flagship Great British Beer Festival in 2019. Unlike casks, they're very difficult to vent successfully, so are more often used with more highly carbonated beers served at lower temperatures. They can also be dispensed using a beer engine, and Batemans is one brewery that deliberately racks them with a lower yeast count to avoid developing an overly aggressive carbonation.

The burgeoning craft beer market has prompted several other manufacturers to come up with alternative designs, some of which look superficially like membrane kegs but lack the membrane, including Ecokeg and KeyKeg's own Unikeg. As these don't separate gas from beer, they're best considered as conventional kegs that happen to be made of plastic.

Tanks

Tank beer is beer kept at the pub or bar in permanent tanks with a greater capacity than conventional casks or kegs and often delivered by tanker. Some versions apply the membrane keg principal on a grand scale using 500- or 1,000-litre polythene-lined and integrally cooled and insulated steel tanks, often displayed in the bar as a talking point. These are typically used for unfiltered, unpasteurised lagers that may well count as live beer, though require a high turnover given the quantities involved.

Some brewery taprooms and brewpubs sell beer either direct from cylindro-conical fermenting vessels, or by racking it into similar-looking cooled dispense tanks. These don't have inner membranes, so carbon dioxide or mixed gas is introduced into the tank as the beer leaves it. Both systems are pressurised, so the results are more carbonated and therefore served cooler than cask.

Bag-in-box

Simple, cheap bag-in-box systems comprising a collapsible and refillable polythene container with a built-in tap inside a cardboard carton have long been familiar as a lightweight method of providing draught beer at home or for events and parties. There are two main sizes: 20 l polypins and 10 l minipins. Some brewers are hesitant about putting fermenting beer in containers like these, concerned they won't handle the additional carbonation, or protect the contents sufficiently to ensure best quality, so fill them with bright beer for rapid consumption.

Some brewers have, however, successfully conditioned beer in bag-in-box containers, and even served it from handpump using connector taps that are

widely available thanks to the format's popularity with small cidermakers. The problem is in venting without disturbing the sediment. One method is to allow the beer to settle with the container on its end, vent through the tap and very carefully tilt the box into dispense position so the sediment slides to the bottom. The other is to pierce a pinhole in the top of the bag and seal it with sticky tape once the beer is vented, but this prevents subsequent refilling. Beer treated this way is arguably the functional equivalent of proper cask and accepted at some beer festivals as such.

Bottles and cans

There are various ways of preparing 'small pack' beer, as brewers call it, the oldest of which is bottle conditioning, where the beer gains its carbonation from fermentation in the bottle, often with the help of priming and/or reseeding with additional yeast. With sufficient skill and expertise, even canned beer can be treated in this way, as it is, for example, at Moor in Bristol. Many modern craft brewers produce unpasteurised and unfiltered bottled or canned beer, sometimes with no force carbonation: such beer, though it may well count as live, isn't strictly bottle conditioned as it doesn't undergo significant additional fermentation. Other beers are filtered and centrifuged so contain minimal amounts of yeast, and may be at least partially force carbonated, but are left unpasteurised to avoid any stale or cooked flavour, while big commercial brands are often pasteurised.

What all these beers have in common is that they're not amenable to venting: their carbonation isn't released until the container is opened, at which point it's advisable to drink them as soon as possible. Certain pouring techniques help disperse carbonation, as explained in Chapter 2, but in terms of mouthfeel and drinkability, even bottle-conditioned beer has more in common with keg than with cask.

Another important difference is that, while cask beers are typically drunk within a few weeks of brewing, small pack beers tend to hang around for longer, at distributors, retailers and in drinkers' homes, with more opportunity to become stale and oxidised. Brewers tend to design them with this in mind, for example brewing bottled versions of the same brand at a higher strength than draught versions. Bottle conditioning can help as active yeast consumes oxygen, and higher alcohol and more robust flavours lend more resilience.

Hop aromas are particularly quick to decline, which is why brewers often put short best-before dates of perhaps three months on their more hop-forward brews. However, this creates difficulties with wholesalers and retailers who prefer products with at least a year of shelf life. Most are best drunk well within that margin, though a few, particularly stronger bottle-conditioned beers, may develop and improve with age for several years.

Growler fills

Growler is an American term of uncertain origin for a container intended to be filled with a larger-than-normal quantity of draught beer for the customer to enjoy at home. The term is relatively new to the UK, but the practice certainly is not. Contemporary containers vary, from two- or four-pint wax paper cartons or plastic bottles to custom-made plastic or glass US-style growlers: big brown jug-like bottles with handles on the neck designed for multiple refills.

Cask beer in a growler should be treated like cask beer in a glass and rapidly consumed. If the container is closed tightly immediately after pouring and the beer is put in the fridge as soon as possible, it might be good for a couple of hours, particularly in cooler weather. But it will have lost some of its carbonation during pouring and picked up oxygen too, so shouldn't be regarded as anything like a proper bottled beer. The same goes for keg if it's simply poured from the tap, though some specialist outlets have more sophisticated counter-pressure systems which purge the container of oxygen before filling.

Another variant goes by the unfortunate name of crowler: a large can, typically of around a litre capacity, filled under counter-pressure with its lid seamed on immediately afterwards. You should get away with keeping beer filled this way unopened in the fridge for up to three days, but once opened treat as draught beer and drink quickly. Neither counter-pressure growler fills nor crowlers work with cask.

Minikegs

Preferred by many brewers for selling larger quantities of beer direct to the consumer, the attractively rugged 5-l minikeg is a 25 cm-tall container with a tubby bilge, looking reassuringly like a miniature cask in vertical extraction mode, but with a built-in tap on the side, close to the bottom. There's another plastic valve on top which, significantly, allows the vessel to be vented.

Some breweries put bright beer in minikegs, but some treat them like proper casks, filling them with beer containing sufficient yeast and sugar to provide a continuing fermentation. In this latter case, the minikeg is effectively dispensing cask beer: the only significant difference is in the size and shape of the vessel, which of course will have some impact on yeast behaviour. Much like casks, minikegs need to be left to settle after transport, then vented, and left to stand for at least a further 24 hours before the first pint is poured. The tap is positioned conveniently above the level of any sediment. Like casks, they have a two- or three-month shelf life if kept sealed but need to be finished quickly once you start emptying them. They're non-returnable, but once emptied can be put in the household recycling just like cans.

The only challenge to running your own home cask cellar with minikegs is temperature. They're too big to fit in many household fridges, which are invariably too cold, so unless you're lucky enough to have a real cellar, or an unheated garage or outhouse during cooler weather, or can afford a dedicated adjustable fridge, you'll need to resort to the damp cloth method. At the Windsor & Eton brewery in Windsor in 2012, I tried samples of the same IPA

from naturally conditioned minikeg, conventional cask and filtered bottle side by side: though there were slight differences between cask and minikeg, both had the freshness and gentle sparkle of cask beer and neither was obviously inferior. The bottled version tasted like a closely related but notably different beer, with a higher carbonation that masked some of the subtler hop notes of the recipe.

There's a pressurised variant of the minikeg, with an integral carbon dioxide dispenser like the type found in soda fountains to push the beer out, replacing the vent. Then there are proprietary systems like Heineken's Blade and AB InBev's PerfectDraft, which require investment in compatible equipment. These also use compressed gas with integral cooling, so the experience is more keg than cask.

4 The flavour of cask

Beer, it's often said, offers the widest diversity of taste experiences of any alcoholic drink for those who are prepared to explore it fully, thanks to the infinite variety of its multiple ingredients and the complexities of its manufacturing process. Cask beer is no exception. It's a method or format rather than a style and even if, as we'll see, it arguably lends itself best to a narrower repertoire than the full-on widescreen experience, there's no reason in principle why pretty much any shade of beer, from the most straightforward session brew to the most complex mixed fermentation geek bait, can't be given the cask treatment. Nevertheless, that treatment will always affect our perception of a beer's flavour and character in a particular way, not so much because of its flavour-active contents but its presentation and that often-overlooked quality known in the food and drink industry as 'mouthfeel', in particular its lower carbonation and warmer serving temperature.

Over many years of drinking and thinking about cask beer, and talking to other drinkers, whether enthusiasts or otherwise, about their experience of it, I've concluded these two qualities are cask's most important defining features. Campaigners have often championed cask on the grounds that it's 'live' and still fermenting rather than a 'dead' pasteurised product like industrial keg beer, and this doubtless contributes to its freshness and the subtleties of its flavour evolution. But the same could be said of bottle-conditioned beer, and I've met many dedicated cask drinkers who, though they accept the logic of 'real ale in a bottle', nonetheless enjoy it less than cask. If you unpack their reasons, they often say it's because bottled and canned beer of any kind is 'too fizzy' or 'too gassy', which, as we have seen, is because there's no way of venting it like cask. And a more carbonated product naturally lends itself to a cooler serving temperature.

Cask is like a wonderful vintage Cheddar compared with a processed cheese.

SUSAN CHISHOLM, quality manager, Greene King 2022

The absence of filtering also makes a difference, and not only to flavour complexity. 'You end up with a lot more proteins in the beer,' explains Susan Chisholm, 'so you get a richer, more mouth-filling experience.' Many other craft beers are unfiltered too, but combined with the effects of carbonation and temperature, the mouthfeel of cask is particularly full and satisfying. To understand how all these elements and others interact in our enjoyment of a great beer, we'll need to dig a little deeper into the science of flavour.

Taste and appreciation

The word tasting is a little misleading when applied to the experience of enjoying food and drink. The sense of taste is certainly involved, but is by no means the end of the story. All our senses are arguably engaged in assessing what we put in our mouths, and our experience of the overall environment at the time also makes a difference. Taste and smell are capable of conjuring powerful memories, which partially explains, for example, why Guinness apparently always tastes better in Ireland to those who have drunk it when on holiday there.

Inside the brewing industry, systematic tasting has long been recognised as a tool for ensuring consistency, perfecting recipes for new products, and identifying potential problems. Human senses are still much more discriminating in many respects than even the most sophisticated items of lab equipment, and since at least the 1970s many brewers have taken heed of feedback from formal tasting panels working within a well-defined and consistent framework. Beer competitions, whether for home or commercial brewers, also aspire towards objectivity by encouraging rigour in sensory analysis. The experience of tasting and judging panels is very different from enjoying beer 'in the wild', as beer lovers who join them for the first time soon discover, but some of the same skills can be applied beneficially to both.

Common sense

Beer appreciation really does engage all the senses. The least obvious, and least important, is **hearing**, but the reassuring hiss that almost invariably accompanies the opening of a bottle or can is, like the pop of the Champagne cork, both part of the experience and a useful indication that the contents are carbonated. Draught beer is a little different. In a busy pub, sound contributes more to the ambience than communicating anything distinctive about the beer. But if it's quiet, the creak of a handpump and the gushing of liquid into a glass at least raises pleasant expectations.

Sight, on the other hand, is surprisingly important. For obvious evolutionary reasons, we're well-equipped to make judgements about potential consumables by sight before they get anywhere near our mouths, and these visual impressions shape our expectations. 'Colour is the single most important sensory cue when it comes to setting people's expectations regarding taste and flavour,' writes Oxford psychologist Charles Spence (2015), before citing extensive scientific evidence in support of the chef's maxim 'we eat first with our eyes'. Inappropriate colours can confuse our identification of flavours, more intense colours may be associated with more intense flavour, and certain colours are actively off-putting.

Beer, with its layered presentation of a distinctively coloured, though usually translucent, liquid crowned by a thick, contrasting head, has a particular aesthetic visual appeal, as graphic artist John Gilroy understood when he effectively launched modern beer marketing with his campaigns for Guinness in 1929. Experienced drinkers interpret colour as a clue to the likely flavour. The darker the beer, the more intense its malt flavours are likely to be, though expectation and reality don't always match. Many people associate the darkest beers with the roasted notes of porters and stouts and are often disoriented when they try a much softer dark mild for the first time.

As discussed in Chapter 3, British cask drinkers traditionally associated clarity with quality, and would return anything visibly hazy without even a sip. Although that association is loosening, most brewers still strive to ensure their products look good, both the liquid itself and its branding and packaging. But despite its contribution to our overall pleasure, appearance isn't a foolproof measure of quality. Beer judges learn not to overestimate its importance, and industry tasting panels sometimes use opaque glassware and coloured light to reduce visual distraction.

Smell is the most important contributor to our experience of flavour. Try tasting something with a distinctive flavour while holding your nose: the sensation will be much degraded and you probably won't be able to identify the flavour in a blind test. Now release your nose: the difference can be dramatic, as if the film has shifted from a grainy black-and-white VHS tape to pin-sharp HD. You should try this if you remain unconvinced by my advice on leaving headspace in the glass. Something similar happens when a bad cold bungs up your nasal passages: you'll likely say you can't taste anything, but your sense of taste is working fine. It's the sense of smell that's temporarily disabled.

Olfaction, as it's known scientifically, is complex and still only partly understood. It results from clusters of receptor nerve cells that fire when they detect specific odourant molecules. Information from other senses is first processed through intermediary structures, but, uniquely, impressions of odours go straight to the brain itself. They're processed in the subconscious parts of the brain associated with long-term memory and emotion, which

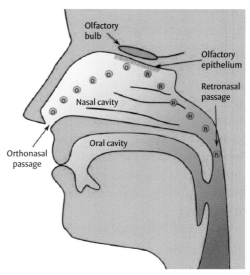

explains why aromas can be so evocative in a way we struggle to put into words. Most of the receptor cells, around six million, are concentrated in the olfactory epithelium, a 5-cm² patch high up in the nasal cavity. It's not clear how many different odours we can distinguish: the number regularly quoted is 'about 10,000', but we have several hundred different types of odour receptors that work in various combinations and some researchers speculate we may be capable of discriminating millions of different smells.

Though the appreciation of aroma usually begins with putting something under the nose and sniffing, technically known as orthonasal olfaction, it doesn't stop there. A passageway behind the soft palate allows odours to waft into the nasal cavity as we eat and drink, reaching detectors lower down the epithelium. The physical shape of the various cavities encourages this process, known as retronasal olfaction, as we exhale. There are differences in our responses to orthonasal and retronasal stimuli, which helps explain why many people find certain notorious foods, like stinky, rind-washed cheese or Indonesian durian fruit, smell repellent but taste delicious.

Given the richness of smell, **taste** may seem the poor relation, but it remains vital to our enjoyment. Taste originates from taste buds, microscopic receptor cells which, like those in the olfactory system, respond to specific compounds. The biggest concentration, typically between 2,000 and 8,000, is on the tongue, where they're embedded in structures called papillae: it's the latter, not the taste buds themselves, that form the tongue's visible texture. We have similar cells elsewhere in the mouth and in other parts of the body, though we're not always conscious of their working.

Taste receptors can distinguish only a handful of basic tastes. Depending on your age, you'll probably know four or five of these from general knowledge: bitter, salty, sour, sweet and the more recently discovered umami. There's now evidence for a sixth, rancid fat, and possibly more. You may also have seen the tongue map, allocating certain tastes to certain areas, but it turns out the receptors are much more evenly distributed across the tongue, with a little more sensitivity to bitter at the back and sour at the sides.

We're hard-wired to find three of the basic tastes pleasant because they're associated with nutritionally valuable foods. Salty indicates salts containing sodium and potassium, minerals essential to healthy body function. Sweet indicates carbohydrates providing a concentrated source of energy. Umami is a Japanese word meaning 'deliciousness' and refers to the savoury, meaty taste found in soy sauce, yeast extracts, cured meats, mature cheese, mushrooms and similar foods. It's triggered by amino acids indicating the presence of protein, another key component of a healthy diet. We evolved in an environment where such tastes were scarce and our motivation to seek them out was an important survival mechanism. Our failure to adjust our behaviour to a world where they're available in profusion explains some of the public health problems linked to diet in more prosperous nations.

In contrast, we're instinctively wary of the other basic tastes. Bitter in nature is associated with alkaline toxins: think bitter almonds and cyanide. We're particularly well-equipped to detect it and may even distinguish different kinds of bitterness associated with different compounds. Sour is our taste response to acidity, as found in unripe, indigestible fruit or food contaminated with hazardous bacteria. The occasional sour beer festival at London specialist beer bar Mother Kelly's is promoted with a drawing of a woman with her eyes tight shut and her tongue sticking out – a well-known gesture associated with sour or bitter taste reflecting the urge to expel whatever's causing it from the mouth.

Yet these two tastes are among the mainstays of beer flavour. The apparently paradoxical depiction of revulsion on the poster doesn't deter drinkers from flocking to the event, and the most prevalent cask beer style is even called 'bitter'. It's a powerful indication of how our instinctive responses are mediated through our consciousness and experience. As children, we often dislike bitter greens like Brussels sprouts and spinach, but learn to appreciate them as we get older, developing 'acquired tastes' as we say. Many of us had the childhood experience of sneaking a sample of beer (or another alcoholic drink) and wondering how on earth grown-ups drink the stuff. We may never shake ourselves free of those childhood impressions, but if we do, there will usually be an inner paradigm shift, a moment when we 'get it' and find a new territory of flavour has opened to us.

Last, but by no means least, is the sense of **touch**. The industry uses the term mouthfeel for the way food or drink feels in the mouth; another word, particularly used in connection with wine and other drinks, is body. As we chew food or swirl liquid, a complex array of detectors in the surface lining of the mouth and in the muscles provide impressions of physical properties like texture, weight, viscosity and temperature. It's customary at a beer tasting to provide tap water, as a palate cleanser and so that participants don't have to drink alcohol merely to quench their thirst. But I also encourage them to contrast water and beer in terms of mouthfeel, noticing that the beer is denser and more viscous, with a fuller body, thanks to complex carbohydrates, proteins and alcohol.

The most marked contrast is in carbonation, registered as bubbles of carbon dioxide bursting against the surfaces of the mouth. Interestingly, a further aspect of touch plays a role here: our perception of pain, as triggered by certain types and intensities of pressure or other things that threaten cell damage, like extreme temperatures or corrosive substances. While the prickle of a good beer is pleasantly stimulating, the same sensation dialled up in intensity becomes unpleasant, as it sometimes is with cheap and very heavily carbonated soft drinks.

Some sensations we think of as flavour also turn out to be a kind of pain. Capsaicin, the substance that makes chillies taste hot, isn't detected by taste buds but by pain receptors that respond in a similar way to dangerously high temperatures. As with the 'bad' tastes, our perception is nuanced by experience, otherwise half the world's cuisine would be very different. Such substances aren't regularly found in beer unless deliberately added, for example, in a chilli stout, but other 'painful flavours' are more common, like the heat of fusel alcohols in strong beer. Carbonic acid formed when CO_2 bubbles meet water in saliva is detected in a similar way, contributing to the 'bite' of carbonation.

Astringency is another 'flavour' perceived through touch. Tannins and phenols reduce the lubricating ability of saliva, producing the puckering sensation most familiar from red wine and tea and contributing to the perception of a lighter body. In beer, astringency is usually unwelcome in anything above barely detectable levels, but tannins are readily extracted from grains during a mash that's too hot or too alkaline and are present in the vegetal parts of hop cones.

Finally, sensitivity to temperature is part of the sense of touch, with extremes triggering pain. Drinking cool liquids is physically cooling as the liquid absorbs some of our body heat, but the sensation of drinking is also pleasing as it's associated with rehydration, which is essential for health. The marketing of numerous big brand beers plays on this, sometimes to the extent that it's the only virtue the advertiser wants to tell you about.

Temperature affects flavour perception in other ways. It's widely assumed that the sensitivity of our taste buds is suppressed at lower temperatures, and this is certainly true for sweetness and bitterness, both key to beer, though there's evidence that coolness enhances salt and sour flavours. Also, chilled liquids release their volatile aromas less readily. Both contribute to beer flavour becoming better defined as the liquid warms. Cellar temperature of 12°C is still cool with respect to our body temperature (37°C), but tastes and aromas will be much easier to detect than at a keg temperature of 6°C.

As if flavour wasn't complicated enough, there are wide variations in the way each of us perceives it, determined by our genes, abilities and experience. It's sometimes said that each of us lives in a unique world of flavour, but there's enough commonality to allow meaningful conversations, so tutored tastings are not entirely pointless. We have different thresholds of sensitivity to different substances, and some of us can't taste certain substances at all. Women, on average, are more sensitive to flavour than men, and this sensitivity is enhanced during pregnancy. As with other sensory processes, our abilities decline with age, but increased experience partially compensates for the loss. Eating or drinking something with a particularly strong flavour temporarily reduces our discrimination, while habits like smoking do more long-term damage. And we all have our own preferences resulting from a complex combination of innate ability and learning: just because your genes have made you more sensitive to bitter flavours than average, for example, doesn't mean you can't learn to like them.

The upshot of all this is that, in tasting, there's no right and wrong, and you have every right to your own preferences. Don't worry if you just can't get that guava, malt loaf, old books or freshly crushed grains of paradise that the other tasters are raving about, or if you find that scores for beers on Untappd are in inverse proportion to their drinkability. Given the wide variety of beer flavours, not everyone will like everything.

Alcohol

You can't ignore the fact that the intoxicating properties of alcoholic drinks, including beer, are part of their appeal. The compound responsible is alcohol, or more precisely, ethanol, as chemically speaking there are numerous alcohols, of which ethanol has the simplest molecular structure. It's absorbed into the blood through the stomach lining and functions as a psychoactive drug, slowing and blocking communications between brain and nerve cells. Its effects range from mild euphoria and the lowering of inhibitions to motor function impairment and unconsciousness, depending on the amount consumed and the speed of consumption.

So long as you don't keep topping up the levels in your bloodstream by continuing to drink, the short-term effects are only temporary: ethanol is broken down relatively quickly by enzymes in the liver, first into acetaldehyde, then into a substance called acetate and finally into water and carbon dioxide which are easily excreted through the familiar channels. The long-term health impacts of excessive and repeated consumption are indisputably more serious and long-lasting, including liver disease, high blood pressure, certain kinds of cancers and mental health issues.

The UK health service currently advises a weekly limit of 14 alcohol units per week, spread over at least three days. A unit is 10 ml of ethanol, the amount an average adult metabolism can dispose of in an hour. A litre of 4% ABV beer contains four units, giving a weekly limit of 3.5 litres, or just over six pints – less, of course, if double IPAs or imperial stouts rather than, say, best bitter are your tipple of choice.

The advice stresses that this limit defines 'low-risk' drinking and that there's no such thing as a 'safe drinking' level, insisting that 'the previously held position that some level of alcohol was good for the heart has been revised' (NHS 2019). Yet peer-reviewed scientific papers, albeit funded by the brewing industry, are still concluding that 'moderate beer consumption... is associated with decreased incidence of cardiovascular disease and overall mortality, among other metabolic health benefits' (Marcos and others 2021).

The role of alcohol in the character of a beer is often overlooked. It contributes particularly to mouthfeel: even some of the best-tasting low alcohol beers give themselves away with a thin, watery quality that's very hard to disguise. It can also help extract flavours from other ingredients, which may play a role in dry hopping.

Relearning to taste

The final complexity of flavour is that, in everyday life, we experience it as a single sensory impression of a particular food or drink, rather than consciously analysing its individual components, just as we recognise faces in one glance rather than thinking individually about the shape, colour and proportions of the features. Of course, there's no problem with continuing to enjoy beer as most other people do, but if you want to take a deeper journey into its flavour and character, you can train yourself to prise apart those overall impressions in a more analytical way. You don't need a genetic predisposition to be 'good' at tasting, so long as your senses function normally. There's no evidence that skilled tasters are any more physically sensitive or discriminating than anyone else, just more experienced and aware.

1. Before you start, reduce interference from other sense impressions. Try to sit somewhere quiet, well-lit and away from strong smells. Don't eat spicy or other strongly flavoured food immediately beforehand and avoid wearing scent. Don't eat while you're tasting, except perhaps something very bland like plain, unbuttered bread or water biscuits. Have tap water to hand.

2. Generally, taste lighter flavoured beers before more intense ones: a rule of thumb is to taste in ascending order of ABV, but consider other factors too. A 4% roasty porter or hoppy session IPA might be better tasted after a 5% special bitter, for example.

3. Be ready to take at least a few notes. Even if you never read them back, putting your impressions into words helps hone your senses. Don't worry about using the 'right' words, just describe your own impressions in a way that makes sense to you. There's a bit more about terminology below, but tasters usually evolve their own language, often through comparison with other familiar flavours and by borrowing terms from others that resonate with them. The important thing is to use them consistently.

4. Get an appropriate measure in an appropriate glass, with plenty of headspace to develop both head and aroma, and so you can swirl the contents without spilling: for example, a third pint in a glass big enough to hold two-thirds. A stemmed goblet that tapers inwards towards the top is a good choice (see above for more about glassware). In a pub or bar you likely won't have much choice, but if they have appropriate glassware and are helpful enough to accommodate you, it's worth asking. You could also ask for a half in a pint glass, or simply drink some of the beer before you set to work.

5. Put your hand over the glass, swirl the beer a little, hold it up to the light and assess its **appearance**. Consider its colour, clarity, or 'brightness' as brewers say, and head. How thick and dense is the head, and what colour? Typically, it'll be off-white but can vary from bright white to dark tan on some very dark beers. Consider **head retention** – how rapidly does the head decline? Haze may be deliberate and isn't necessarily a bad sign but could influence your expectations. With cask beer, you're unlikely to see many visible bubbles, if at all – compare this with a freshly poured keg or canned beer.  How pleasant do you find the appearance? Is it encouraging you to taste the beer? Do you have any expectations of flavour based on appearance?

6. Swirl again with your hand over the glass, then release your hand, put the glass up to your nose and take a good, deep sniff to appreciate the **aroma** (or **nose** as some wine tasters say). Try to describe what you smell, perhaps repeating the process a couple more times to pin things down. Some tasters find they get subtly different impressions if they take several short, sharp sniffs while passing the glass quickly under the nose: this can help pin down certain aromas. Tasting expert Melissa Cole recommends you try these 'bunny sniffs'  first to give yourself time to adjust to any particularly strong odours (2018:19).

7. Take a sip, perhaps half a mouthful, but don't swallow it straight away. Swirl it around with your tongue to see how the flavours develop and note the retronasal aromas as you exhale. Try to describe what you taste, smell and feel. The flavour impression in your mouth is known as the **palate** and the sensation of it is the **mouthfeel**.

8. Now swallow the beer to assess the **finish** or **aftertaste**. There are significant differences between taste buds in different parts of the tongue and mouth, and even wine tasters, who are known for spitting, know that you need to swallow at least some of the liquid for the full flavour. This is where the drier, bitter flavours, and perhaps tart, sour ones, become more pronounced.

9. Don't take another mouthful immediately but give the finish time to develop and see how long it lasts. Swallowing itself sometimes yields distinct flavours – this is often when astringency shows up. Bitterness typically increases in intensity after you've swallowed a mouthful, then slowly recedes.

10. Try different ways of sampling. If you take a gulp and swallow it straight down, you'll likely get more sweetness than if you hold the beer in the mouth. Alternatively, slurp a bit of air over the liquid to release more of the complex aromatics and drier flavours. This is a professional taster's trick which needs to be done carefully. Take no more than half a mouthful, keep still with your chin parallel to the floor, open your lips slightly and slurp gently.

11. Reflect on the beer as a whole. What style do you think it is? How does it compare to other beers in that style? Does it have any off-flavours (of which more below)? Is the flavour in balance, with its individual components complementing each other, or does one component predominate in a way that skews the overall drinkability? Importantly, do you like it? Do you want to finish it? Would you drink it again or recommend it to others? What do you like about it and what don't you like about it? If it's a beer you've drunk before, how does it compare to other samples?

12. Clean your palate with water between beers.

13. Try leaving some of the beer and returning to it later: it'll be warmer, less carbonated, and may well be modified in flavour. Avoid doing this in direct sunlight, though, as off-flavours can result.

14. Don't try too many beers in a session. The more you drink, the more your senses are dulled. This is why wine tasters spit, and though your drink is likely weaker than theirs, it's still intoxicating. You can also get 'palate fatigue'. If you're not enjoying a beer, give yourself permission to leave it unfinished and mark the expense down to experience.

15. Don't lose the knack of simply enjoying a beer. Perhaps close the session by getting another glass of the one you liked the most, or another favourite, and drink it in the normal way.

Judges at the Great British Beer Festival

There are other things you can do to focus your sensory apparatus. Look for local taste training or courses, or consult the books I suggest under Further Reading. If you're a CAMRA member, enquire about local tasting panels, or get together informally with like-minded people. Look out for tutored tastings at specialist pubs and breweries and hear what the brewers have to say about their beers. Visiting breweries is a good opportunity to learn about the brewing process and sometimes to taste malts and handle and smell hops. There are formal programmes too, like the Beer and Cider Academy courses and the Beer Judge Certification Program for homebrewers. Your skills are transferable, so it's illuminating to try applying them to other drinks, and even food. It doesn't have to be prestigious stuff like fine wine, malt whisky, single estate coffee or *haute cuisine*: though all these have their rewards. You might like to ponder, for example, precisely what it is about the flavour of your favourite everyday tea or soft drink that makes you like it.

Beer flavours

Flavour terminology

Discussing flavour is challenging partly because of the lack of clear and consistent terminology. English, and, it appears, most other languages, lack specific words for aromas comparable to those for colours. Instead, we describe such sensations in terms of familiar things that cause them: smoky aroma smells like smoke and floral like flowers, roasty flavour tastes like something that's been roasted, fruity like fruit and so on. Early beer writers resorted to such broad, relative and subjective terms as 'malty', 'hoppy' and even 'beery'. Practically every beer contains hops, so when exactly does it qualify as 'hoppy'? And does your idea of a 'beery' flavour agree with mine?

The brewing industry grappled with such conundrums in the 1970s when several international trade bodies backed a project led by brewing chemist Morton Meilgaard aimed at developing a consistent flavour terminology (Meilgaard and others 1979). Its best known and most influential output was the flavour wheel, which took a selection of common flavour terms, grouped them hierarchically into tiers, added some concise explanations, and arranged them around a wheel so that similar flavours were close to each other. For example, 'cereal' is split into 'grainy' ('raw grain'), our old friend 'malty', and 'worty', a distinctive flavour more familiar to brewers than drinkers. 'Grainy' is further split into 'husky' ('husk like, chaff'), 'corn grits' (as in maize) and 'mealy' (flour). Characteristics of mouthfeel are included too. There have been numerous variations and adaptations of the wheel since, both simpler and more complex than Meilgaard's, including some that interpret a tool originally intended for professional brewers in a way that's more accessible to drinkers and enthusiasts. An updated rendering of the wheel as a spriral is reproduced below.

BEER AROMA SPIRAL
Version 2

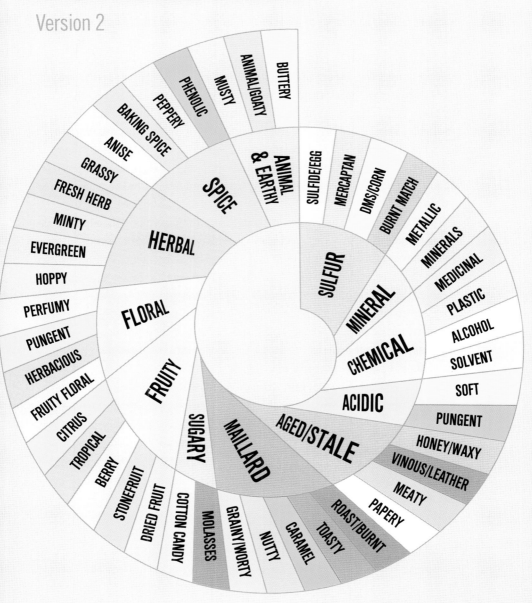

Decoding cask beer flavours

Let's try sampling that inviting glass of cask beer and see what we find. Most likely it's on the regular beer colour spectrum of pale yellow to black, unless it's a speciality with fruit or some other addition. Likely, it has at least some head, and if in a traditional style should be 'pin bright' and clear but could be hazy if left unfined.

Early beer writers weren't wrong: beer does indeed usually smell and taste of malt and hops. The flavour of most common beer styles is built on the relative contribution of these two key ingredients. Malts contribute sweetness from residual sugars, offset by bitterness from hops, and in darker beers, from roasted malts. A good start when evaluating a beer is to consider its place on the axis between these two poles, though much more will be going on beyond this in any beer of character, as its multitudinous aromas and additional flavours dance around the sweet-bitter framework. Whether or not the results are attractive depends on what brewers call balance and drinkability. An overly malty beer with little else going on may be bland and boring, but an excessively hoppy beer without a firm malt base is unpleasantly toxic, as many craft brewers have found to their peril in recent years.

The aromas of malt and hops are more complex than you might expect. Pale beers normally have just a light cereal note, while darker malts lend more intense aromas: brown bread, biscuits, malt loaf, malted breakfast cereal, caramel, toffee or nuts. The latter covers a wide territory encompassing almonds, hazelnuts, peanuts, walnuts or sometimes coconut, a flavour that can develop in the roasting process even if no coconut is added. In combination with other aromas, malt can suggest honey or treacle. Porters and stouts made with very dark roasted malts often have coffee, chocolate, burnt and smoky notes that sometimes shade into dried fruit like prunes or raisins, or yield a leathery scent.

I hinted at the diversity of hop aromas when introducing hops as an ingredient above. Traditional European varieties are typically resinous, herbal, earthy and possibly woody, with noble hops offering delicate grassy and lightly spicy notes that shade towards vanilla and meadowsweet. Fruit notes tend to be dark orange marmalade, grapefruit zest, lemon or, sometimes, blackcurrant, known to some tasters as catty or ribes. Floral notes might include rose, geranium, juniper, elderflower, lavender or heather.

US and Australasian hops widen the fruity vocabulary considerably. Citrus notes allude to grapefruit, sweet orange, tangerine, lemon, lime or bergamot, alongside stone fruit such as peach, apricot or cherry, and aromatic tropical fruit like mango, passion fruit and lychee. Resinous notes shade towards pine, spruce and roasting herbs, sometimes with suggestions of soap, cheese, bitter spices, disinfectant or, for some tasters, the sulphur-tinged flavours of onions and garlic. Floral aromas are also common.

Equally important aromas don't derive directly from the ingredients but are developed by yeast during fermentation. Many of these, arising from esters, are also fruity and can be difficult at first to disentangle from hop aromas, but they may remind you of rising dough, fresh bread, apple skins, aniseed or fennel, aromatic grapes and white wine, pear or pear drops, or, in higher concentrations, banana, bubblegum or solvents. In traditional cask styles, they tend to have a low to moderate presence determined by the behaviour of the brewery's house yeast. You may also detect buttery diacetyl and the boiled cabbage and struck match notes of sulphur compounds.

Speciality beers, particularly those influenced by Belgian brewing and Bavarian Weissbier, often employ more expressive yeasts, producing not only increased amounts of esters but phenols, with their spicy clove, aniseed, medicinal and wet plastic notes. Wild yeasts add other pungent and complex funky aromas evoking animal comparisons – goat, wet dog, mouse – but are also capable of exotically floral, pungently herbal and spicy scents that are sometimes likened to marijuana. Tasters familiar with traditional cider often name this as an obvious comparison as it shares the characteristic scent of wild fermentation. Sourness is evident from aroma too, with lactic acid smelling of yoghurt, sour milk and lemon, and acetic of vinegar. In contrast, lager styles should lack yeasty and sour aromatics, excepting perhaps traces of diacetyl and sulphur.

While many of the aromas persist in the palate, they're not always a good guide to how the beer will taste. Typically, beer smells sweeter than it tastes: fruit is sweet, but fruity-smelling beer can be unexpectedly dry. Sweetness is usually evident immediately while bitterness develops afterwards, sometimes very quickly, sometimes more slowly, becoming more assertive in the finish. Sourness and tartness behave in a similar way. Though most beer, including traditional cask, isn't designed to be sour, lesser elements of acidity are common, in citrus and other fruit flavours, roasted malts and carbonic bite. Other aromas, like strong fruity esters, phenolic spices or roasty chocolate and coffee, clearly follow through on the palate.

Salt and umami rank lower on the beer flavour hierarchy. Though salt is often added to help achieve an appropriate water profile, it's not intended as a flavouring, except in a handful of minority styles. As well as its characteristic taste, salt contributes to a fuller mouthfeel. Other salty compounds derived from brewing water and malt can add a mineral-like note. Umami, sometimes referred to as autolysed taste, is produced when yeast cells die. It's very rare in cask beer, though turns up in long-aged bottle-conditioned beer where its contribution can vary from an interesting hint to an overwhelming and unwelcome soy sauce or Marmite character. Fat-related tastes are more likely to occur in specialist styles, with some mixed fermentations yielding mildly cheesy and waxy character, but sometimes shading into unwelcome rancid notes.

The basic tastes are modified by aromas to produce a range of flavours. Sweetness may remind you of honey, confectionery, jam, brown sugar, caramel or molasses. It can combine with the aromatics of malt and yeast to suggest muesli and other cereals, or a variety of baked goods: bread, brioche, croissant, toast, digestive biscuits, cake. Or it may yield further nutty and woody character. Bitterness varies from the high notes of white grapefruit zest through several variants of pepper to the low throb of earthy salad greens. While toast and roast are most obvious in darker beers, hints may be detectable in lighter styles, such as amber-coloured bitters.

Turning to mouthfeel, most cask is best described as medium bodied: not water-thin, but still easily drinkable and not too dense, with a moderate carbonation. Astringency is unwelcome except in the smallest of doses as it undermines this comfortable character. Stronger specialities are likely to be denser, sometimes combining with other characteristics to suggest milk or cream, evoking richly textured fabrics like velvet. Chocolate flavours help bolster this impression in stouts. Stronger beers can also seem 'boozy' with the hot sensations of fusel alcohols.

Grains other than barley contribute their own character. Wheat lends a lightly tart, grassy character and is sometimes used to increase haze and body. Oats are another favourite for this latter purpose, contributing a silky mouthfeel, though their porridge flavours may not be welcome in excess. Rye has its own distinctive spicy, nutty aroma and flavour familiar from rye bread. Lactose adds sweetness and mouthfeel, contributing to the creamy impression of milk stouts.

Added ingredients like fruit, herbs and spices bring us back to the question of balance. In most cases, their flavours are familiar from other drinks and foods, and you'll be interested to see how they work in the beer. If you've bought a beer described as a plum porter or a lemon and thyme saison, you may be disappointed if you can't taste the added ingredients. We might also question the brewer's judgement if such flavours overwhelm the contribution of the core ingredients. It's your call, but you may wonder whether a beer that just tastes of, say, strawberry and cucumber, while lacking a characteristic malt and/or hop note, is any different from an alcopop or hard seltzer.

One further characteristic associated with cask beer is a borderline off-flavour that, as seen in Chapter 2, some drinkers undoubtedly find appealing in very modest concentrations. It's the musty note resulting from slight oxidation as the cask empties, a slight whiff of damp wood or earth: some people simply call it 'casky' and one particularly imaginative taster terms it 'old castle'. Any deliberate encouragement of it is playing with fire, as it shows the beer is starting its descent into staleness. I personally prefer my cask as fresh as possible.

Off-flavours

The term off-flavour is common in brewing circles, and I've used it several times here, but, like so much else, it turns out to be problematic. According to the *Oxford Companion to Beer*, off-flavours are 'the result of undesirable concentrations of flavor-active compounds' (Bird 2012:623). But context is everything in determining desirability, and sweetness or bitterness could be described as off-flavours if they're excessive or inappropriate to the style. The term is usually reserved for a handful of compounds that can emerge during fermentation and afterwards, which, although sometimes welcome in modest concentrations, are always unwelcome in excess and a sign that something has gone wrong. Specialists are trained to recognise them by deliberately spiking a neutral-tasting beer with the relevant compounds in concentrated form.

Checking for off-flavours is a basic step in evaluating a beer and finding them during a competition normally sends the culprit on a short-cut to the slops bucket. But first ask yourself if the flavour is appropriate to the style and whether you think the brewer intended it, which admittedly involves some speculation. It's not unknown for a brewer to market a beer unintentionally contaminated with wild yeast or acid bacteria as a 'sour' or a 'farmhouse ale', then find themselves struggling to replicate it if it sells well.

The usual suspects, some of whom we've already met, are:

Acetaldehyde An intermediate compound produced during the conversion of sugar to alcohol, this has a distinctive, sharp, green apple flavour that is almost always unwelcome. It's a sign the beer hasn't fermented or conditioned sufficiently and is sometimes found in cask beers that haven't been given sufficient time in the cellar before serving.

Acetic acid The active ingredient in vinegar, produced when *Acetobacter* bacteria break down acetaldehyde and alcohol in the presence of oxygen. It can be desirable in small amounts as part of the complex flavour of sour, barrel-aged and mixed fermentation beers, where it's often reminiscent of balsamic or cider vinegar, though its pungent acidity rapidly becomes overbearing. It's all too familiar, and invariably unwelcome, in cask beers that have hung around on the bar for too long.

Autolysed A characteristically umami-meaty taste like soy sauce or (British-style) gravy which results from yeast cells dying due to stress or old age, rupturing their walls and releasing the contents in a process known as autolysis, meaning 'self-destruction'. It's almost entirely unwelcome, not just as a flavour but as an indicator of a brewer's failure in their duty of care. It's ultimately unavoidable in long-aged strong beers, and in this context might contribute added complexity in modest quantities.

Butyric acid The flavour of this indicator of unwanted bacterial infection is traditionally described as 'baby vomit' or 'rancid cheese', not something most of us want in our beer.

Caproic and caprylic acid Waxy, goaty flavours familiar from goat's milk, particularly associated with wild yeast and therefore a desirable characteristic when balanced in wild fermentation or farmhouse brews, where they can mellow with age, becoming intriguingly perfumed and fruity. They're often present alongside phenols, prompting other animal-related tasting notes. In the days when breweries had stables full of dray horses, brewers talked about 'horse blanket' and today you'll hear 'farmyard', 'wet dog' and 'sweat'. Unhealthy or stressed brewer's yeast can introduce them where they're not welcome.

Diacetyl An inevitable by-product of fermentation largely reabsorbed by yeast cells during a properly managed conditioning. It has the distinctive aroma and flavour of butter, or, in higher concentrations, butterscotch or cinema popcorn. In high concentrations it smells to me like sweaty socks. In sensible quantities it adds an extra dimension to certain styles, including some bitters and pale lagers, but can easily become sickly and overbearing.

Dimethyl sulphide (DMS) A sulphur-based compound reminiscent of canned sweetcorn, boiled cabbage or tomato juice, it originates in malt but is largely driven off during boiling and venting. It's accepted in moderation in certain pale lagers but is unlikely to contribute positively to cask ale.

Fusel alcohols Beer can contain traces of up to 40 of these more complex alcohols, particularly at high ABVs, giving hot and solvent-like flavours that are undesirable in excess. They tend to break down over time, which is how strong beers of 10% ABV or more can end up as deceptively smooth and 'dangerously drinkable' given sufficient time to mature.

Hydrogen sulphide Another sulphur compound produced during fermentation, particularly by stressed yeast, but usually dispersed through carbonation. It can add interest at low concentrations: thanks to the sulphurous local water, the Burton snatch was once regarded as an indicator of a good Burton-brewed pale ale. But a whiff of 'struck match' can quickly develop into the unwelcome stench of 'bad egg'.

Isovaleic acid Resulting from the oxidation of alpha acids in old hops, this has a cheesy, slightly rancid aroma. While aged hops are used in some wild fermentation beers, the cheesy note mellows as the beers themselves are aged. If present in fresh cask beer, it's a sign the brewer really needs to clear out the hop store or change their supplier.

Lactic acid The result of a lactic fermentation involving *Lactobacillus* or *Pediococcus* bacteria, this has a milder flavour than acetic acid, reminiscent of lemon juice. While a key ingredient of sour and wild fermentation beers, it's unwelcome when recipes aren't designed around it, as with most common beer styles, where it indicates unwelcome bacterial contamination.

Lightstruck An off-flavour produced after the beer is brewed, when ultraviolet light, a component of sunlight, stimulates a reaction with hop acids. The result is a sharp, sweaty aroma known in North America as skunky. It's a particular problem with bottled beer packaged in clear or green rather than brown glass but can even arise when you take your pint out in the sun.

Mercaptan Another always unwelcome compound smelling of rotting vegetables and blocked drains, caused by stressed yeast or bacterial infection.

Metallic An excess of ferrous sulphate from metals in water or poorly kept brewing vessels results in this always unwelcome aroma. An easy way to test for it is to dab some of the suspect beer on the back of your hand and sniff: if it's present, you'll get an unmistakeable whiff of wet steel.

Oxidised Exposing beer to oxygen causes a variety of stale aromas, of which the most distinctive is the note of paper, wet cardboard or old books. In strong beers intended for long ageing in wood or bottle, it can add an attractive complexity reminiscent of sherry, but in an everyday session beer designed for drinking fresh, it's simply stale and off-putting.

Phenolic A variety of spicy, clove-like, smoky or medicinal flavours associated with substances called polyphenols. They're produced during fermentation by wild yeasts and certain brewer's yeast strains, and are desirable characteristics in styles built around them. They're also present in smoked and peated malts and expected, though highly divisive, in beers made using these. Otherwise, they're unwelcome, particularly when they result from chemical contamination.

Cask styles

Pioneering beer writer Michael Jackson is widely credited with developing the modern concept of beer styles in his *World Guide to Beer* in 1977, though of course beer has long been offered in a range of different types and strengths. Among Jackson's many achievements was the shift in systematic awareness of other brewing techniques and styles from the national to the international level, just at a time when homebrewing and microbrewing were emerging to challenge the dominance of the big brewing groups and their streamlined range of bland industrial beers. Thanks to this, porter is once again commonly available on British bars, tripel is produced in New Zealand brewpubs as well as Flemish monasteries, and gose, a style near-extinct in its eastern German homeland at the dawn of the 21st century, is a mainstay of North American craft brewing, admittedly often in rather liberal interpretations.

When the *World Guide to Beer* was published, the current *Good Beer Guide* needed only three symbols to define the cask repertoire of British breweries: one for bitter, one for mild and one for the occasional 'old ale or special' (Hardman 1976b:244). In the years since, the offer has diversified in a way unimaginable to 1970s drinkers. Nonetheless, the most successful and enduring cask beers tend to cluster in a more restricted handful of styles, including those traditional ones recognisable from early *Good Beer Guides*. They're generally moderate in strength, subtle in flavour and high in drinkability, qualities that dovetail well with cellar temperatures and restrained carbonation.

Beer styles are tricky things. Aside from a select few that have protected designations, there's no single authority to define and enforce them. Breweries apply style names with a broad brush as a marketing tool, sometimes even reinventing names if they think it will help the beer sell, thus the various milds relabelled simply as 'dark' in recent years, a practice since extended by renaming bitter as 'amber'. Formal competitions for both home and commercial brewers require more precision: organisers issue detailed style guidelines to which beers are expected to conform. But styles evolve and creative brewers won't be held back from innovating, so the rules can't be set in stone. Keeping up with the ever-expanding diversity of the industry has prompted some competition organisers to increasingly granular distinctions: the prestigious World Beer Cup organised by the Brewers Association (2022) in the US currently recognises 103 categories, many of them further subdivided.

CAMRA's own competition, the Champion Beer of Britain (CBoB), inaugurated in 1978 and initially focusing exclusively on cask, has always used a smaller set of styles. These time-honoured categories struggled to cope with 21st-century developments, and after extensive consultation were recently revised and expanded, though remain much simpler than many other systems. The revision resulted in 12 judging categories, most encompassing a number of beer styles, reflecting the fact that, due to the ingenuity of brewers, many beers do not strictly adhere to any particular beer style (CAMRA 2020). While I've been guided by them in the discussion that follows, I haven't always adhered to them.

All the beers considered in detail are excellent in their own way, but I've chosen them as illustrative examples without any implication that they're the most outstanding representatives of their style.

Mild ale

As we'll see in Chapter 6, mild ale was in many ways the original cask beer, the basic 'running ale' of the mid 19th-century brewer. Those milds were generally paler and stronger than are typical today, when the term is associated with dark amber and brown beers of very modest strength. At the Champion Beer of Britain competition, beers up to and including 4% ABV are accepted in the basic mild category, but most well-known commercial examples are 3.5% or less, some dropping below 3% while remaining remarkably well-packed with flavour,

like **Hook Norton Hooky Mild** at 2.8%. Paler and stronger versions have never quite disappeared and are becoming more common as brewers draw on historical inspirations. What unites them is their relatively low bitterness and greater emphasis on malt character compared to bitters and pale ales, a reminder that they evolved as beers intended to be drunk young and fresh rather than stored for long periods, and therefore required fewer hops.

Mild was the default British beer between the mid-19th and early 20th centuries and remained the style of choice in the heavily industrialised areas of South Wales, the Midlands and the North for several decades more. Its sweetish flavour, drinkability and modest strength made it an ideal refresher and restorative after a hard and thirsty shift at the mill or pit. Unfortunately, this association saddled it with a so-called 'cloth cap' image unhelpful in the aspirational decades that followed. Mild has long been regarded as a threatened style, targeted by CAMRA for enhanced support with an annual Mild Month promotional campaign every May since 1977. Today, even in redoubts like the Black Country, its traditional constituency is dwindling with age. But there are encouraging signs that it may finally be losing its baggage. Several newer, more craft-oriented breweries have done a good job of selling mild to younger drinkers who appreciate both its lower alcohol and mellower flavour compared to more fashionable styles.

Dark mild

Hobson's Champion Mild, brewed in Cleobury Mortimer, Shropshire, not too far from its West Midlands heartlands, is a good example of the traditional dark, lower alcohol variety at a particularly modest 3.2%. It's made with Maris Otter pale malt darkened with a little crystal and chocolate malt. Dark amber to brown in colour, with a smooth and sticky head, it has a rich and decidedly malty aroma reminiscent of sticky malt loaf: dusty cereal, caramel, chocolate and baked vine fruit. The malt character takes on suggestions of roasted hazelnuts on a soft-textured palate that starts sweet and then dries out in a way that's more toasty than bitter. The hops, Worcestershire-grown Fuggle and Golding, are very restrained but add an interesting herbal note to the finish, with a dab of blackcurrant fruit.

Milds are still relatively easy to find in and around Manchester, though **Hydes Dark Ruby**, from a family brewer now based in Salford, is one of those now trading under an alias. A typical 3.5%, it really does have a ruby tinge to its dark brown appearance, with a beige head. The aroma suggests dry grain, with some chocolate and light fruity blackcurrant. The texture is relatively light, but comforting malt cereal and dark toast aromas fill the mouth, conspiring with aromatics from yeast and hops to suggest liquorice. The hops show typical restraint in the finish, with a gentle but earthy and very English note over caramel tones, with a hint of roast grain expressing itself as the flavours fade.

Pale mild

Pale (or light) milds are now considerably rarer but one notable regularly brewed example is **Timothy Taylor Golden Best** from the much-admired family brewer in Keighley, West Yorkshire. Describing itself as 'the last of the true Pennine light milds', at 3.5% it's just as drinkable as the darker versions but notably different in character. It's made entirely with pale malt from Golden Promise barley, yielding a rich golden liquid with a creamy white head. There's a definite note of fruit on the aroma, perhaps red apple and rosehip, driven by the house yeast. Pale malt gives a delicate, plain biscuit impression on the palate, revealing more of the hops (Styrian Golding, Fuggle, Golding), which become lightly bitter even before the finish, with tantalising tea-like notes. The finish is initially surprisingly sweet, with blackcurrant and apple tart: it soon dries out with lightly peppery and resinous hop but remains soft and soothing. Taylor's beers have a very distinct character and it's interesting to compare this with **Boltmaker** bitter, which has a similar recipe but is stronger (4%) and notably hoppier.

Strong mild

Brewed at 6% to a 1921 recipe, **Sarah Hughes Dark Ruby**, from historic Black Country brewpub the Beacon Hotel in Sedgley, Dudley, provides a glimpse of mild's more muscular past. A creamy beige head offsets a very dark-brown beer with red highlights, a colour obtained just with Maris Otter pale and crystal malts. The malty aroma has notes of burnt toast threaded with black cherry fruit and an early whiff of lightly resinous Fuggle and Golding hops. The extra gravity lends lusciousness to a richly malty palate with more fruit, perhaps plum. A gentle throb of leafy, earthy hop bitterness offsets toffee and toast in the finish. The beer is a great example of how yeast and hops add tantalising complexity to a firm malt base without overstatement.

Strong pale mild is only found as an occasional special, often recreating an historic recipe.

Bitter

Bitter is often considered the signature cask beer. By the time the modern beer consumer movement emerged in the 1960s and 1970s, it was the best-selling one, and by the 1980s was (and still sometimes is) the only cask style available in many pubs, particularly in the south of England. Until very recently, pretty much all English brewers made at least one bitter, and most likely two or more, using the time-honoured brewer's expedient of making the same basic recipe in several different strengths with perhaps a minor tweak or two. More recently there were worrying signs that it was heading the same way as mild as a terminally unhip endangered style, derided by a new generation of craft beer aficionados as 'boring brown bitter' and ignored by many new start-ups. But like mild, it seems to have recovered a little, with several admired newer breweries adding a cask bitter to their range.

'Bitter' is a relative term: most bitters are polite compared to more contemporary pale ales. They typically aim for a rounded flavour with a good balance between biscuity malt, fruity yeast, lightly resinous hop aromas and an earthy, autumnal, lightly bitter finish achieved with classic English varieties, although imported hops aren't unknown.

Most bitters are amber to mid-brown in colour, typically achieved using 10–20% crystal malt and sometimes other coloured malts alongside pale malt. Originally, they were paler, and some still are, particularly in the West Midlands and northwest England, while others deepen to nut-brown. Strengths range from 3% to 5.5% or more: the entry-level versions (around 3–4%) are often termed **ordinary**, or sometimes **boys' bitter**, with stronger ones (around 4–4.8%) as **best**, or **special bitter** if towards the top of the range. **Extra special bitter** (ESB), following the Fuller's model considered below, is typically above 5%.

Adnams Southwold Bitter (3.7%), first brewed in 1967 by the well-known Suffolk family brewer, is a fine example of an English ordinary bitter that's still dry hopped in cask with Fuggle, also used in the boil. A small dose of black malt is added to the customary mix of pale and crystal malts to achieve a classic glowing amber colour. A hint of fruit and grassy, hedgerow-like hops add interest to a caramel-scented aroma, while the palate has herbal hops over stewed fruit and caramel. Herbal bitterness offsets rounded sweetness in the finish, with a late subtle crack of burnt toast and black treacle from the roasted malt. The beer often has a slight astringency, which develops further if it's aged

in the cellar, yielding an even more complex beer with lemon tea, orange and red wine notes.

Woodforde's Wherry (3.8%) was the first beer made at this Norfolk Broads microbrewery when it opened in 1981, named after a type of sailing boat once common locally. Though now described as an amber ale, it's a lighter and more modern interpretation of a bitter, a golden beer with more delicate and floral hop notes. It has suggestions of honey and a crisp, fruity hop presence on the aroma, a full and notably malty palate, with the whiff of an empty grain sack, offering good support for subtle lemon, kiwi fruit, grape and quinine-bitter notes. The crisp finish turns peppery, developing quite a hop bite, though with admirable restraint.

Harvey's Sussex Best Bitter (4%) is an English classic from the one of the UK's most famous family breweries. First made in 1955, it's a great demonstration of how a simple, traditional recipe – pale and crystal malt, locally grown Fuggles, Progress, Golding and Bramling Cross hops – acquires unmistakable individuality from an expressive house yeast. The amber-brown beer has a copper sheen, and an aroma that wafts fine orange peel, grassy resins and apricot jam over honey biscuit malt, sometimes with a light hint of buttered toffee. The palate has a similarly biscuity malt character, with notes of autumn fruit, roast nuts and light yeasty esters. Dryness in the mouth balances a sweetish background, and after a brief burst of juicy malt on the swallow, firm, earthy, peppery hops grip an indubitably bitter finish while leaving room for more delicate notes of honey and orange.

Bathams Best Bitter (4.3%) from the revered, traditional, small family brewery at Brierley Hill, Dudley, is an excellent example of the pale West Midlands variety: it's pale gold, or 'straw-coloured' in the brewery's own terms, with a sticky white head. The aroma has suggestions of fresh-picked Williams pears, with lemon, spice and a gentle but characteristic sulphur hint. The palate is soft and complex while remaining crisp and refreshing, with bready, slightly sweet malt that turns chalky-dry, lightened by suggestions of lemon and sweet cherry. Pear hints return in the finish, with more fruity sweetness and lingering resinous bitterness. It's another good demonstration of how much house yeast character can add distinctiveness to a simple recipe of English malt and hops.

Butcombe Original (4%) was the only brand to emerge from its brewery just outside Bristol for 18 years after it was founded in 1978, and the unusual level of dedication to getting a core beer right helped turn it into a regional icon, which, according to the *Morning Advertiser,* was the UK's ninth best-selling cask beer in 2022. 'Lots of people round here will choose which pub they go to according to how good the Original is,' says brewer Mike Jordan. It's a classic pale amber southern bitter with a light suggestion of roast and chocolate from a touch of black malt, immediately hoppy on the palate against plenty of cracked toffee malt. Bitter orange marmalade and peppery bitterness present themselves in the finish.

Marble Manchester Bitter (4.2%), from a much-admired veteran micro-brewery, nods to the celebrated golden, hop-forward bitters of its home city, most obviously the once-revered Boddingtons Bitter (which moved outside Manchester when the Strangeways brewery closed in 2005 and was discontinued as a cask product by current owners AB InBev in 2012). It's not a clone say the brewers, but more a 'collective memory' of the old Boddies. US hops – Cascade, Ekuanot and an experimental hop – lend a contemporary twist, with citrus and apricot on the aroma and a no-nonsense bitter grapefruit zest palate, shown off by a light, grainy, malt backdrop and softened with subtle fruit and elegant herbal notes. Bitterness in the finish compels you to another mouthful.

A summary of English best bitters would be incomplete without mentioning **Timothy Taylor Landlord** (4.3%), a classic, dry, mid-amber Yorkshire example with a typically lively condition and creamy head. Styrian Golding and Fuggle hops and an expressive house yeast yield lightly floral, fine marmalade, berry and rosehip aromas, some of which persist into a fruity, malty palate with bold endive bitterness. The peppery finish is balanced with cracker biscuit malt.

Batemans XXXB (pronounced locally as 'Triple XB', 4.8%), launched in 1978, is a satisfyingly malty deep-amber beer darkened with crystal and chocolate malts from a picturesque historic brewery at Wainfleet, Lincolnshire. A slightly dusty, sacky aroma with raisin and peanut heralds a more assertive palate, with layers of caramel toffee, toasted rye bread and raisins laced with snappy black pepper. There's more toffee malt with autumn fruits and hazelnut chocolate on a finish with a late bitter throb. Slovenian Bobek hops add a floral note, alongside the classic tones of Golding for aroma and Challenger for bittering, while the extra alcohol adds obvious weight compared to the brewery's equally delightful ordinary bitter **XB** (3.7%).

Fuller's ESB (5.5%) began in 1969 as a seasonal simply named Winter Brew. It proved so popular that it was added to the core range in 1971 as Extra Special Bitter, a novel phrase indicating its extra strength compared to other specials. Named joint Champion Beer of Britain in the inaugural competition in 1978, it was widely imitated by US craft brewers in the 1980s and 1990s, spawning a recognised

international style. A modest dose of crystal malt alongside pale produces a rich amber colour; Golding is used as a dry hop alongside Challenger, Northdown and Target in the copper. Initial notes of fresh, chaffy hopsack and freshly ground pepper give way to walnut, fruit cake and rum on the aroma. There's plenty of malt on the palate, blending bittering resins with plums, raisins and dried citrus peel, with a fresher orange note from the house yeast. A suggestion of red wine develops in a lingering, mouth-filling, peppery-earthy finish: very much a classic southern English bitter dialled up a couple of notches.

Pale ale

Bitter, as we'll see, developed from older styles of pale ale, but paradoxically the term pale ale today is more likely used for some of the most contemporary and popular styles: often yellow- and golden-coloured ales but sometimes amber, foregrounding hop aroma and character, which first began to make their presence felt with the rise of microbreweries in the 1980s.

Golden ale

As described in Chapter 7, golden ale, sometimes called summer ale, or blond ale in CAMRA judging, appeared in the 1980s as a cask beer intended to compete with premium lager, with a similarly golden colour and something of the same refreshing quality. It went on to challenge bitter as the most popular cask style. The early classic is **Hop Back Summer Lightning** (5%), first brewed in 1988 at the Salisbury pub where the brewery began and still well worth seeking out today. The recipe uses English hop East Kent Golding in a way that emphasises its aroma against a 100% pale malt base. It's a straw-coloured beer with a white head yielding alluring fragrances of gooseberry, pineapple, and grassy meadows, with a crunchy apple crispness over substantial creamy, cracker-like malt on a palate with plenty of hop character too. The finish is also crisp, lightly fruity, and lettuce-bitter, both satisfying and refreshing.

Another interesting and award-winning European-hopped golden ale from a veteran microbrewer, founded in Essex in 1981, is **Crouch Vale Brewer's Gold** (4%), named after its single hop, an early 20th-century cross from Kent now grown widely in Bavaria's Hallertau, where Crouch Vale sources its supplies. An 100% extra pale malt grist creates a pleasing gold beer with grapefruit and spice over clean grain on the aroma, and more aromatics on the palate: hints of elderflower and muscat grape. The bitter finish is quite intense for the style but dissipates before it outstays its welcome.

Both beers are now classed by CAMRA as 'blonds' to distinguish them from the variants with US or Australasian hops discussed below.

American pale ale

As the influence of US craft brewing increased in the early 21st century, the term 'pale ale' took on an increasingly transatlantic hue though the use of imported hops. One of the early breakthroughs, from 1993, was **Rooster's Yankee** (4.3%) from Harrogate, essentially a golden ale with Cascade, the signature hop of the early US craft movement. It's still available today and packed full of delightful grapefruit zest, lime and pear flavours. **Oakham JHB** (Jeffrey Hudson Bitter, 4.2%), which, despite its designation, has always been pale gold, appeared the same year. Now brewed in Peterborough, it uses Mount Hood and Challenger to create tantalising tangerine, pear, peach and stewed apple notes.

Today, Oakham is more famous for a cask beer that puts the spotlight on one of the newer, even more intense Pacific Northwest varieties. **Oakham Citra** (4.2%) was launched as the first UK beer hopped with 100% Citra in 2009 and rapidly became the brewery's best seller. The beer is straw-coloured with a greenish hue and a good white head. A citric, piney aroma has hints of mango and lychee and the slight spring onion note often associated with particularly pungent hops, but it's balanced in with crisp and tasty malt on the palate. Floral hints and lemon pepper set up a resinous zesty grapefruit finish.

Other outstanding cask examples include **Fyne Ales Jarl** (3.8%) from Argyll, made with Citra, and **Brewster's Hophead** (3.6%) from Grantham, which blends US hops like Cascade with English varieties. Rather stronger is **RedWillow Wreckless** (4.8%), where cask dispense helps create a rich, pillowy mouthfeel to support vivid notes of mango, lemon, blackcurrant and pineapple, and a hint of garlic from Citra, Amarillo and Simcoe hops.

India pale ale (IPA)

The most dramatic example of the repositioning of pale is India pale ale, which, as explained in Chapter 7, began as an English ale made strong and hoppy to withstand long maturation. In its home country, this eventually evolved into a beer indistinguishable from bitter, with modest alcohol and hop rate. It was known in this form in the US in historic brands like Ballantine's IPA, which was withdrawn in 1996, but by that time US drinkers applied the term more readily to stronger pale ales liberally dosed with domestic hops. These originated in

West Coast craft brewers' attempts to imitate 19th-century British recipes. That usage has since spread to many other countries, including Britain, where some enthusiasts now insist certain longstanding brands aren't 'real' IPAs.

Perhaps the most celebrated UK cask version of an **American-style IPA** is **Thornbridge Jaipur** (5.9%), first brewed in 2004. This has always used a generous mix of US hops, currently Ahtanum, Centennial, Chinook, Columbus and Simcoe, but remains sublimely balanced and drinkable. The delicate gold beer has quite a sharp citric aroma, with white grapefruit, pine and blackcurrant. Key to the balance is a full body and a rich malty backbone, providing a stage for lemon, grapefruit and estery pear flavours and a firmly bitter finish that's bracing rather than overpowering. Another punchy modern IPA well worth trying from cask is **Rooster's Baby-Faced Assassin** (6.1%), with a beautifully clean peach and passion fruit-slanted Citra hop character and plenty of body to support it.

Beers that use traditional British hops in a similar way and at similar strengths to create a **British-style IPA** are much harder to find, particularly in cask, though there are a few more bottled versions. If you see one, try it: old warriors like Fuggle and Golding, though they lack intense fruit, are still capable of shining in larger doses with their subtler herbal, earthy and autumnal notes and smooth bitterness.

British pale ale

The closest link back to the early draught versions of England's world-conquering pale ale is probably **Marston's Pedigree** (4.5%). Although now part of the Carlsberg stable, it still spends some of its time fermenting in the last remaining union set at Marston's Albion brewery in Burton upon Trent. As with many older styles, the grist includes a portion of glucose sugar, and it's hopped with whole leaf Fuggle and Golding. The amber beer has a toffee aroma with leafy hops and the occasional whiff of sulphur, with the hops lending a curiously creamy note to the palate alongside earthy resins and apple and orange fruit, and a similar light, fruity character on a moderately bitter finish. But there's nothing to distinguish it from a regular special bitter.

An excellent heritage Burton pale is **Burton Bridge Draught Burton Ale** (DBA, 4.8%), from a brewpub active in the town since 1982. Not to be confused with a Victorian-style Burton ale as explained below, it's a recreation of the once much-admired Ind Coope Draught Burton Ale, launched by national group Allied in 1976 in response to growing interest in cask and based in turn on an old export recipe for the brewery's once premium pale ale Double Diamond. A whiff of struck match betrays its origins over distinctly fruity and floral notes and a deeply malty, piney and earthy palate.

Perhaps the most derided of these 'devolved' pale ales among beer snobs is also one of the best sellers, from one of the UK's biggest cask breweries: **Greene King IPA** (3.6%), made with pale, crystal and black malt and hopped with Challenger, Pilgrim and First Gold. I've long regarded this as an innocuous, mildly flavoured brew, but my view was challenged during a brewery visit in 2022. I was welcomed to the 'Bogey Hole', an on-site clubhouse for retired employees. A fresh firkin of IPA is dropped off here every day, in prime condition from the brewery cellar, dressed in a cooling jacket and dispensed on vertical extraction via a handpump with a very short line. One of the members offered

me a beer, promising it would be 'the best pint of Greene King IPA you've ever tasted'. It was a beautiful bright amber, perfectly carbonated and yielding a thick head, even without a sparkler, with nutty caramel and a hint of hopsack on the aroma. The toasty palate had some tantalising orchard fruit esters alongside spicy hop resins, and the finish had more of a bitter grip than I was expecting, with the subtle crack of black malt adding interest to the earthy spice. I still think there are more interesting beers in the same broad style, but it was an object lesson in the capabilities of cask at its best and freshest.

Pale ale variants

The burgeoning popularity of pale ales and IPAs has unleashed a wave of brand extensions, with numerous potentially confusing modifiers applied to the basic style names. Many beers tagged with these are more likely to be in can or keg. However, there are numerous cask examples of **session IPA**, a style that aims to maintain the hoppy punch of a contemporary IPA but at a 'sessionable' strength more suited to sinking in pints. **Brass Castle Session** (3.6%), with various US hops, and **Siren Lumina** (4.2%), fragrant with Hallertau Blanc and Mosaic, among others, are good examples.

Another old term enjoying new currency is **table beer**, indicating a lower strength beer of perhaps 2–3% ABV, which is refreshing to drink alongside food.

Perhaps the most influential UK example is fragrant but easy-drinking **Kernel Table Beer** (around 3%) from the renowned London craft brewer, mainly supplied naturally conditioned in bottle or keg but in cask in selected outlets.

The most fashionable pale ale variants of recent years are the hazy, juicy **pale ales** and **IPAs**. These are often dubbed **New England** or **East Coast**, **NEPA** or, in stronger versions, **NEIPA** (both, confusingly, pronounced 'neepa'), since a prominent early example originated in Vermont. These achieve most, and sometimes all, of their assertive hop character after the boil, with generous dry hopping during fermentation and conditioning, yielding intense aromas with very little bittering. Dry hopping tends to leave a natural haze, which fans associate with the style, prompting some brewers to cloud the issue still further with yeasts that settle less readily and/or additional wheat and oats, to the extent that some examples look like carton orange juice or liquidised vegetable soup. Personally, I find many of them lacking in balance, and the better examples benefit from a livelier carbonation than cask typically provides, although they're not unknown in the format.

Dry hopped and **double dry hopped** are other likely indicators that the beer will be hazy with an emphasis more on hop aroma than bitterness: the latter term may either mean twice the amount of hops or that they've been added twice during conditioning. A related style is raw pale ale or IPA, mentioned in Chapter 1: the wort used for these beers is never boiled, helping preserve aroma and minimise bitterness. Lactose and fruit puree eliminate bitterness almost entirely in **milkshake IPA**, a particularly extreme expression of the hazy, juicy fad.

Pacific indicates Australian and/or New Zealand hops used instead of, or alongside, US and other varieties. As mentioned above, these tend to be vividly fragrant but less aggressively citric and piney than their US counterparts, often with tropical fruit suggestions. Other geographical terms are **West Coast**, which has become more commonly used since the advent of East Coast pales to indicate the earlier interpretations from West Coast brewers, leaning more towards the English model in brightness and pronounced bitterness from kettle hops in the finish. **Mountain** invokes the Rockies as a halfway house between west and east.

Belgian indicates the use of Belgian ale yeasts, likely adding spicy, lightly phenolic flavours. **Kveik** indicates the use of kveik yeast, discussed in Chapter 1. Though it can be used in a variety of styles, in modern brewing it's more commonly deployed in hazy, fruity pales. Adjectives eclectically borrowed from other brewing traditions indicate increasing strength. **Double** when applied to IPA normally means 7.5% or above, while **triple** or **imperial** edges towards 10% and above. **White** indicates some wheat character, **red** a deeper amber colour and likely the presence of rye. I'll deal with **black** under porter below.

Amber and red ales

Red ale is a term applied to several distinct styles. **Irish red ale** is an amber session beer, broadly like a bitter though often with a dose of roasted malt or barley to give a hint of roast in the finish. Belgian-style reds are usually mixed fermentation beers. More common on this side of the Irish sea are red and **amber ales** inspired by modern US models, adding extra colour to a pale ale with caramelised malts and extra aroma and flavour from fruity and piney US hops, an effective combination if well-judged. 'Red' often implies a dose of rye malt, which indeed adds a ruddy colour as well as the characteristic pungently spicy flavour of the grain. Beers like this are more likely to be keg or canned specialities but may well pop up in cask and can work well in this format.

A self-declared red ale widely available in cask is **Tiny Rebel Cwtch** (4.6%), which develops from its brewers' liking for malty best bitters. From a thoroughly modern craft brewery in Newport, South Wales, founded in 2012, it uses Citra hops for both bittering and aroma alongside a complex grist of pale, crystal, Bavarian speciality and wheat malts. Pine hints lace a digestive biscuit and caramel crunch aroma, with lime and dark orange marmalade alongside salted caramel on an enveloping palate. The finish is piney bitter with plenty of malt and dark fruit and a hint of liquorice. The Welsh name rightly plays on the beer's comforting qualities: pronounced to rhyme with 'hooch', it means 'hug'.

Dark and strong ales

Brown ale

Brown ale is beer made with brown malt, or with a blend of other malts to give a deep-brown colour, deeper than the amber of the typical bitter, inevitably introducing more intense malty notes, though not as roasted as porters. Historically in the UK, brown ales were primarily bottled beers, often a bottled version of a dark mild recipe, with two distinct regional specialities: a sweetish, lower-alcohol London variant represented by Mann's Brown Ale, and a drier, stronger style typified by Newcastle Brown Ale. More recent US-inspired brews tend to be stronger (around 5%) with fruity New World hops lacing a generous malt backdrop: they may be labelled American brown ale.

Old and Burton ale

The original **old ales**, also known as stock or XXXX ales, were strong beers matured for long periods in large casks and vats. With one partial exception, there are no surviving traditional examples of the aged versions, though many craft brewers offer wood-aged specialities, discussed as mixed fermentation beers below. The remaining old-established cask brands, though lightweights compared to their predecessors, are stronger than average, and dark, sweet and complex.

The best-known example still in regular production is also one of Britain's most famous beers. **Theakston Old Peculier** (5.6%) derives its aberrant spelling from its hometown of Masham's medieval status as a 'peculier', with its own ecclesiastical court. Made with crystal and roasted as well as pale malt, with English Challenger and Target bittering hops and Fuggle for aroma, it's a very dark ruby-brown colour with a fine tan head and a smooth aroma, with hints of dark fruit, toast and varnished wood. The palate is immensely complex, superbly integrating toffee malt, plum, sultana, liquorice and treacle. A whiff of pear-like ester and a hint of cough candy offset a finish that turns quite bitter with rosehip and salad-green notes. The effect is simultaneously stimulating and comforting, just what you'd want from a big dark beer.

A closely related style is **Burton ale**, not to be confused with Burton *pale* ale, but a darker and sweeter brew originating in the celebrated brewing town. It's very close to old ale in character and in 1940s London the terms were used interchangeably, according to pub chronicler Maurice Gorham (2011:102). The best-known surviving example is seasonal **Young's Winter Warmer** (5.2%), now brewed at the Eagle brewery in Bedford, with a chestnut-ruby colour from a generous dose of crystal malt and brewing sugar. It has fruit cake and sappy red fruit notes on the aroma, a nutty, toffee-tinged bittersweet palate turning dry with hints of cherry, and slightly tarry burnt toast on the finish lifted by lightly resinous English hops.

Barley wine

The seemingly contradictory term **barley wine** has been used since at least the 1870s by some breweries to distinguish their strongest beers, not only invoking the strength but also the cachet of wine, though other words have been used for strong ales, including **stingo**. Such beers are more likely to be found in cans, bottles and kegs and only find their way into cask on special occasions, but if you spot one, it will likely be worth trying. One example is **Fuller's Vintage Ale** (8.5%), introduced in 1997 as a bottle-conditioned version of the brewery's Golden Pride, which in turn was essentially a strong version of the basic pale ale/bitter recipe used for beers like London Pride and ESB. Vintage is one of those rare beers that achieves additional complexity through bottle age, but a small amount turns up in cask at festivals and other events: a rich amber beer with sweet notes of orange and apple fruit, toffee, brown bread and a spicy, chewy, peppery finish. **Harvey's Christmas Ale** (8.1%) appears seasonally, as its name suggests: a Burgundy-hued beer with an oily palate carrying suggestions of cherry and almond.

Scottish ale

In the 1970s Scotland was noted for producing distinct styles of modestly hopped, malty, sweetish, caramel-tinged 'shilling' ales, evolved from milds, which tended to dark amber or brown in colour, at varying strengths. Ranges typically comprised **60/-** ('sixty shilling'), sometimes called **light**, at around 2.5–3.5%; **70/-** or **heavy** at 3.5–4%; and **80/-** or **export** at around 4.5–5%. **90/-** or **wee heavy** was reserved for descendants of the particularly dark, strong (7–10%) beer known as **Scotch ale** which was once renowned in the export market.

Sadly, the shilling styles have suffered a particularly sharp decline. As everyday beers, they were squeezed out by lager, and newer micro and craft breweries have largely neglected them in favour of a more international repertoire. Pasteurised keg and canned 70/- and 80/- from big brewing groups, and even 60/- if you look hard, are still available, though now often brewed south of the border.

There are some honourable exceptions, such as **Stewarts 80/-** (4.4%), from a microbrewery just outside Edinburgh mainly known for modern pale and hoppy brews. In a sure sign of increasing rarity destabilising terminology, this describes itself as a 'classic Scottish heavy'. It is dark reddish-brown with a thick yellow head, good carbonation and notes of zesty marmalade over a dusty, husky malt aroma, the whiff of a well-stocked malt store. A medium-bodied, chewy palate builds in toasty, roasty malt character, with more marmalade fruit, a little astringency and a throb of hops. There's a slightly vinous character on the finish, typical of the style, along with a lingering citrus note.

Fyne Ales, on a farm at the head of Loch Fyne in Argyll, is celebrated for hoppy pale ale Jarl but pleasingly also offers **Highlander** (4.8%). Though not described as an 80/-, it occupies overlapping territory: the amber colour is achieved in the time-honoured way with crystal malt alongside pale, though the hops are more contemporary: Challenger and Mount Hood from the US and Celeia from Slovenia. They lend a suggestion of red berry and cherry to a toasty, nutty aroma, with a honeyed sweetness and suggestions of liquorice on the malty palate. I got a faint strawberry and peach note on the finish, alongside spicy herbal hops and toffee.

As with other strong beers, wee heavy or Scotch ale is more readily found in bottle, can or keg. The style has become part of the international craft repertoire. It's been popular in Belgium since the 1920s and is now more commonly brewed there and in the US and Canada than in Scotland.

Porter and stout

One of the questions I'm most frequently asked at beer tours and tastings is: 'What's the difference between porter and stout?' The short answer is that there isn't one, as no distinction is consistently applied. The long answer requires recounting some history, which I'll do in more detail in Chapter 6, but to summarise: **porter** is the earlier and more inclusive term, with stout porter used for the stronger variants, eventually shortened to simply **stout**. When strengths declined and ranges contracted in the 20th century, the now much weaker descendants of the old stouts proved more tenacious than the even weaker porters, which were defunct in mainland Britain by the 1950s. Then in 1978, a small handful of British brewers reintroduced cask beers labelled 'porter', inspired by beer writer Michael Jackson's account of this 'lost, though not forgotten, beer' (1977:156). The people who devised and marketed these revivalist examples positioned them as distinct from the best-known stouts of the day, primarily Guinness, which itself had originated as a stronger porter. Porter and stout subsequently re-established themselves securely among the repertoire of British, and indeed international, brewers, though now loosed from the consistent nomenclature of the past.

Today, beer competition guidelines distinguish numerous sub-categories of stout and porter, with some authorities suggesting that, while the former achieves its bitterness largely from roasted malts, the latter depends more on hops. This view is reflected in the CAMRA guidelines which refer to 'flavours and aromas resulting from the roasted grain malts' in stouts and 'roasty notes… balanced by a hoppy character with some fruit' in porters (2020:8). But the labelling and branding practices of many breweries provide counterexamples, and CAMRA combines both styles together for judging.

What all these beers have in common is the use of darker, roasted malts like brown, chocolate and black malt, and sometimes roasted unmalted barley, alongside pale malts. These give a very dark brown or near-black colour, often with ruby highlights, and a distinct roasted flavour, often with suggestions of chocolate and coffee. Though some examples use actual added chocolate and coffee, roasted malts can express these flavours strongly without such assistance: coffee is roasted in the same way and develops much of its character through the process. Such beers contrast with other styles, like mild, which can be equally dark but uses a different balance of speciality malts to achieve a sweeter and more rounded flavour without the roasted edge.

Session stout and porter

It may seem ironic from a historical viewpoint to go to Burton on Trent for a good example of an everyday cask porter but **Burton Bridge Burton Porter** (4.5%) illustrates obvious roasted qualities in a medium-bodied beer with excellent drinkability. As the brewery says, it's 'very dark brown but not black', using crystal and chocolate malts, with a light tan head. The aroma has light coffee and cream alongside fruity blackcurrant and liquorice notes, while you may catch some apple from the house yeast on the malty and lightly bitter but still refreshing and slightly astringent palate. Chocolate and charred malt develop alongside a bitter buzz in the finish, provided by Target and Challenger hops. There's an evident overlap with some of the darker bitters, like Batemans XXXB above, but a roasty edge too, which deepens in many other examples.

Peter Amor once brewed for Guinness, so it's perhaps not surprising that a session-strength dry stout became a highlight of the range when he set up his own microbrewery in Herefordshire in 1985, though in cask- and bottle-conditioned form rather than nitrokeg. **Wye Valley Wholesome Stout** (previously sub-branded Dorothy Goodbody's, 4.6%) remains an impressive beer, combining a notably smooth and soothing mouthfeel with unapologetically dry and bitter flavours from Northdown hops and a dose of roasted barley. The beer is a very deep brown but not quite black, with a creamy fawn head and coffee, malt, fruit and a suggestion of yoghurt on the aroma. This slightly sour impression follows through on the palate, a demonstration of darker malts adding acidity. Malt breakfast cereal and dark chocolate flavours give way to earthy salad bitterness, salt and roast on the finish, with a late cigar ash note.

Oatmeal stout

Oatmeal stouts – or **oatmalt** or simply **oat** stouts – include oats in malted or unmalted form to help promote a creamy, silky mouthfeel alongside a little distinctive flavour.

Castle Rock Oatmeal Stout (4.6%), from a brewery established in 1997 that's since become the biggest in Nottingham, is a dark ruby colour with a slightly smoky aroma, almost reminiscent of fried bacon. The mouthfeel is beautifully smooth and dense, with hazelnut chocolate and a tangy blackcurrant note. Chocolate orange, coffee and chewy malt on the finish remain smooth, with a mild roast note. Besides oats, it has a complex grist, including Munich, crystal and chocolate malt, with Phoenix, a lightly piney and citric 1990s hybrid English hop, accounting for some of the orange character.

Given the Scottish fondness for oats as a foodstuff, it's no surprise to find several excellent oatmeal stouts north of the border. **Loch Lomond Silkie Stout** (5%), from a microbrewery founded in 2011 and now based near Dumbarton, has a pungently toasty crack to the aroma, as if some of the oats have been turned over in a hot, dry frying pan. There's a hint of fruit too, with New Zealand Pacifica hops used alongside First Gold, adding notes of blackcurrant liquorice and angelica to very smooth, slightly candied palate. The finish is lightly sweet and too short to yield any troublingly intense roast, but very satisfying. It's named after a mythical seal that can shapeshift to human form when on land.

Other porter and stout variants

Milk stout is made with lactose, the unfermentable sugar which adds sweetness and a luscious, slightly sticky mouthfeel sometimes described as 'milk gum' to the finished beer. Increasing interest in sweeter beers has helped a style once associated with elderly ladies find hip new fans, though often in versions stronger than the original model, Mackeson, from the early 20th century, which is now only 2.8%. Lactose finds its way into other styles, like the milkshake IPAs mentioned above.

Bristol Beer Factory Milk Stout (4.5%), from a microbrewery founded in 2003, has become one of the classic revivalist versions and is regularly available in cask. The brewery claims the recipe was found on the wall when it moved into its current site in 2004, part of the former Ashton Gate brewery that closed in 1931. This very dark-brown beer with a cappuccino head has a roasty aroma with a whiff of smoky bacon and fruit, and obvious sweetness on the palate soon balanced by coffee roast, light berry acidity and a hint of mint toffee. There's a slightly tarry note to the roast finish, but the lactose smooths things out, leaving a subtle sweetness on the tongue. When the brewery collaborated with Craft Beer Chocolates on a range of beer truffles, Milk Stout was immediately in the frame, but the beer is skilfully balanced and certainly not oversweet.

Most breweries rely on hoppy pale ales or best bitters to lead the sales, but at **Titanic**, founded in 1985 in Stoke-on-Trent, a strongish, fruit-flavoured porter has unexpectedly emerged as the best-seller. **Plum Porter** (4.9%) adds natural plum flavouring to a beer darkened with dark crystal malt and hopped with English Pilgrim and Golding, German Herkules and Slovenian Celeia. The deep-red liquid has dark chocolate and plum jam on the aroma, with perhaps a suggestion of blackberry pie. The flavouring is obvious on the palate, with more plum and blackberry notes and a rose-like perfume, but well-balanced with dry, roasty and chocolate notes. Earthy bitter hop flavours grip the finish but folded into gentle fruit and chocolate. Other fruit additions like cherry can work well with porters and stouts if subtly accomplished.

Vanilla is another sympathetic additive that blends well with the chocolate flavour of darker malts. **Brass Castle Bad Kitty** (5.5%) is a longstanding speciality from a craft brewer now in Malton, North Yorkshire, named after two misbehaving brewery cats. The brewery avoids lactose to keep its beers vegan-friendly but adds extra lusciousness with oatmeal in this very dark-brown beer. There's light vanilla toast on the aroma, along with a plummy fruit suggestion that recalls Titanic's famous porter, though no plums are added. The palate is full, chocolately and slightly sweet, with coffee and a light hint of vanilla that expresses itself as custard on the finish, drying to toasty malt laced with mint, clove and a very late whiff of smoky ash.

A beer bearing the designation **oyster stout** may simply be claiming to work particularly well in the traditional pairing of stout with oysters. But oyster shells, once readily available in cities like London where these shellfish were a staple food, were previously used for fining and filtering beer, in the process adding salty flavours. Some brewers have revived this practice, and may even add oyster flesh or juice, so ask if this is a concern for you.

Coffee and chocolate are curiously popular additives, given that roasted malts can provide these flavours without them. **Double chocolate stout** usually indicates the beer contains both chocolate malt and actual chocolate or cocoa. **Coffee stout** is sometimes called **breakfast stout**, although the term is best not taken seriously as a serving suggestion. Caffeine in the added coffee finds its way into the finished beer, though typically at a much lower concentration than in proper coffee, with its stimulant properties largely cancelled out by the depressive effects of alcohol. Coffee flavour can easily dominate, so the recipe must be carefully balanced to distract drinkers from wondering why they just didn't have an espresso (or an espresso Martini) instead.

There's no consistent system for classifying the stronger porters and stouts, although those of perhaps 6.5–8.5% may be labelled **export** or **foreign extra**, and those 9–10% or more are usually termed **imperial** or **imperial Russian**. Recently, 'imperial' has been generalised to other particularly strong beers but its use in this sense dates from the late 18th century when London-brewed strong stouts were popular in the Russian empire. As with other strong beers, these are more readily found in other formats, but occasionally pop up as cask specials: expect a rich body with deep, lingering layers of complex roast malt.

Black IPA is a contemporary style, first introduced at a Vermont brewpub in the 1990s. Style guidelines often use the alternative term **Cascadian dark ale** to avoid the apparent contradiction, but, as with barley wine, it's obvious what's intended: the assertive hop aroma of a modern IPA combined with the dark colour and flavour of roast malts. I agree with Canadian beer writer Stephen Beaumont, who regards black IPA as simply a particularly hoppy form of porter, so I've dealt with it here, as its flavour profile sits better alongside darker beers.

The challenge is in balancing assertive hop bitterness and aromas with the equally assertive bitterness and astringency of the malts to create something that tantalises the senses rather than feeling like it's dissolving your teeth. In my experience, more fail than succeed, and examples are much rarer than they once were. Good ones, when they do appear, are worth trying. **Windsor & Eton Conqueror** (5%) is still available on cask as a winter seasonal: it uses a good dose of Cascade alongside Summit and various dark malts to combine pine and grapefruit notes with brown toast and suggestions of blackberries. Peppery, herbal hops sit comfortably with roast malts in the finish.

Other styles
Cask lager and related styles

Lager, as explained in Chapter 1, is distinguished from ale by its use of a different yeast and a long, cold maturation period. There's no reason why it can't then be cask conditioned, but it arguably expresses its flavour better at a lower temperature and with a little more carbonation, ideally naturally evolved during its long lagering period.

A rare regularly available premium cask lager is **Harviestoun Schiehallion** (4.8%) from a Clackmannanshire brewery founded in 1983. Made with pale pilsner malt and a little wheat malt for head retention, and the German noble-style hop Hersbrucker, as well as Challenger and Slovenian Celeia and Bobek, the straw-coloured beer has a crispness that survives well on cask when kept well. The grassy, floral hop character has notes of red grapefruit and elderflower, with a notably bitter finish balanced by firm bready malt.

Originally, the term **pils(e)ner**, or **pils**, was a German adjective meaning 'of Plzeň', the city in western Bohemia, called Pilsen in German, where the first truly pale lager was brewed in 1842. This sense persists among Czech speakers, who would never dream of referring to a beer from anywhere else as a pilsner. When Bavarian brewers adopted pale lagers, they came up with another distinction: the standard brew, which was more malt-forward and closer to the previous taste for darker lagers, was known as a **helles**, meaning 'light', while a pilsner was a more heavily hopped interpretation, with more hop aroma and bitterness, thought to correspond more to Czech preferences. The distinction is retained in Germany, and by brewers inspired by

German models, but otherwise all specificity has been lost, and in most countries 'pils' simply means a standard session pale lager, most of which are if anything closer to helles.

Märzen (pronounced 'mare-tsen') is a slightly stronger (5.5–6%), maltier lager, a shade darker than helles, of the style particularly associated with the Munich Oktoberfest. **Vienna** is made from Vienna malt for a deep gold or amber colour and a more biscuity character: a cask version (4%) produced as a special by Titanic in 2022 was so successful it's likely to return. **Bock** is strong (7% and up) lager made seasonally in both light and dark variants – the word means 'billy goat'.

Amber and dark (**dunkel**) lagers might make even better candidates for cask treatment, but are rare in the UK even in other formats. One notable strong dark lager (above 7%) that sometimes shows up on cask is **Baltic porter**, a beer made to a porter recipe but fermented as a lager with a lager yeast. It has the roasty character of more traditional porters and stouts but without yeasty fruit.

One welcome recent development is the proliferation of decent unpasteurised non-cask craft lagers in UK brewing, making for interesting comparisons with cask. Among the names to look out for are Bohem (London), Braybrooke (Market Harborough), Donzoko (Hartlepool, Edinburgh), Geipel (Denbighshire), Lost and Grounded (Bristol), and Utopian (Devon).

Speciality grains

Beers made without barley malt are now extremely rare, so where another grain is named on a pumpclip, this means that, while enough of it has been used to add an identifiable character, it's unlikely to account for more than 50% of the grist.

The best-known **wheat beer** styles are both hazy ales. **Witbier** ('white beer') from Brabant in Belgium uses unmalted wheat, typically spiced with coriander seed, dried orange peel and sometimes other ingredients. **Weissbier** (also 'white beer') or **Weizenbier** ('wheat beer') from Bavaria uses malted wheat and yeast strains that produce high concentrations of esters and phenols for a fruity, spicy, banana and clove character. Classic examples of both are typically even more highly carbonated than lagers so they don't transition to cask particularly well, but I've encountered specialities inspired by them.

I've already mentioned rye in connection with red IPAs, and oats as used in hazy, juicy IPAs and oatmeal stouts – both are sometimes included in other styles to similar effect. A highly distinctive option is smoked malt, recalling the days when all malt would have retained smoky flavours from drying over open fires. **Rauchbier** ('smoke beer'), lager and wheat beer using a proportion of beechwood-smoked malt, is a speciality of Bamberg in Franconia, northern Bavaria: the results tend to divide opinions sharply, but brewers who love the style have sometimes experimented with their own versions. Very small proportions of smoked malt are occasionally included in the grist of porters, stouts and other dark styles to more subtle effect. Another option is **peated malt**, dried over peat, as featured in Islay and some other Highland whiskies. Contrary to the assumptions of many US craft brewers, such malt was never a characteristic ingredient of Scottish beer styles but can still contribute to interesting specialities.

Saison and other Belgian styles

Belgium shares with Britain a rich beer culture and a continuing tradition of ale brewing, and over the centuries has adopted and adapted several British styles, including porter, pale ale and Scotch ale. But there are big differences too: among them a wider diversity of surviving local traditional styles, many employing unusual techniques; no real surviving equivalent to cask, with draught beer almost entirely from pressurised keg (though often unpasteurised); bottle-conditioned beer much more popular; and a preference for sweeter beers with more emphasis on expressive yeasts than assertive hop character. In the absence of any other information, 'Belgian' applied to a beer made outside the country indicates the use of a typical yeast strain, leaving plenty of fruity esters and, often, spicy phenols in the finished beer. Belgian IPA is a good example: a well-hopped contemporary IPA fermented with a Belgian yeast.

The Belgian style name that most commonly appears on non-Belgian beers is undoubtedly **saison**. While in its homeland it's usually a strongish golden ale fermented with an expressive but otherwise conventional yeast, many of the world's contemporary craft brewers have reinterpreted it as the sort of mixed fermentation brew discussed below. The benchmark versions tend to be designed for bottle and keg, so don't necessarily transfer straightforwardly to cask. Very occasionally seen in cask versions are monastic-inspired styles like **dubbel**, a dark but not roasty beer, often with chocolate and banana notes, at around 7%, and drier, spicier, golden **tripel** at around 9%. Arguably more suited to the format are versions of **enkel** ('single') or **patersbier** ('fathers' beer), a hearty, yeasty pale ale at around 4.5% of the sort the monks drink themselves.

Wood-aged, wild, mixed fermentation and sour beer

Wooden casks, vats and tuns for ageing beer were once ubiquitous in British breweries of any size, but the current generation relearnt the techniques of using them from the Belgians, often via the US craft sector. Today, the sort of vessel a brewer from a century ago would recognise as a vat is more likely known as a foeder (pronounced 'fooder') or foudre, using the Dutch or French word respectively.

The exception, perhaps unexpectedly, is the **Greene King** brewery in Bury St Edmunds, where a stock ale known as **Old 5X** (12.5%) is matured in three 100-barrel (16,366 l) oak vats, two of them venerable antiques, for at least two years. Last time I tried this very dark brown beer at the brewery, it was a highly complex blend of stewed fruit, brown toast, liquorice humbugs, vine fruit, caramel and oaky wine, with dashes of goat's cheese, wet plastic and soy sauce. Greene King seems afraid to share this treasure: it's blended with a Burton ale to create bottled speciality Strong Suffolk but only appears solo as a very rare cask treat at selected festivals.

Another traditional example was **Gales Prize Old Ale** (9.3%), a dark ruby beer aged in wood-lined tanks at a historic brewery in Horndean, Hampshire, and sold in bottle-conditioned form. New owners Fuller's brewed a batch just before they closed the brewery in 2006, and proportions of this have occasionally been blended and released, most recently at Dark Star in Sussex in Autumn 2022. Some appeared in cask form and proved a rich and fruity treat, with notes of plum, orange, cherry, chocolate, tobacco, damp wood, peach schnapps and the sort of thick balsamic vinegar that works well on ice cream. Sadly, Asahi closed Dark Star almost immediately afterwards so the future of POA is uncertain.

Meanwhile, craft brewers have found a variety of routes into more complex fermentations, as explained in Chapter 1. Such specialities are a minority taste with low turnover, so tend to be presented in other formats, but sometimes appear in cask. Their flavours vary widely but they share some of the character I've already mentioned for the traditional examples. Wild yeast notes can range from goaty and spicy to intensely perfumed and fruity. The yoghurt sourness of lactic acid is usually present, and perhaps a hint of vinegary acetic acid too, though hopefully not too much. Added fruit will make its own contribution, and of course the basic flavours of the malt and hops should also be evident.

Wood itself can add oaky, vanilla, nutty, coconut and toasty notes which will vary according to the extent it has been charred and the number of times it's been refilled with beer. When first delivered to the brewery, refill casks normally contain at least some of their former contents, which will have a particularly heavy influence the first time they're used for beer. Ex-bourbon casks are particularly common for barrel ageing because bourbon distillers are obliged to use fresh casks for every batch, but beer is also aged in casks previously used for table wine, sherry, port, malt whisky, rum, tequila and other beverages.

Variations
From the wood

I'm still agnostic on whether oak as a material for everyday trade casks has a significant impact on their contents. Unlike barrel-ageing, wooden casks here are used in the same way as steel or plastic ones. The beer is only intended to remain in them for the shortest possible period: just enough time to reach the pub, settle and condition, to be poured and sold within days if not hours. Traditionally,

breweries tried to minimise the influence of the wood by choosing materials carefully, filling new casks with a soda solution and leaving them to soak before use to leach out tannins, and most of those in circulation have been reused so many times that the oak itself is unlikely to impart much in the way of flavour. Contact is reduced even further in larger casks with a lower ratio of surface area to liquid. Objective assessments are difficult: wooden casks are now very rare, and it is highly unlikely to find the same beer available from steel or plastic to make an accurate comparison.

James Atherton, founder and co-owner of Beerblefish brewery in London, has served the same beer from both wood and steel at events and didn't notice a difference. Any subtle variations, he says, would likely be due to factors like oxygen pick-up in transferring to a wooden cask and in temperature exposure. 'The better insulation of the wood,' he says, 'would smooth out temperature transitions in the yeast and beer but given the volumes the effect would only be tiny.'

During 2022, I tried Theakston Old Peculier twice from wooden casks and once from steel, all on separate occasions. There are no consistent differences in my notes: I found all three samples in excellent condition and rated them very highly, remarking on all three occasions on the rich malts, liquorice and blackcurrant and plum fruit. But Simon Theakston says the wood adds subtle oaky vanilla notes which increase the complexity. 'If Old Peculier in steel is 100%,' he says, 'in wood it's 100% plus'.

Rob Shacklock is probably one of the world's greatest enthusiasts for wooden casks: as well as chairing the Society for the Preservation of Beers from the Wood (SPBW), he's a master cellarman and licensee of two Tyneside pubs, the Heaton Tap and the Seven Stars, and maintains his own population of 59 casks which he sends to breweries for custom filling. 'Yes,' he says, 'the taste is different. The wood gives it a different dimension, it imparts flavours and seems to round the beer off nicely.' You can judge for yourself at the SPBW's annual Woodfest event, which typically features at least 60 cask beers from the wood, many of them prepared especially for the festival.

Unfined

As explained in Chapter 2, finings encourage yeast solids to sediment rapidly so beer quickly drops bright ready for sale. Some brewers now avoid them, partly because they're traditionally derived from fish sources, though vegan alternatives are now available, and partly because they're considered to reduce the intensity of flavour and aroma. An unfined cask yields a hazy beer if treated in the same way at the pub as its fined counterparts, and the brewer intends it to be served this way, but if it's left long enough, the contents may drop bright of their own accord.

And some yeasts flocculate so readily that finings are hardly needed. Marble Beers, for example, no longer fines its casks, though its beers rarely look markedly hazy.

It was flavour rather than dietary requirements that inspired Justin Hawke to become the most prominent early champion of unfined cask beer. Originally from California, Justin spent time in the army stationed in Europe, where he discovered the delights of German brewpubs and British cask. After brewing professionally in the US, in 2006 he bought the defunct Moor brewery, located on a farm in rural Somerset, reopening it in 2007. Initially he worked alongside Arthur Frampton, who had founded the brewery in 1996, and learned to add the customary finings to each cask.

> But I'd also fill swing top bottles from the fermenter before it went into cask, to bring beer home, and it was always better than the same beer drunk in the pub. I started doing more research and remembered that what I loved best about German brewpubs was the naturally hazy beer. There are flavour compounds in yeast, and the finings are stripping them out. Hop oils bond to yeast cells, so when you drag those down to the bottom you're also reducing the hoppiness.

Realising the emphasis traditionally placed on brightness by many licensees and drinkers, he realised he needed an ally in the trade. He found one in James Scrancher, now the brewery's retail manager but then managing the Queens Arms, Corton Denham. James and his colleagues agreed to take an unfined version of Revival, a 3.8% bitter brewed to mark the resurrection of the brewery, as a house beer. 'Compared to the fined version, the flavour was like day and night,' continues Justin. News slowly spread, but the local West Somerset CAMRA branch remained to be convinced. They agreed to offer fined and unfined versions of an Australian-hopped golden ale called Southern Star, now known as So'Hop, at the Minehead Beer Festival. 'Not only did the unfined version prove massively more popular, it won beer of the festival. It got to the point where I wondered why we were using finings at all and just dropped them'.

Justin admits there's still some education to be done around the issue:

> Unfortunately, people don't distinguish levels of haze. A beer is either bright or it's not, and if it's not, a landlord will say it's meant to be like that. But there's a level of haze that's desirable and a certain point where it becomes chicken soup, not the way I want my beer to be. In the early days, though we had knowledgeable champions, we also had some unscrupulous people who used it as a means of cutting quality.

Moor is now one of the best breweries in Bristol, a city with a particularly strong brewing community, and quality is never an issue in its taprooms and favoured pubs. All its beers are unfined, unfiltered and unpasteurised, and naturally conditioned whether in cask, keg or can. **Moor Illumination** (4.3%) is a golden best bitter made with English pale malt and Slovenian hops, moderately hazy with a lightly grainy lemon-tinged aroma and some pear fruit from the yeast. A slightly floral burst of peppery hops on a bready palate sets up a hint of Riesling grape on a crisp finish with developing rooty bitterness. This is a straightforward beer, but the low-intervention treatment makes the most of the hop and yeast flavours.

Gluten-free

Gluten is a protein present in barley, wheat and rye and products made from them, including most beer. About 6% of the population are intolerant to it to varying degrees and can suffer digestive problems and symptoms like headaches and fatigue if they consume it. Such symptoms are usually temporary, but almost 1% of people have a genetic condition known as coeliac disease, where gluten causes an autoimmune reaction that permanently damages the gut lining.

Brewing and fermentation naturally break down at least some gluten and the amount left in the finished beer is typically relatively low, but still likely to cause problems to those who need to avoid it. Gluten-free (GF) beers have long been made using naturally gluten-free grains like maize, millet, oats, rice and sorghum. These require different mashing techniques: their resemblance to beers made with malted barley is partial at best and they're rarely celebrated for their flavour.

By careful choice of grains and control of brewing and fermentation, some brewers have been able to reduce gluten to undetectable levels using traditional methods. More assured reductions can be obtained with a proprietary enzyme known as Brewers Clarex, derived from a fungus and originally developed to reduce haze. The results are indistinguishable from ordinary beers and certainly much more pleasant than the alternative grain products. Tasting treated and untreated samples of the same brew side by side, I've sometimes noticed a reduction in flavour, but several breweries have now gone over to producing all or most of their beers this way and are designing recipes that take flavour impacts into account.

Westerham Brewery in Kent now produces enzyme-treated GF beers across its range, and owner and brewer Robert Wicks worked with sensory experts to ensure they have as much character and complexity of flavour as the original untreated versions. But the brewery is also noted for its cask, and Robert reminded me that avoiding gluten in cask beer is problematic. The problem isn't at breweries, which are perfectly capable of producing GF cask, but at pubs, where cask lines are regularly swapped between different beers, so if the lines aren't thoroughly cleaned between casks, there's a risk that gluten from a previous cask could contaminate a GF beer. Westerham's keg beers, in contrast, tend to be on dedicated lines, thus reducing the risk.

Gluten concentrations below 20 parts per million (ppm) are practically undetectable and, in UK law, products below this level can describe themselves as gluten-free. But even lower concentrations can be troublesome for some people, particularly those with coeliac disease, who need to think carefully and consult medical professionals before deciding what they should and should not drink. In the US and some other countries, only beers made from gluten-free ingredients can be labelled gluten-free, with enzyme-treated beers designated 'gluten-reduced'.

Low- and no-alcohol

One of the most dramatic changes on the beer scene in the last decade or so is the proliferation of tasty and characterful low-alcohol options, as increased lifestyle concern coincides with increased discrimination among the beer-drinking public.

There are various ways of producing a lower alcohol beer. The long-established method is to make a conventional beer then remove the alcohol. You can simply boil it off by heating, which also drives off much of the flavour and introduces a cooked note familiar from the industrial options of the past. Less damaging treatments including fine filtering and vacuum distillation. The beer is then likely to require further intervention, including force carbonation, to render it palatable. Alternatively, with a careful choice of ingredients and strict control of mashing and fermentation, you can brew a beer naturally lower in alcohol and even naturally carbonated too. This is the method adopted by many of the new arrivals, some of whom have reached down to 0.5% this way, and at least one producer, cuckoo brewer Big Drop, has experimented with putting a beer of this strength in cask. Meanwhile, there's a long tradition of cask beers that are just a little bit stronger. I've already mentioned Hooky Mild at 2.8% ABV, and there are numerous others.

Brewers are now very skilled at getting plenty of flavour into lower alcohol beers, but the dimension that often trips them up is mouthfeel. Alcohol helps contribute to fullness of palate, so its absence can make the beer seem watery, particularly as it's swallowed. Carbonation in a keg or canned beer helps disguise this but isn't quite so much help in cask, so very skilful use of malt is needed to ensure the drinking experience remains satisfying.

The description 'low-alcohol' can only be used in the UK of beverages under 1.2% ABV, while anything below 0.5% is 'de-alcoholised' and anything below 0.05% is 'alcohol-free'. However, 0.5% is the upper alcohol-free limit in the rest of Europe, the USA and many other countries so, confusingly, some imported beers above 0.05% use this description. Beers between 1.2% and 2.8% are officially referred to as 'reduced alcohol'.

Is cask always best?

I've intimated a few times already that some beers fare better in other formats. Cask works miracles on relatively low-strength beers with subtler flavours, its lower carbonation and slightly warmer serving temperature bringing out all the nuances of traditional styles like bitters and milds, and more recent innovations designed for it, like golden ales. But a lager, which lacks the sort of yeast complexity most evident when the beer's a bit warmer, is arguably shown off to best advantage with a little extra coolness to emphasise its crisp edge.

Cask treatment can overaccentuate the already strong flavours of beers like heavily hopped modern IPAs and sours, rendering them overwhelming and cloying, while the additional fizz and cooler temperature of a keg or chilled can

rounds off the edges and helps them zing. I've judged cask competitions in the US, where not only is cask rare, but its association with relatively unassertive session beers is less embedded and flavoured specialities much more common. 'The problem with cask in the US,' says Chicago-based Cask Marque assessor Steve Hamburg, 'is that they've got that great big shive hole in the top, and brewers can't resist putting stuff in.' Tasting some of the results was a good demonstration that cask conditioning isn't always appropriate.

Traditional strong styles like barley wines and imperial stouts, on the other hand, often work well in cask, revealing their full splendour a few degrees above cellar temperature, at perhaps 16–18°C. But beers like this are rarely found in cask, because they're strong and expensive and licensees consider themselves unlikely to empty a cask in a short enough timeframe.

London's Kernel brewery has recently added casks after building a formidable reputation on bottle- and keg-conditioned beers. Founder Evin O'Riordain prefers to reserve cask conditioning for lower alcohol, more subtly flavoured and darker beers, believing the brewery's hop-led pale ales and IPAs are better in other formats. 'It seems to work with anything malty', he says. 'With our porters and stouts, they're already quite big and heavy. I wondered if the lower carbonation of the cask would make them feel heavier still but instead it smooths and rounds them out and really improves the texture.'

Darron Anley, founder and owner of Berkshire's Siren brewery, now mainly a producer of contemporary keg and canned styles, is another fan of malty cask beers, including stouts like the brewery's Champion Beer of Britain winner Broken Dream, a coffee milk stout. But the brewery discontinued the cask version of its flagship IPA, Soundwave, in 2015, because 'we didn't think it was the right showcase, with the lower carbonation the beer tasted too grassy and not as clean as we wanted it to be.'

But expectations can be upended. Rooster's in Harrogate is a noted pioneer of punchy, hop-forward pale ales using US varieties, but 65% of its volumes are still in cask, with eight handpulls in its own taproom. Commercial director Tom Fozard opines that 'there are certain styles of beer that clearly don't belong in cask, like saison, New England IPA and kettle sours, they benefit from effervescence and a slightly cooler temperature.' Though most of the cask offerings are at typical session strengths of 3.5–4.5% ABV, the rather stronger and emphatically hoppy Baby-Faced Assassin, at a sturdy 6.1%, also presents well in the format.

The cask and keg versions of Thornbridge Jaipur, mentioned above, are made with different yeasts, the fermentation is managed slightly differently, and the keg version is force carbonated. Over the years, I've heard a few keen cask drinkers confess that they prefer the keg version. I used to think I agreed with

them, but I asked brewers Rob Lovatt and Dominic Driscoll which they preferred, and both unhesitatingly answered 'cask'. The keg version wasn't available at the taproom, so we compared the very similar bottled version. It was also very tasty, with plenty of those fine pine and grapefruit hops, but there was a whiff of sulphur on the aroma which would have been vented from the cask, and a suppression of yeasty complexity which allowed a slightly sweet lemon sherbet note to come through. I'll opt for the cask version in future.

Ultimately, it's best to set aside what you know about the ingredients, methods and processes used in the production of a beer and trust your own senses in evaluating it. More and more, it seems, drinkers are what CAMRA chief executive Tom Stainer calls 'dispense agnostic', choosing a beer by its brewer, style and ABV rather than the way it's poured, and are as likely to choose cask as keg. Doubtless they would concur with the point once expressed eloquently by the Campaign's co-founder Michael Hardman (1976) who concluded that 'the only way to judge the quality of the beer is to drink it'.

Cask beer and food

Beer is food

There's an often-repeated story that Bavarian monks refer to beer as *flüssiges Brot*, 'liquid bread'. The phrase is said to originate in the 17th century when Minim friars at the Paulaner cloister in Munich took to brewing a strong doppelbock, the ancestor of today's secular Paulaner Salvator, to sustain them while fasting during Lent when solid foods were proscribed. This may well be one of those uncritically repeated myths so common in the beer world, but the link between bread and beer is compelling. Both are made from similar ingredients, and brewing and baking have been co-dependent on each other, with a shared reliance on arable farming, since ancient times. And though it's wise not to overstate the health benefits of beer, it does have nutritive value, like bread. There are numerous examples of governments encouraging people to choose beer for public health reasons in preference to spirits, which are practically devoid of other nutrients besides alcohol. So a daily *Maß* (then just under 1.1 litres) of doppelbock may well have helped sustain a hungry brother through a chilly Bavarian March.

The table below gives the recommended daily allowance of selected nutrients for adults aged 19–64 alongside the quantities typically found in a litre of beer. It's adapted from a similar table provided by brewing scientist and writer Charles Bamforth, partly based on his own data from 2002 (2003:83), updated with current British guidelines (Public Health England 2016). The figures aren't specific to cask beer, but this will be broadly in line with other formats, perhaps towards the higher end for nutrients related to yeast. Kilocalorie (Kcal) is the accurate term for the unit most of us simply call a calorie. I'm aware that energy isn't strictly speaking a nutrient, but it plays a crucial role in dietary recommendations and fits well into the table.

Beer has been the only thing that has permitted generations of Englishmen to endure the cooking of English cooks without murdering them.

'A Drinker' (1934:63)

I'm not suggesting that, for example, anyone tries to hit their target for niacin by drinking three or four litres of beer, and we also need to remember that the benefits of beer are partially offset by the potential harms of alcohol – a litre of 4% beer a day works out at twice the recommended limit – but the table does show that, in moderation, beer can contribute to a balanced diet.

Nutrient	Unit	Adult daily recommendation		Amount in litre of beer
		MALE	FEMALE	
Energy	Kcal	2,500	2,000	150–1,100
Carbohydrate	g	At least 333	At least 267	0–61
Fat	g	Less than 97	Less than 78	Negligible
Protein	g	55.5	45	3–5
Niacin	mg	16.5	13.2	3–8
Vitamin B6	mg	1.4	1.2	0.07–1.7
Vitamin B12	µg	1.5	1.5	3–30
Folate	µg	200	200	40–600
Vitamin C	mg	40	40	Up to 30
Magnesium	mg	300	270	60–200
Potassium	mg	3,500	3,500	330–1,100

The figures also underline that beer's big contribution to nutrition is in terms of energy, some of it in the form of sugars but mainly as alcohol. On average, the stronger the beer, the more calorific it will be. The good news is that only a negligible amount is in the form of fat, which dieticians advise should account for only a small proportion of our energy intake. But all the same, just one litre of a strong beer could satisfy around half the daily energy requirement.

The beer belly is not just a myth dreamed up by people who like to poke cruel fun at middle-aged men in socks and sandals, but it's no more a reality than the wine belly, the chip belly or the cream cake belly. Some promoters of fad diets have attempted to distinguish between 'bad carbs' and 'good carbs', with beer allocated to the former camp, but there's no scientific basis for this.

The persistent belief that beer is more fattening than wine is often cited as one of the reasons why it's less popular among women. In reality, wine contains more sugar on average than beer, but both derive most of their calories from alcohol and wine appears to score better because, although it's usually stronger, it's typically served in smaller measures. The NHS website (2020) counts the calories in a 175 ml glass of 12% wine as 133, which it helpfully explains is equivalent to three Jaffa cake biscuits. But there are 239 in a pint (568 ml) of 5% beer, equivalent to a standard size Mars bar.

To set things on a level playing field, while the beer contains 0.42 Kcal per ml, the wine has 0.76, as you'd expect from a drink that's higher in alcohol. If you enjoyed the beer from, say, a third-pint glass, you'd only need to subtract a little more than one and a half biscuits from your daily Jaffa cake intake to compensate. Studies have found that overindulgence in alcohol of all kinds, not just beer, is a risk factor in obesity.

Beer with food

Beer writers and other industry influencers have been proselytizing for beer and food pairing for many decades. The grain offers a wider range of flavours than the grape, we argue with considerable justification. Beer can be fruity, floral, rich, tannic and even sour, just like wine, but it can also be biscuity, roasty and bitter in a way wine cannot. Even the most ardent oenophiles admit that wine struggles with certain foods, like chocolate and curries, while beer copes admirably.

Diners usually agree, if you can persuade them to experiment. It's always hard to change old habits, and wine's sophisticated image counts for much, not to mention the fact that it's generally pricier, with retail mark-ups more generously in favour of the restaurateur. Hospitality staff rarely recommend beer with food, and matching suggestions are rarely printed on menus.

Where beer earns a place on the table, it's normally in a bottle, an analogue to the wine experience – some brewers have retained their bottling lines rather

than switch to canning, with all its advantages, mainly because a significant part of their trade is with dining establishments who consider glass makes for a more elegant presentation than aluminium. A pint seems like an alien interloper in this environment, and even most gastropubs don't do much in the way of cask. And while there's now beer aplenty, though precious little on cask, in the more US-inspired corners of the informal dining sector, there's more to gastronomy than pizzas, pulled pork and loaded fries.

The more accessible and less expensive option is to serve beer with food at home. Bottles and cans suggest themselves for convenience, but if you're close to a good cask pub that fills growlers, you can fetch one in ideally no more than an hour or two before the meal: put it in the fridge as soon as you get home. If you're catering for a larger number of guests, a 5-l minikeg is worth considering, though look for a live rather than a bright one, follow the brewer's advice and order in sufficient time for it to condition and settle.

Pairing guidelines

Flavour, as we've seen, is highly complex and there are no clear-cut rules, though a few basic guidelines will help steer you towards successful matches. But in the end, it's up to you: if you find you like drinking imperial stout with braised fennel, it's your choice.

Match intensity Most authorities agree this is the most important parameter: the intensity of flavour should be broadly equivalent in both food and beer. A rich, assertively flavoured beer will overpower a delicate dish and vice versa. Intensity in beer is often linked to hop aroma and bitterness, but expressive yeasts, darker malts, higher strengths and the effect of ageing can increase it too. Traditional cask styles range from highly delicate to robust enough to tackle the average curry, but don't tend to reach the extremes of big modern IPAs and strong bottled and canned beers.

Complement This means matching flavours, for example serving a chocolatey oatmeal stout with chocolate. But due regard must be paid to intensity: a particularly rich chocolate dessert like a torte may merit something stronger like a foreign export or imperial stout. Complementing is relatively foolproof but rather safe and predictable, so is best enlivened by combining with the next tactic.

Contrast You could try complementing spicy food – a Thai curry, say – with a particularly hoppy and spicy pale ale, but you might find that all these strong flavours shouting at once is overwhelming. The contrasting flavours of a softer, sweeter, maltier beer, perhaps one of the stronger dark milds, may be more successful, as well as presenting an intriguing succession of sensory experiences. Both food and beer are usually complex enough to enable simultaneous

complementing and contrasting. Consider that most humble of beer snacks, the potato crisp: the starchiness of the potato complements malt, but the brittle texture and salt provide a striking contrast, and the latter also has the virtue, from the licensee's perspective at least, of increasing thirst.

Cut Beer can offset the fattiness of rich foods by refreshing the palate between mouthfuls. One way of doing this is with acidity; for example a sour beer with a rich cream sauce. But beer also has the advantage of carbonation, with gas bubbles that literally scrub the palate clean, loosening the fat: this is one good reason why it's such a great partner to cheese, much more so than table wine, despite common assumptions. The effect is a little reduced in cask with its lower carbonation, so it's important to ensure such beer is in top condition, with plenty of life, and that you look after those growler fills carefully.

Proximity and seasonality Claire Bullen and Jen Ferguson include this one in their recent book (2019:14), quoting an adage familiar to wine sommeliers, 'what grows together goes together'. They admit that the more distant relationship between brewing and agriculture reduces its applicability but insist 'there are still cases in which traditional, location-specific styles pair well with food from the same respective regions…[and] beers made with seasonal ingredients… tend to pair well with comparably seasonal dishes.' Contemplating a good vegetarian haggis with a pint of richly malty and complex Fyne Ales Highlander, or a green hop ale enjoyed on the Kent coast on a warm September day with freshly picked local leeks and savoy cabbage: I get the point.

Pairing by style

Mild

Tasting and pairing expert Melissa Cole (2018:23) includes this on her list of go-to food pairing styles, and with good reason. Dark mild is a gregarious beer, thanks to its rich, sweet tones of dark malt without the bite of roast or too much potentially problematic hop bitterness, and interesting yeasty highlights that help pinpoint fruity and gently spicy flavours. Try it with lighter beef dishes, vegan charcuterie, lasagne, chopped liver, macaroni cheese, moussaka, Singapore noodles, Ploughman's lunch, garlic sausage and stews.

For cheese companions, try loose-textured British styles like Caerphilly, Lancashire and Wensleydale, or mature Dutch and Alpine cheeses like Gouda and Gruyère. It's useful as both an ingredient and accompaniment to malt loaf, and its affinity to umami works particularly well with mushrooms, including wild species. Consider it, too, with Mexican and Tex-Mex classics, where it makes an interesting substitute for the amber and dark lagers served in their native habitat.

Pale milds work a bit more like lighter bitters or golden ales, but with less hops to worry about, making them great with asparagus, a notoriously difficult challenge for wine.

Bitter

While a golden, northern-style bitter is another good partner for asparagus, the more amber-shaded, maltier interpretations are impressively flexible, particularly alongside traditional British grub: fish and chips, of course, but also curry if relatively fruity and not too intense, sausage and mash, shepherd's pie and even a fry-up breakfast. Ordinary and best bitters will 'accentuate fresh fish flavors rather than overwhelm them,' says brewer and food pairing pioneer Garrett Oliver (2003:110). 'The best British malts are made from "maritime" barley varieties that are grown close to the sea. Perhaps this accounts for the whiff of sea air that characterizes several of my favorite bitters.' He also suggests those with an apple note from the yeast are perfect with pork chops.

Maltier bitters work well with roast chicken and pizza as well as sweet biscuits and traditional pastries like Eccles cakes. Richer, stronger bitters pair with Middle Eastern aubergine-based dishes like imam bayıldı, roast beef and Yorkshire pudding, Scotch eggs, pork pies, salmon and even game like wild pheasant. Hoppier ones will work as a mouth-watering aperitif.

A pint of bitter regularly accompanies a Ploughman's lunch and does the business with the cheese and onions, but mild does even better when the bread is considered. Obatzda, the Bavarian beer snack mashup of Camembert-style cheese, butter, onions and paprika, is classically matched with a malty lager, but an amber best bitter that's not too hoppy makes an interesting alternative.

Golden ale

Like Muscadet or Riesling, these are obvious choices for white fish and other, more delicate dishes. Also consider smashed avocado on toast, green leaf salads and paella. Hummus can work, though if it has a strong sesame tahini flavour, a maltier choice may complement it better.

Most everyday French cookbooks include potage à la bière, a simple soup made with beer, butter and flour flavoured with garlic and nutmeg and topped with slices of toasted baguette, with the option of toasting cheese on these to make gratinée à la bière. Recipes normally recommend standard lager, but golden ale would make a fine alternative, with the same beer served alongside.

Pale ale

Today, this is most likely to be the contemporary variety with New World-style hops, and while hop fragrance is useful, too much bitterness can be a problem. Consider it with fuller-flavoured fish and seafood like roast monkfish, salmon and scallops, but also chicken wings, toasted cheese sandwiches, fried halloumi, kebabs, pizza, risotto, gently spiced rice dishes or desserts like pineapple upside-down cake and tarte tatin. Tarka dal and chapati is another good match, but the darker and creamier dal makhani needs something a bit punchier, like an IPA or a red ale. Pale ale can work with mussels, so long as it's easy on the hops, but a Belgian-style version is best here.

IPA

The US-influenced pales that dominate contemporary brewing immediately invoke US brewpub standards like burgers, nachos, pizzas and loaded fries. The West Coast versions are thirst-provoking enough to make a good aperitif. But shouldn't an India pale ale go with Indian food? Yes, so long as you choose one with plenty of malty body and floral, fruity aromas, which can work with aromatic spiced dishes from other culinary traditions – Mexican, Thai and Vietnamese among them. And not forgetting jerk spices, jambalaya and other Cajun treats.

More surprisingly, IPA pairs with certain sweet treats like carrot cake and salted or chilli-spiced chocolate, though both the sweetness and bitterness will tend to underline each other. Strong IPAs with pine and onion notes work well with mature cheddar. Ripe, rinded cheese like Brie and Camembert, as well as pork and lamb chops, are even better with an English-style IPA if you can find one.

Red ale

The examples that combine biscuity malt with citric hops and other spicy flavours pair wonderfully with black bean dip, fried chicken, hot dogs with fried onion and mustard, and pizza. They can also work well with tacos, depending on the filling – if it's more delicately flavoured, a lighter beer will be better.

Brown ale

Rich malt and moderate roast flavours, and perhaps some hop presence, pair with spit-roast and barbecue meats and a range of beef dishes, including spaghetti bolognese. Spicy stuff with noodles and rice is another option: try Sichuan mapo tofu, coconut curries or Korean dishes with kimchi. Loose-textured cheese like Lancashire, so long as it's mature and flavourful, is delicious on Jamaican spiced bun in a traditional Caribbean combination, and brown ale pushes it up a notch further. Drier brown ale goes with a crisp salad, particularly if the dressing is made with a nutty-flavoured oil, and is an interesting match for kulfi.

Old and Burton ale

Unsurprisingly, Theakston Old Peculier is a popular and appropriate choice to accompany roast beef and Yorkshire pudding. Expanding on the theme, these dark, rich beers also pair with beef or nut wellington, beef stews, steaks, hotpot, duck, roast quail and sticky toffee pudding.

Barley wine

This is the cheese beer *par excellence*, yielding divine flavour combinations in partnership with some of the world's most pungent dairy products: vintage cheddar; Stilton, Stichelton and other big, blue, creamy and spicy cheeses; and stinky rind-washed varieties like Époisses, Evenlode and Stinking Bishop. But also consider it with anything big and rich, such as game, pâté and even crème brulée or crema catalana.

Scottish ale

Shilling beers are surprisingly flexible, matching, among others: barbecued foods; gratins and other dishes with creamy sauces; haggis, including the vegetarian version; lamb chops; and crunchy salads, particularly with nuts. Strong Scotch ale (90/-) is an obvious pairing for local game like grouse and venison, or as a digestif if you can resist the lure of the whisky list.

Porter and stout

Oysters were once in plentiful supply in cities like London and Dublin and washing them down with the equally cheap and ubiquitous porter was known as the 'poor man's lunch'. Guinness was still promoting its brews as a natural accompaniment to oysters in the 1930s, but since then the bivalves have gone upmarket and joined the Champagne set. The original fortuitous combination remains effective, though: as Michael Jackson puts it, a dry stout's 'tanginess seems to tickle the salty flavours of oysters'. He further observes that 'the combination works almost as well with clams and other molluscs, and with crab and lobster' (1993:253).

We could add ham, salami and other cured meats, meatloaf, patatas bravas, ribs, scallops and rich stews among other matches. New Yorker Garrett Oliver (2003:138) likes porter with a Reuben sandwich on pumpernickel. Sweets work well with the dark stuff too, riffing on the coffee and chocolate flavours. Mark Dredge (2022:90) suggests coffee stout with blueberry pancakes for brunch, though an ordinary stout with coffee character would do the job as well.

Sensory expert Christine Cryne, who regularly hosts beer and chocolate matching workshops, suggests Titanic Plum Porter with white chocolate. Then there are savoury chocolate dishes like mole poblano. Smoked porter works with smoked food like fish or bacon, while milk stout flatters ice cream.

Oatmeal stout

The silky texture works well with buffalo or cauliflower wings, chilli con carne and its meat-free versions, banana desserts, milk chocolate, bannocks and proper salted porridge.

Imperial stout

This is best reserved for the more intense dishes: beer and food dinners often close with a rich chocolate dessert and an impy, and the beer will work with fine dark chocolate on its own. But cocoa beans don't have to be involved: black and red fruit in a creamy dessert is another option, or the very best quality vanilla ice cream, the sort that might otherwise merit a splash of aged affinato balsamic vinegar. Imperial stout also pairs with rich game and matches the punch but complements the creaminess of full-flavoured blue cheeses.

Wild, mixed fermentation and sour

Lighter, unflavoured or lightly citric sour beers work with goat cheese, pickles and light seafood. True wild fermentation beers match rich cheeses, especially washed-rind ones, although in its home territory Belgian geuze lambic is more typically served with plattekaas, a mild and lactic farmhouse curd cheese, on brown bread with spring onions and radishes. Black pudding, mussels, pâté and duck are other options.

Fruit desserts seem an obvious choice for fruited sours but matching the fruit often doesn't work as well as expected: pairing, say, a red berry-flavoured beer with a chocolate dessert is more likely to be successful. If a beer is sour enough, it can be substituted for vinegar in salad dressings.

Spiced and flavoured

Such beers add another ball to juggle with, and if you wanted a particular spice flavour you could always add it to the food. Wheat and other light-coloured beers spiced with coriander are useful all-rounders, making a great match for falafel and various Indian, southeast Asian and Mexican dishes laced with the fresh herb. They can also work with delicate fish, mussels, ceviche, salads with citrus dressings, and subtly flavoured vegetables like celeriac and fennel.

Beer in food

Cooking with beer, or *cuisine à la bière* to give it a more sophisticated air, is often bracketed in with food pairing but is quite a different topic, a branch of cookery rather than beer appreciation. It might sound like something dreamt up in a Shoreditch restaurant, but it has a lengthy pedigree. Everyone's heard of beer battered fish, onion rings and other indulgent deep-fried savouries: the beer's grainy notes meld with the flour in the batter and its carbonation is a handy shortcut to a frothy foam, yielding a crisp and lacy coating. Beer helps tenderise the meat and contributes sweet and fruity flavours to steak and ale pie or Flemish carbonnade. Making Welsh rarebit with beer is attested by no less a chef than Auguste Escoffier (1903:1196): he recommends pale ale, some later recipes suggest stout, but I prefer brown ale or dark mild.

This is not the place to go into further detail, particularly as cask beer is the least likely ingredient in a home kitchen. Carbonation and fresh flavours are lost during cooking, as indeed is alcohol, unless you're incorporating cold beer into something like a salad dressing. It's not worth making a special effort to cart a freshly-poured growler home from the pub just to cook with it – a can or bottle will do as well and be more convenient. A pub kitchen is a different matter. I know of pub chefs who use up casks that are starting to go stale: a little acidity may be intrusive in a pint but can make a positive contribution to a pie filling.

5 Beer in casks (and other vessels): 7000 BCE–1700 CE

There's a widespread assumption that cask is the way beer was always done until all those new-fangled kegs, bottles, cans and gas cylinders came along. A piece by 'a brewery cellars manager' in a 1923 manual for licensees asserts that cask beer 'has existed from the time brewing was first instituted in this country'. Some 50 years later, the newly founded CAMRA defended cask as the traditional product which big brewing groups were trying to abolish. We now know much more about the history of brewing than we did then, yet you can still read that cask 'dates back to the middle ages', as the website of one family brewer puts it.

It turns out cask beer as we know it is as much the result of evolution and change as any other product. Beer *in* casks was around in medieval times and, indeed, earlier. Beer that's still fermenting to some extent at the point it's consumed was the only option until the microbiological advances of the later 19th century. But neither of these is quite the same as modern cask-conditioned beer, which, like so much else in brewing, is a child of the industrial age.

One useful way to look at brewing history is in terms of the struggle to ensure beer is consistently palatable. Pioneering biochemist Louis Pasteur noticed that 'beer and the wort used to produce it are essentially alterable liquids' (1928:21; the French term *altérable* is particularly associated with substances liable to oxidation). He contrasted beer with wine, which ferments much more reliably, and, with its higher acidity, antioxidant content and, typically, alcoholic strength, is more robust to transport and store. One of his more famous quotes (1866:56) is 'Le vin peut être à bon droit considéré comme la plus saine, la plus hygiénique des boissons' (Wine can perhaps rightfully be considered the cleanest, the most hygienic of drinks). It's often misinterpreted as a comment on the supposed health benefits of wine drinking, but Pasteur was drawing attention to wine's comparative microbiological stability compared to beer.

The simplest way of meeting this challenge is to drink beer as quickly as possible after fermentation, and for many centuries most breweries were small undertakings with thirsty drinkers close at hand. The changing seasons presented a greater challenge. Wine needed to keep because its production immediately followed an annual harvest. Beer was made with dry ingredients so in theory could be brewed year-round, but warm summer weather made successful fermentation difficult: the yeast worked too quickly, creating off-flavours; exceptionally hot weather could kill it; and unwanted infections were more common. Early brewing scientist Michael Combrune designated the brewing season as 'that part of the year in which the medium heat of the day is at, or below, 50°F (10°C)', which in his home city of London at the time stretched from the beginning of October to the middle of May (1762:121).

Higher alcohol content, the addition of preservative herbs and spices, including hops, storage in cold cellars and caves, and later, filtration, pasteurisation and cask conditioning itself were all strategies to prolong shelf life, an objective that became ever more important as brewing evolved into a large-scale industry and beers were distributed both nationally and internationally. To understand how British brewers eventually developed cask beer as a reliable means of delivering a drinkable pint, we need to begin with the evolution of the beers that preceded it.

Ancient and medieval beer

Given the complex succession of processes involved in modern brewing, the question arises of how humans discovered beer in the first place. Mead is widely believed to be the oldest alcoholic drink, as wild yeast will ferment honey diluted in water, although this is largely informed speculation. Wild yeast also readily ferments overripe fruit, as explained in Chapter 1. The pathway to beer seems less obvious, until you consider that soaking raw grains in water, milk or some other liquid is a simple way to soften them, rendering them digestible and nutritious. In the process, they will begin to germinate, increasing their sweetness and nutritive value, laying the foundations for malting. Sprouted grains left in a liquid exposed to air attract wild yeasts and ferment, particularly if sweetened with honey and/or fruit, resulting in a crude, turbid beer with a much lower alcohol content than yielded by modern mashing and fermentation regimes, but significant just the same.

The earliest known archaeological evidence of brewing to date was discovered in 2018 in the Raqefet Cave near Haifa, Israel. Researchers found stone mortars once used by the Natufian people, to grind wild barley or wheat for brewing a gruel-like beer some 11,700 to 13,700 years ago. This was a particularly significant find, as the Natufians were pre-agricultural semi-sedentary foragers, while previous evidence of ancient brewing was from later cultures that, unsurprisingly, practised large-scale cultivation of grain.

The Raqefet discovery places the known origin of brewing much further back than the previous earliest evidence, from China around 9,000 years ago, and returns it to its traditional home, the Fertile Crescent of antiquity, a broad inverted U-shaped ribbon stretching from Luxor to the Persian Gulf. Mesopotamia, mainly in modern-day Iraq, was the cradle of the 'Neolithic revolution' from around 10,000 BCE, witnessing the development of cereal cultivation, the wheel, and cursive script among other innovations. Barley has been cultivated here for over 10,000 years, with the earliest brewing finds, in Iraq and Israel, dating from around 8500 BCE.

There's a longstanding debate among anthropologists and archaeologists over whether bread or beer came first, initiated by US academic Robert J Braidwood in 1953. Braidwood was sympathetic to his botanist colleague Jonathan Sauer's view that 'thirst rather than hunger may have been the stimulus behind the origin of small grain agriculture', or, in other words, humans began cultivating grains primarily so they could brew beer, not bake bread. Many disagreed, arguing that leavened bread soaked in liquid provided a more plausible route to the serendipitous discovery. The puzzle may never be entirely solved, but the recent evidence from Raquefet of brewing long before grain cultivation lends weight to the 'beer first' hypothesis.

What's certain is that beer had great value to our ancestors. As we've seen in Chapter 4, it's inherently nutritious, particularly in terms of energy; unlike raw grains, it's also readily consumable and would have been easier on the teeth than the bread of the day, which often contained residues of sand and ash. But it's also intoxicating, and therefore linked to spiritual, religious and ritualistic practice, and, through these, to social cohesion.

Much of the earliest archaeological evidence for beer is in contexts which suggest its use in ritual. Perhaps the earliest written description of the brewing process is in the *Hymn to Ninkasi*, a religious work in praise of the Mesopotamian goddess of beer, known from tablets inscribed around 1800 BCE but likely composed earlier: it's detailed enough that modern brewers have attempted to brew beers based on it. The Egyptians believed that the god Osiris invented beer and drinking it was an act of worship. There's a much-retold myth that originates in the *Book of the Heavenly Cow*, compiled around 1323 BCE: the sun god Ra orders 7,000 jars of beer dyed with red ochre so they resemble blood; his bloodthirsty daughter Hathor drinks the beer and is thus pacified and distracted from a murderous rampage, averting the destruction of humanity.

Knowledge of malting and brewing spread north and west from the Middle East. Remnants of a malt-containing drink dating from 3910 BCE were identified in the 2010s at Hornstaad-Hörnle, Baden-Württemberg, Germany. During the Iron Age, beginning around 1000 BCE, beer and mixed beverages made with grain and honey were well established among the Celtic and Germanic people who occupied much of what

Drinking beer through a straw in ancient Egypt

we now recognise as the European 'beer belt', stretching from Ireland to Slovakia and Poland. Unfortunately, such people left few written records.

We learn more from Greek and Roman authors, who were from wine-drinking countries and felt pity for poor northerners whose appalling climate denied them the pleasures of the grape. 'The land produces neither vine nor oil,' observes Sicilian geographer Diodorus Siculus in around 35 BCE, 'and as a consequence those Gauls who are deprived of these fruits make a drink out of barley which they call *zythos* or beer.' (1935: Book V:26.) Pioneering Greek physician Dioscorides, writing around 60 CE, discusses beer under its old Celtic name *kurmi* as a substitute for wine, but warns that it 'causes headaches, breeds ill fluids, and hurts the tendons' (2000:2:110 p231). The renowned historian and politician Tacitus, writing about the Germanic tribes at the end of the 1st century CE, says they make a drink from 'barley or other grain… fermented into a certain resemblance to wine.' He drily observes that, while 'they satisfy their hunger without elaborate preparation and without delicacies, in quenching their thirst they are not equally moderate'(1942:Ch 23).

Pliny the Elder notes that 'the people of the Western world' have intoxicating drinks made from grain 'steeped in water' (1855:Book 14:Ch 29), and underlines the connection between brewing and baking by noting that in Gaul and Spain bakers use the barm from beer fermentation as a leaven: 'hence it is that the bread in those countries is lighter than that made elsewhere' (Book 18:Ch 12).

When did brewing begin in Britain? There's plausible but inconclusive evidence at the neolithic village of Skara Brae on Orkney, inhabited in 3180–2500 BCE, while pottery sherds from very large vessels recovered from the Balfarg henge

Brewing residues from c400 BCE found alongside A14 in Cambridgeshire

monument at Glenrothes, Fife, in use from the 4th to the 2nd millennium BCE, have deposits of what might be oat and barley beer. Both barley and wheat were widely cultivated throughout the Bronze and Iron Ages, at least from the time of the Beaker people, who migrated to Britain around 2000 BCE, continuing under their successors the Celts and the Belgae. We can assume they all brewed too, though archaeological evidence is hard to find as wooden vessels are unlikely to survive. The remains of ingredients sometimes do, and a dig in 2019 alongside the A14 in Cambridgeshire unearthed barley and oat granules from around 400 BCE which showed signs of being milled, mashed, boiled and fermented (MOLA Headland 2019). Brewing is well-attested in Roman Britain, and another recent excavation, at Tempsford in Bedfordshire, revealed the remains of what is highly likely a 1st century maltings, with an oven used to dry out malted spelt (National Highways 2022).

After Roman rule ended in 410, much of Britain was forcibly colonised by Germanic-speaking people from northwest Europe and Scandinavia: Angles, Saxons, Jutes and, later, Danes. All these were from beer-drinking nations, and the cultivation of barley, wheat, oats and other grains for food and brewing continued throughout the Anglo-Saxon period. Missionaries determined to re-establish Christianity first arrived in 596, and subsequently monasteries became centres of brewing knowledge and much else, as elsewhere in Europe.

'The long eighth century', between 650 and 850, witnessed considerable change and development: the climate warmed, political consolidation brought more stable trading conditions and the use of heavy ploughs in the large open fields of big estates increased agricultural efficiency. This is reflected in a large archaeological site at Sedgeford in Norfolk where a substantial maltings complex from around 800 was revealed in the 2010s: excellent malting barley is grown in the area today, but the complex seems mainly to have been malting rye. Ian Hornsey (2003:247–248) cites references to beer in early Welsh laws, and as the drink of choice in a 10th-century English monastery.

The Norman Conquest of 1066 did nothing to change England's status as a beer-drinking country: the new ruling class descended from beer-friendly Scandinavians and Normandy has long been known for brewing, as well as cider-making. Norman managerial skills placed grain cultivation and brewing on a more organised footing. Although beer is scarcely mentioned in the Domesday survey of 1086 (one exception is in the description of Bury St Edmunds abbey), the text confirms that the main grain crops were wheat, oats, barley and rye. With beer consumption at around two litres per head per day, perhaps as much as one-third of the sown land was used to produce alcoholic drink. Barley was then less popular as a brewing grain: oats, or a mixture of oats and barley, were preferred.

Greater social organisation meant greater regulation and, inevitably, taxation, a factor that has loomed large in the industry since. The first national tax to affect beer was the so-called Saladin tithe in 1188 to fund the Third Crusade: this wasn't specific to brewers, but they weren't exempt, and were required to give up 10% of their stock to the exchequer. The next year, the City of London introduced a licensing requirement for all alehouses, most of which were also breweries, and applied fire regulations to those that weren't built of stone, banning the use of fuel other than wood at night. The Assize of Bread and Ale, introduced in 1267 and lasting for several centuries, was a much more sweeping piece of legislation, controlling weights and measures for the two staples and linking prices to ingredients costs. It also introduced the office of ale conner to assess quality. It was enforced largely with fines, but persistent offenders might find themselves flogged.

A glimpse of medieval ecclesiastical brewing is provided by figures from London's St Paul's Cathedral in the early 13th century showing that in a year the cathedral brewhouse produced 308,289 litres, the level of output you'd expect from a decently sized microbrewer today. In the process, it consumed 88,500 kg of oats, 40,225 kg of wheat and 30,550 kg of barley. Every canon received a generous weekly allowance of 30 gallons (240 pints, 136.4 l) – we can only assume he was expected to share it with subordinates. Compare this plenitude with the voluntary poverty of the Franciscan friars: Thomas of Eccleston, who later joined their number, recalled that when he first met Italian Franciscans soon after their arrival in London in 1224, he saw 'the brethren drink beer of such sourness that some preferred to drink water' (1909:9).

The earliest reference to London brewers acting collectively is from 1292, when they complained about prejudicial treatment by the City's sheriffs. By 1361 a 'fraternity of brewers' met regularly at All Hallows-on-the-Wall church. This evolved into the Brewers' Gild which, in 1438, received a royal charter and became one of the official City Livery Companies: it still functions today as the

Medieval brewhouse

Worshipful Company of Brewers, commonly known as the Brewers' Company. Similar organisations in other towns and cities were slow to get started, with many not incorporating until the 16th or 17th century.

Detailed recipes and technical descriptions from pre-industrial days are rare. Brewing was a familiar domestic practice taught by example and most people would no more think to record how they brewed than how they did the washing. An exception is in *Le tretiz* ('The Treatise'), a lengthy poem written around 1234 by nobleman Walter de Bibbesworth. Its purpose is to teach aristocratic children French, and it does so by describing everyday life on a country estate in light-hearted verse. There's lots on malting, but de Bibbesworth admits he's a little shaky on the details of brewing:

> The malt is then ground, infused well with hot water and allowed to drain for a while out of the mash tun, until the brewer decides that it is brewed as she wishes. Then she takes the mash of wheat or barley and by the yeast and wort, which sharpen our wits, carries out her true brewing duties. I don't know everything, but each process completes its own part, until you have good ale that puts people so much at ease, some take too much (1990:14).

While much of what de Bibbesworth describes remains familiar, hops are conspicuously absent from his account, not because of his self-professed ignorance but because this was centuries before their widespread adoption in British brewing.

The ascent of hops

I've already said that the hop is the only one of the four key ingredients inessential to brewing, and in historical terms it's a latecomer. Set against a history dating back 11,000 years or more, hops only attained their current ubiquity in the last 500. That's not to say they're not important, quite the reverse. Their adoption is one of the things that marks the birth of modern brewing, making all the familiar styles of today possible.

Hops grow wild, so evidence of their use isn't necessarily evidence of cultivation. Neither is it evidence of their use in brewing, as they were also valued for pharmacological and culinary reasons. Pliny the Elder is widely credited with the first written reference to hops in around 77 CE, which is why a much-admired West Coast IPA is named after him. He briefly namechecks a plant he calls *Lupus salictarius* ('willow-wolf'), which is usually translated as 'hop' due to the similar derivation of *luppulo*, modern Italian for 'hop' (1855:Book 21:Ch 50). But the application of plant names often changes over time, and in the absence of any further description we can't be sure which plant Pliny intended. He certainly doesn't mention it in connection with brewing, listing it instead alongside other plants with edible shoots.

The archaeological record, though, suggests hops may have been used in beer, at least on an occasional basis, for a very long time, with evidence from the 1st millennium BCE in Italy and the Czech Republic, and in Germany between 250 and 850 CE and the Viking world between 725 and 925. Then there's the Graveney Boat, an Anglo-Saxon cross-Channel cargo vessel built around 895 and abandoned 55 years later in the mudflats off Faversham, Kent, where it was rediscovered during drainage works in 1970. Among its cargo was a considerable quantity of hop cones. Despite the location, in what's now one of the most celebrated hop regions, it's highly unlikely at that time that they were grown nearby: they were either carried to the boat from a distance or were being imported. The fact that they were cones, separated from other parts of the plant, raises the possibility they were destined for the brewhouse.

The first written reference linking hops with brewing dates from 822. In that year, Adalard, the abbot of Corvey, on the river Weser in what's now Nordrhein-Wesfalen, Germany, compiled statutes governing the management of his newly built abbey. He assigned the porter the duty of securing supplies of sufficient malt and hops to brew beer for the community's needs. These hops were gathered from the wild, but cultivated hop gardens are recorded at Bavarian monasteries

Hukins Hops, Kent

in the mid-9th century, and French monasteries in the same period required tenants to supply them with the plant in quantities that imply cultivation.

Another monastic source is often cited as the first confirmed reference to boiling hops to extend a beer's shelf life: philosopher, composer and physician Hildegard von Bingen, mother superior of a community of nuns on the Rhine near Mainz. In *Physica*, likely written in the 1150s, she notes that, though the hop 'is not much use for a human being … its bitterness inhibits some spoilage in beverages to which it is added, making them last longer.' (1998:36.) A later passage on boiling ash leaves in a wort or mash for beer suggests hops were also boiled (124).

Boiling is the breakthrough that unleashed the full potential of hops as a beer ingredient. As outlined in Chapter 2, though the aromatic essential oils migrate into beer at cooler temperatures, bitter acids, with their powerful preservative and stabilising properties as well as their characteristic taste, require prolonged boiling to make them soluble. Raw hops, as was likely with the earlier finds, were just another aroma component, though doubtless a pleasant one. But boiling hops in wort added a new dimension, yielding a beer that was not only long-lasting and less prone to going sour but had a clean bitterness and resinous character, balancing the sweetness of the malt in a way other herbs and spices could never quite nail. Lars Marius Garshol (2022) divides the introduction of hops into two phases, the first when they were just 'one beer herb among many' and the second when they were boiled. 'It's really the second phase,' he concludes, 'that corresponds to hop usage as we know it.'

How that second phase came about is unclear. The energy required to boil wort is a major commitment of resources when you're dependent on gathering firewood or peat, and metal vessels are rare and expensive. It seems, nevertheless, that brewers did this even in pre-hop days, perhaps to concentrate it and make stronger beer, as well as boiling water and allowing it to cool for mashing. The well-documented aspirational architectural plan for the abbey at St Gallen in Switzerland, drawn up around 830, includes three brewhouses which, historian Richard Unger tells us, each have 'four ranges for heating water and boiling wort', with stoves of the same design as in the abbey kitchens (2004:28).

Brewers working in less state-of-the-art conditions sometimes dropped red-hot stones into mash or wort. There are later records of boiling unhopped ales, while some farmhouse brewers in countries like Finland still boil the whole mash without adding hops. Other herbal additives were, most likely, at least sometimes boiled, either with the mash or wort, and often for a very long time. Writing in 1588, physician and herbalist Tabernaemontanus recommends boiling for three to four hours, whether hops are used or not (Herz 1964:112). Brewing historian Martyn Cornell (2009) speculates that the practice of boiling hops to extract dye could have resulted in a greater understanding of its potential benefits for beer.

The preservative effects of boiling hops enabled the development of an export trade in beer, first exploited by the north German port cities of the Hanseatic League, like Bremen and Hamburg. It's likely that large-scale hop cultivation first developed in the vicinity of these cities. In 1252 the League began exporting hops down the North Sea coast to Flanders via Brugge (Bruges) and soon it was exporting finished beer more widely to the Low Countries. Not only did this new beer contain hops, it was also made mainly with barley malt, rather than oat malt like most of the local brews. Its increasing popularity fuelled the emergence of a major medieval industry: by the 1370s, 43% of Hamburg's craftsmen were brewers, working at 457 breweries, of which 181 produced exclusively for export to the Low Countries, with 30,000 hl a year sent through Amsterdam alone. At their peak, the Hanseatic breweries produced 500,000 hl a year between them, most of it for export.

Dutch and Flemish brewers looked on with frustration. They were within the jurisdiction of the Holy Roman Empire, where the *gruitrecht* (gruit right) applied, a stealth tax on brewing in cities. Almost without exception, every brewer was obliged to use the secret herbal blend known as *gruit*, probably consisting largely of bog myrtle (*Myrica gale*), available only from a monopoly supplier – the *gruithuis* (gruit house) – at a hefty surcharge, which was a major source of civic revenue. In the 1320s, when the Count of Holland briefly banned German imports, the county's brewers won the right to brew hopped beer if they paid duty equivalent to the *gruitrecht*, and over the next century or so hopping became the norm in the Low Countries.

The region provided the staging post for hopped beer to reach Britain, crossing the North Sea to East Anglia. The earliest relevant British records are from the 1350s. Beer from Amsterdam was imported to Great Yarmouth in 1361, and a total of 100 barrels (164 hl) landed at Colchester in 1397–98. The earliest record yet found of hopped beer brewed in England is also from Yarmouth, in 1398–9: the brewer was a Dutchman and likely used imported ingredients.

Hop cultivation followed later, almost certainly in Kent with its favourable *terroir* and cross-Channel links: 1524 is often quoted, though it may be 1511 or 1520. The practice expanded in subsequent decades to Essex, Surrey and Sussex. By 1572 it was well-established enough that agricultural writer Leonard Mascall covered it in detail alongside advice on managing orchard trees and vines. He suggests not only growing hops from seed then selecting the best roots but also transplanting and cultivating good wild hops found in hedgerows. He says his text is 'Englished' from Dutch sources, but proudly claims 'one pound of our hop dried and ordered, will go as far as two pound of the best hop that cometh from beyond seas' (1572:90).

So different was this new kind of malt liquor that English speakers coined a new word for it. Previously, all beer was known as 'ale', from the Old Norse *öl* (modern Danish and Norwegian *øl*, Swedish *öl*), another reminder of the strong brewing heritage of Scandinavia. The hopped variety was distinguished by borrowing the word used in the places it came from: 'beer', from the Dutch (and German) *bier*. The words have subsequently shifted in meaning several times: today, all these beers, hopped or unhopped, would be considered ales, made with ale yeast.

Several brewing histories present ale and beer as a battleground in Tudor culture wars, with hops decried in various petitions to Parliament and denounced as a 'wicked and pernicious weed', a quote sometimes attributed to Henry VIII who was allegedly responsible for outlawing them between 1530 and 1552. Cornell (2007) points out that there are no government records of any such petitions or laws, so the vociferousness of resistance is at least exaggerated.

It's clear, though, that both the authorities and brewers were, for some time, anxious to preserve the distinction between ale and beer: the various local bans on hops turn out to be bans on hops *in ale*. Beer brewers organised separately from their ale-brewing competitors who were granted their own London gild in 1493. Initially, they were mainly immigrants from the Low Countries, often Protestants fleeing political instability and sometimes repression at home, and vulnerable to bouts of xenophobic bigotry (possibly the explanation for the more colourful accounts of objections to their product).

Tudor physician and writer Andrew Boorde is a much-quoted example of a man with strong opinions on the topic. In his *Dyetary of Health*, Boorde praises good ale as a strengthening 'natural drink' for an Englishman'. In contrast:

> Beer is a natural drink for a Dutchman. And now of late days it is much used in England to the detriment of many Englishmen, specially it killeth them the which be troubled with the colic and the stone and the strangulation, for the drink is a cold drink yet it doth make a man fat, and doth inflate the belly, as it doth appear by the Dutchmen's faces and bellies (1542:52–53).

The obvious advantages of hops ultimately outweighed such prejudices. Just three decades after Boorde's diatribe, agriculturalist Reynolde Scot wrote a best-selling manual for hop farmers which made an eloquent case for the fragrant bine, in terms of both preservative qualities and flavour, suggesting that even some ale brewers were now hopping their products:

> Whereas you cannot make above eight or nine gallons [36–41 l] of indifferent ale out of one bushel of malt, you may draw 18 or 20 gallons [82–91 l] of very good beer… for if your ale may endure a fortnight, your beer through the benefit of the hop shall continue a month, and what grace it yieldeth to the taste, all men may judge that have sense in their mouths, and if the controversy be betwixt beer and ale… it sufficeth for the glory and commendation of the beer, that here in our country, ale giveth place unto it, and that most part of our countrymen do abhor and abandon ale, as a loathsome drink… Finally, that ale which is the most delicate and of best account, borroweth the hop (1576:5–6).

By the second half of the 16th century, says Unger (2004:235), English drinkers 'had almost completely accepted hopped beer, with a small minority still preferring ale'. The old style clung on into the 17th century, particularly in rural areas, and as late as 1651 the self-styled 'water poet' John Taylor was still fighting old battles by declaring beer a 'Dutch boorish liquor… a saucy intruder into this land' (1651:11), linking it with heresies. But by now a more common view of ale was as a drink for old codgers and country bumpkins.

What did unhopped ales taste like? Spiced beers are still familiar today, though those made without hops are a rarity. One brewer who specialises in them is Annick De Splenter at the Gruut brewery in Gent, East Flanders, making use of bog myrtle alongside numerous other herbs and spices. I've enjoyed her brews, though find the flavours sweetish and sometimes

Annick De Splenter

slightly medicinal, with nothing quite like the clean bitterness of hops. But then I've grown up drinking hopped beer.

One common misconception is that unhopped ale was always spiced. Certainly, numerous flavour additives were used, even outside the region where the *gruitrecht* applied, including in Britain. Numerous sources, however, make clear that ale was often made simply with malted grains, water and yeast, and the simplest was considered the best by many. Walter de Bibbesworth's 13th-century account quoted above makes no mention of flavour additives. In 1464 the London ale brewers, hoping to protect their livelihoods, petitioned the Lord Mayor to 'forbid the putting into ale of any hops, herbs or any other like thing, but only liquor [water], malt and yeast' (quoted in King 1947:54). Boorde insists that 'ale is made of malt and water, and they the which do put any other thing to ale than is rehearsed, except yeast, barm, or godisgood [all three of which refer to yeast], doth sophisticate their ale' (1542:52). In this context, he doesn't regard 'sophistication' as a good thing. Several authorities speculate that such ale was heavy and sweet, with plentiful residual sugar from an incomplete fermentation – some accounts suggest taking only two days, though Boorde says ale shouldn't be drunk younger than five days.

It may help when imagining an ale without *any* added flavouring to remember that it was most probably fermented by expressive yeasts that contributed flavour-active compounds as well as soured by lactic bacteria. Certain beers today rely on acidic and yeasty flavours to balance the malt, for example lambic, where the hops are deliberately aged to minimise their aroma and bitterness. I once tasted an experimental porter made without hops by the Dolle Brouwers in Diksmuide, West Flanders, where lactic notes and fruity yeast offset dark roast malt flavours and brown sugar sweetness. The old unhopped ales must have been palatable, or they would not have been drunk so readily. But you can also understand how the flavour of hops, as well as their practical advantages, won the argument for beer.

But first I make a protestation
That I am drunk, I know it by my sound;
And therefore, if that I misspeak or say,
Wyte it [blame it on] the ale of Southwark, I you pray.
GEOFFREY CHAUCER (c1385:lines 29–32)

Monks, housewives, alewives and common brewers

English brewers were already exporting significant quantities of beer by the mid-16th century: 'London alone,' says Richard Unger (2004:235), 'exported more than 4,300,000 liters of beer in 1591 going to north Germany, the Low Countries and France.' Better-off people in England's more cosmopolitan cities enjoyed beers imported from Europe, particularly as trade in bottled beer grew in the 17th century. These products moved by convenient sea and coastal routes, but beer, using the term again in an inclusive sense, remained a bulky and perishable commodity to transport by land. For many centuries it was largely made for local consumption by a multiplicity of small brewhouses, in institutions and private homes as well as on commercial premises.

Beer was an everyday drink in the truest sense of the term. Unger writes of a medieval world 'where beer was a necessity, a part of everyday life, a drink for everyone of any age or status, and a beverage for all times of the day from breakfast to dinner and into the evening.' (2004:xiii.) Another historian, Judith Bennett (1996:17), estimates medieval adults may have consumed as much as a gallon (4.55 l) a day, with children drinking lesser quantities. There's a widespread assumption that this is because beer was safer than water, but nobody really made the connection between water and public health until the 1850s. People's reasons for drinking, and often preferring beer were more complex: to avoid the unpleasant taste of contaminated water, which would have been much more common before modern hygiene practices; because beer was more nutritious and calorific, at a time when hard manual work was most people's lot; and doubtless because they liked the taste and the intoxicating effect.

And whether they knew it or not, beer was indeed less likely to make them sick than water, particularly in towns and cities. Brewing was even more of a thirsty industry then than now, and brewers typically had their own water sources like springs and wells guaranteeing clean and fresh supplies. Sometimes they were compelled to, as they were banned from abstracting excessive amounts from public supplies. And wort was further sanitised by boiling.

Most readers will know about monastic brewing, as a small but select group of much-celebrated cloisters brews today, including one in England, Mount St Bernard (Tynt Meadow) in Leicestershire, but nearly all are examples of a revived tradition rather than a continuous one. Medieval British monasteries and other religious institutions certainly brewed, as we've already discovered at St Paul's in

London. St Modwen's Benedictine abbey at Burton upon Trent provides the first brewing records in the famous brewing town in 1295. Henry VIII dissolved this and all other English monasteries and seized their assets in the 1530s, but brewing continued in many other institutions.

Military facilities, veterans' hospitals and almshouses, universities, boarding schools and even medical hospitals brewed. Unger quotes figures for a London hospital that allocated its patients a litre a day in the 1570s, with an extra half-litre in summer (2004:127). Pharmacologist Jonathan Pereira (1847:506–509) records that hospitals were still issuing one or two pints (570 ml – 1.14 l) a day per patient in the 1840s.

Even more numerous and important to the evolution of brewing were the large country estates, providing beer not only for the owning family but for their visitors, staff and farm labourers. 'It is rare to find a country house of any size or age which has no record at all of the existence of a brewhouse,' says historian and researcher Pamela Sambrook (1996:1), who persuasively describes such facilities as 'a missing link between the techniques of the modern commercial brewery and the age-old, and largely unrecorded, processes of the medieval home brewer' (3). Domestic brewers had no commercial imperative to innovate, so retained many ancient techniques.

We know about Marion Harrison's brewing activities from the remarkably detailed description written by her husband, geographer and Essex vicar William Harrison (1889:100–102), in 1577. Her beer was made mainly from barley malt,

Domestic brewhouse at Lacock Abbey, Wiltshire

with smaller quantities of wheat and oats, using a complicated mashing and boiling regime that included 'seething' hops with wort for two hours, half an hour less in winter, and dosing it with concentrated wort flavoured with powdered orris root and laurel berries. Gervase Markham (1623:228), in his best-selling compendium of recipes and advice for 'English housewives', first published in 1615, recalls the days when beers were made without hops but insists the best brewers use them. As is clear from both these sources, the domestic brewhouse, like its neighbour the bakehouse, was a female domain.

It's a common misconception that our ancestors drank only very weak beer. Certainly, processes like malting, mashing and fermentation were less reliable and efficient at that time, but brewers ensured a decently strong result by using much larger quantities of malt than today. Modern attempts to recreate old beers as faithfully as possible include a medium-strength beer based on a recipe from the brewhouse at Dublin Castle in 1574, similar to English recipes of the time, which achieved a respectable 4.5–5%.

Brewers extracted as much fermentable material as they could with multiple mashes of the same grist, which also provided opportunities to make beers of varying strengths. Harrison mashed her grist three times and blended the results to make a single beer, while Markham suggests making two separate beers with two mashes from an 'ordinary beer' recipe and three separate ones from a recipe for strong 'March beer'. An anonymous 'Country Gentleman' writing for 'gentleman and farmers' in 1703 (1724:9) suggests what became the common country house practice of blending worts from the first two mashes to make a strong beer then mashing the same grist a third time for a weaker small beer, also known as a table or household beer, which was boiled with the spent hops left over from the strong beer. Thomas Tryon, writing at the end of the 17th century, considers small beer 'a very ill sort of drink … a gross substance, stinking, harsh, bitter … void of all the seminal or sweet virtues' (1691:25). But for many ordinary country people it was the only beer on offer.

Both strong and small beer typically spent a very short time in open fermenting vessels, perhaps 24–48 hours, before being racked into casks that were left unbunged for several more days as the yeast continued to work. Small beer was then drunk soon after fermentation subsided, while strong beer was bunged and cellared for much longer periods.

As hops were now in universal use, the old distinction between ale and beer eroded. George Watkins (1767:67) uses 'beer' for the strongest variety, 'ale' for a strong beer not designed for keeping, and therefore with fewer hops, and 'small beer' for the weakest kind. Theoretically, the preservative qualities of hops allowed for weaker beers with longer shelf lives, but domestic brewers used them instead to extend the ageing capabilities of strong beers, perhaps because, as Sambrook suggests, 'it was easier to produce a strong product of reasonable quality than a weaker one' (1996:113).

Aged beer was also known as 'stale', not a derogatory term but simply meaning the liquid had stood, compared to the young variety, which was fresh or, later, mild. Markham's March beer 'should have rightly a whole year to ripen: it will last two, three or four years if it lie cool and close' (1623:228). The 'Country Gentleman' says that many of his fellows 'talk of and magnify their stale beer of five, ten or more years old' (1724:17), and recognises that hops are crucial to such longevity (4). The strongest and finest malt liquors came to be known as October ales (or, sometimes, beers), as they were brewed following the harvest and laid down over at least a winter or a summer. William Ellis (1759:73) shares an account of managing them by keeping them bunged until spring, then releasing the bung over the summer to allow for further fermentation, stopping it up again in the autumn.

What's happening here is clearly a mixed fermentation involving wild yeast and bacteria resident in the brewhouse and the casks, taking their time to break down the plentiful quantities of more complex carbohydrates such as dextrins left behind by the imprecise mashing regime. As we've seen in Chapter 2, such processes produce distinctive flavours which evolve further over time and as oxygen seeps in. In terms of flavour profile, the results would be more akin to a Belgian-style sour brown ale, or a modern barrel-aged or farmhouse brew from a specialist craft brewer.

Brewer and bacteriologist John L Shimwell reflected on the process from the more scientifically informed perspective of the 1940s, surmising that the onset of wild yeast activity would occur after a month or so, inducing what brewers then called a 'sick-fret'. He says:

> At this stage, the beer would be far from a palatable beverage, being grossly turbid and having an objectionable mawkish flavor and aroma. This condition, however, would gradually pass off and in the course of a few months the beer would again drop bright and the mawkish flavor would be slowly replaced by a beautiful aromatic wine-like bouquet and flavor…Vinous character only took place in strong beers with a gravity of 1.060° and upwards [likely with a final ABV of above 6%]. In weaker beers, the sick-fret phase would be obtained, but this would persist and would not be replaced by subsequent maturation (1947:22).

Alcohol, hops and the ageing process were powerful weapons in Pasteur's struggle against alterability, resulting in a beverage that was more wine-like in other ways too, with a higher acidity and increased stability and longevity. Brewing in summer was possible in England but was limited to small beer for immediate drinking, while aged strong beer would last until the next brewing season and longer. But perhaps more importantly, drinkers enjoyed the character Shimwell so eloquently describes, prompting more extreme iterations of the style for special occasions, most notably the coming-of-age of the male heir to a country property. A giant cask of the best and strongest beer, perhaps around 12%, was brewed on the day of his birth and cellared, sometimes with fresh doses of hops every few years, until it was ceremonially tapped as one of highlights of his 21st birthday celebrations, a custom dating back at least to 1730 and likely earlier.

By this stage, such beers were pale ales, made with better quality pale malt. It's often said that once all beers were brown, if not darker, because the only way of drying malt was over open wood or peat fires, inevitably singeing it in the process. That's not quite true: perhaps the earliest method of drying malt was to spread it out in the sun, producing a delicately coloured and flavoured and highly efficient grain. Maltsters in ancient Iraq and Egypt doubtless found this easier than those in cloudy northern Europe, but even here it was an option for quantities suited to a domestic brewhouse. Tryon says April and May are the best months, resulting in 'not only the palest [malt], but the most kindly and wholesomest of all others' (1691:59). In the late 16th century iron and steel makers experimented with rendering coal smokeless and free of noxious odours through heat treatment, producing coke, and by the 1640s maltsters in Derbyshire were using this new processed fuel in a more carefully controlled indirect kilning process to produce pale malt on an industrial scale.

Country-house brewing went into decline in the second half of the 19th century as non-intoxicating beverages like tea began to erode the demand for beer, with brewhouses perhaps only used in March and October, making it difficult to maintain yeast cultures. This was also a period when decent cheap beer from commercial brewers was easily available, so most estates turned elsewhere for supplies. 'Not very long ago,' laments brewer Henry Stopes (father of birth control campaigner Marie Stopes), 'almost every good housewife prided herself on the quality of her "home-brewed". The quantity now brewed by women is so small that it does not need notice.' (1895:30). Nearly all domestic brewhouses had fallen into disuse by the early 20th century, though, as we'll see, some of their practices lived on in surprising ways.

Commercial breweries were once also small and plentiful, particularly in towns and cities, and like their domestic country cousins, were largely led and staffed by women. Before the Black Death in the middle of the 14th century, brewing was carried out by women in their homes and sometimes in alehouses – 'brewster', related to the Dutch feminine *brouwster*, was once the everyday term for a female brewer in English. Some brewed only occasionally to raise extra cash, while others were what Bennett (1996:25) terms 'by-industrial', selling beer regularly to neighbours but also brewing for their own multi-occupational household.

Beer was sold informally in a variety of locations, including streets and marketplaces, but following the Black Death brewing alehouses became the norm, sometimes managed by men but sometimes by women known as alewives: 'wife' here has its earlier meaning of 'woman', with no implication of marital status. Alehouses grew dramatically in Tudor times as urban populations rose; the numbers in Canterbury, Kent, for example, doubling between 1577 and 1596 (Clark 1984:225). There's an unpleasant streak of misogyny

'Mother Louse', a mid-17th century Oxfordshire alewife

in the way alewives were often portrayed as unattractive and dishonest harridans, perhaps corresponding to wider changes that were bringing about increasing professionalisation, and masculinisation, of brewing.

'In 1300,' says Bennett (1996:9), 'brewing was a small-scale, local industry pursued by women who worked from their homes … it was unorganized and underdeveloped. By 1600, brewing in many cities, towns, and villages was so large scale and so centralized that it was assuming a leading role – managerially, technically, and commercially – among other contemporary industries. It was also largely controlled by men.' She suggests that the advent of hopped beer played a role: compared to ale, it was more complicated and expensive to brew and required more investment in equipment. It was also largely brewed by immigrants who were predominantly male (77–84).

The 15th and 16th centuries witnessed the increasing emergence of almost invariably male-led 'common brewers', businesses solely dedicated to commercial brewing, so-called because they brewed for the public in common, not for a particular pub or institution, though some of them developed from alehouses. They were particularly noted in bigger towns and cities but weren't unknown in smaller towns and more rural locales. They were often specifically licensed and encouraged by local authorities in the interests of more effective regulation. By the end of the 17th century in Britain, though there were still around 40,000 'victualler brewers', or brewpubs as we might call them today, 750 common brewers were also established. Each group produced roughly the same total

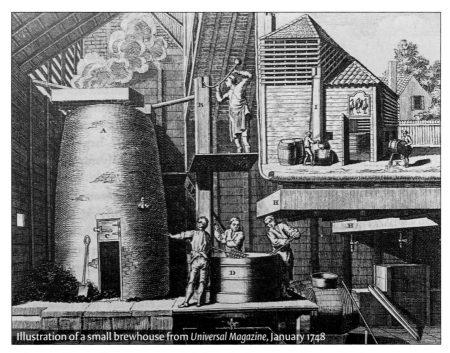

Illustration of a small brewhouse from *Universal Magazine*, January 1748

volume of beer (Hornsey 2003:385), but the latter were increasingly encouraged by the authorities, who found it easier to tax and regulate limited numbers of larger breweries than a multiplicity of smaller ones.

Hopping was now all but universal, barley malt had largely supplanted other grains, and beer exports were growing, but most people still drank their local brews. In rural areas, pale malt was increasingly employed as it was cheaper and easier to obtain closer to the source; in urban areas, more beers were made with cheaper, darker malts. In cosmopolitan London around 1715 adventurous drinkers could track down brews known as mild beer and stale beer – probably cheap brown malt beers – amber beer, various pale ales – including strong and twopenny and examples from Derby, Burton, Oxford, Nottingham and York – and stout, which could have been any strong beer. Elsewhere, some eccentric specialities persisted, like white ale, made in southwest England, with the addition of wheat flour and egg whites, and sometimes spiced.

Brewing is an involved, energy- and time-hungry process, with obvious economies of scale. As the agrarian revolution began to create a more populated, urbanised, productive and economically complex Britain in the last decades of the 17th century, it seemed inevitable that the future of brewing was in bigger, well-resourced, standalone breweries. No one could have predicted, though, just quite how much the industry was about to grow.

6 Cask beer rising: 1700–1914

Porter and pale ale

Over the course of the 18th century brewing transformed from what was effectively a cottage craft into one of the first major large-scale industries, the vanguard of the industrial revolution. The transformation began in the special circumstances of London, where the population grew from around 630,000 in 1715 to 1.1 million in 1800, housing around 10% of the entire country, and providing an unprecedented concentration of thirsty drinkers within the delivery range of a brewer's dray. And what these people mainly drank was a beer called porter, produced at an unprecedented scale. As the century began, historian Peter Mathias estimates, the biggest breweries were producing 8,000 hl (1.4 million pints) a year, or perhaps 16,000 hl at most. By the end of it, the individual annual output of the biggest porter brewers was well over 160,000 hl. Mathias describes one particularly impressive example:

> In 1796, Samuel Whitbread brewed, for the first time in any brewery in the world, over 200,000 barrels [327,320 hl, 57.6 million pints] of porter in a single season. This feat involved raw material costs of perhaps £200,000 [£17.9 million in 2023 prices], the upkeep of a plant which, with stocks, was worth over half a million pounds [£44.75 million], maintaining over 100 horses, and holding to account 500 publicans or more, and perhaps 1,000 other customers, for business which represented nearly thirty million retail transactions (at one quart) from a single unit of production (1959:xxiii).

There are numerous fanciful tales in circulation about the origin of porter, but the more mundane probability is that it evolved from earlier recipes as a way of making a cheap, palatable and relatively consistent mass-market beer in such circumstances. Recipes at the time were determined largely by the available forms of malted barley. Pale malt, gently kilned with smokeless fuel, was considered to make the finest beers, but was the most expensive, particularly in cities like

London, its price inflated further by increases in coal tax at the end of the previous century. Amber malt, as its name suggests, was darker in colour, 'high-dried' at higher temperatures, but still capable of good results. Brown malt was the cheapest but also the darkest and most heavily roasted, kilned over wood fires: it could be made from poorer quality barley as roasting covered up deficiencies gentler treatment would expose. All three were regarded as what we'd now call 'base malts', each capable of at least some production of sugar on its own account, though the darker malts were noticeably less efficient.

Brown malt was used to make brown beer, a simple, unaged 'mild' brew which was then London's default style, one step up from very weak small and table beer. It sold at 2d (around £2.20 today) a 'pot', then the standard measure, comprising a quart, or two imperial pints (1.14 l). But its popularity was challenged by a draught pale ale known as 'twopenny ale', increasingly fashionable though it cost twice as much at 2d a pint, perhaps because it resembled the country house beers familiar to the landed gentry, who were spending increasing amounts of time in the capital. The brown beer brewers responded by using even cheaper malts, and hopping their products more heavily, mimicking the rates typical in country house brewing. This extended the beer's keeping qualities, and the brewers soon discovered that if they followed another rural practice, ageing in wood, the results would be not only more stable but more palatable.

Porter thus evolved as a way of getting the best out of the cheapest brown malts, made with 'inferior sorts of barley' (Aiken 1818:525) and kilned over beech, birch or fir. The heating was so ferocious the starch expanded out of its husk like popcorn, hence the alternative name 'blown malt'. As explained previously, this inevitably reduced diastatic power, and early 19th-century brewing writer William Black calculated brown malt yielded 32% less extract than pale (1849:40–41). To ensure a sufficiently strong result, it was mashed to oblivion. William Ellis (1759:22) describes four mashes of the same grist at varying temperatures, followed by boiling the blended wort with large quantities of cheap hops. The beer was allowed to ferment at higher temperatures than usual, with production continuing throughout the warmer months.

Fresh out of the fermenter, it must have been near-undrinkable. Brown malt, according to Ellis, was 'impregnated with the fiery fumiferous particles of the kiln, [with] a most unnatural taste, that few can bear…[a] strong smoky tang' (1759:11–13), imparting an acrid flavour commonly described as 'empyreumatic'. This was compounded by tannic astringency from the intensive mashing regime, a heavy dose of hop bitterness, and, likely, plentiful esters and off-flavours from a stressed fermentation. The secret was in the subsequent staling, for around four or five months in casks in the early days, extended by the 1750s for up to two

Giant porter tuns overlook square
fermenters at Truman's, London, 1889

years in large vats, sustained by alcohol, hop acids and the additional acidity of
roasted malts. Mixed fermentation and flavour evolution over time worked their
magic to round off the many rough edges, yielding a durable beer with the prized
'vinous' quality. As William Tizard describes it:

> The spontaneous and gradual decomposition which takes place in a large vat,
> creates a peculiarly grateful kind of acerbity and fulness on the palate…
> an amalgamation of distinct flavours… properly denominated mellowing,
> a word significant of becoming ripe, and which lexicographers derive from *mel*,
> honey (1857:439–440).

The beer was originally termed 'entire butt', as the entirety of worts from the
same grist were used for one beer rather than two or more, and as it was then
aged in a butt, a 108-gallon (491 l) cask. It was also still sometimes referred to as
brown beer, an accurate description of its colour, which was typically dark brown
rather than the very dark brown or black associated with the style today. The term
'porter' was familiar since at least the 1720s: the most likely explanation is the
beer's popularity with porters as a recognised London profession, either
'fellowship' porters who unloaded bulk goods from ships, or 'ticket' porters who
delivered goods around the streets on foot. Initially costing 3d a pot, it made for
an attractive mid-priced alternative to mild brown beer and upmarket pale ale.

Such a beer could only have evolved where there was a dense population and
an established network of professional, common brewers. The production
method was beyond the reach of both the alehouse brewer dependent on quick

sale and the domestic brewhouse. The need to offset the impact on cash flow of maturing your flagship product for months and years spurred further economies of scale, and porter breweries swelled accordingly. The Red Lion brewery at St Katherine's, owned by Humphrey Parsons, sometime Lord Mayor of London and hunting companion of Louis XV, was likely the first to upgrade from butts to purpose-built vats known as 'porter tuns', installing several 2,500 hl vessels in 1736, each one replacing 500 butts.

The growth of big brewing accelerated in the 1750s as legislation and rising grain prices finally put an end to cheap gin, infamously the anaesthetic of choice of the urban poor in the first half of the century. As the 19th century dawned, the mammoth Barclay Perkins on Bankside had over 100 tuns holding almost 10,000 hl (1.76 million pints) each – the entire annual output of the biggest breweries of a century or so previously. As well as building one of the biggest rooms in London to house its tuns, Whitbread, at Chiswell Street on the edge of the City, maximised its footprint with several underground concrete tanks, each holding almost 20,000 hl. The most successful brewery owners became extremely wealthy, contributing to government war chests, receiving knighthoods and other honours, buying large country estates and entering politics. In the second half of the century porter brewing spread outside London – it was adopted in Sheffield in 1744 and by 1806 had spread to Bristol, Edinburgh, Glasgow and Liverpool, across the Atlantic to Philadelphia, and perhaps most famously, to Dublin, where Arthur Guinness began making it at his St James's Gate brewery in the 1770s.

Technology drove further growth. London porter brewers began installing steam engines in 1784. The thermometer, perfected by Daniel Fahrenheit in 1714 and advocated by brewer Michael Combrune (1762:30–39), was adopted from the

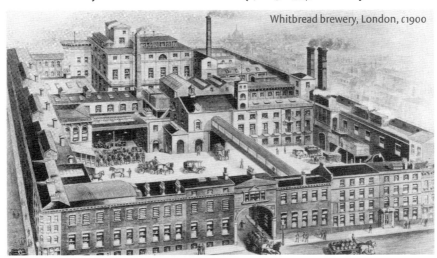

Whitbread brewery, London, c1900

1760s. James Baverstock (1811:26) and John Richardson (1798) both championed the hydrometer or saccharometer in the 1770s. Baverstock first tried explaining the benefits of the instrument to Samuel Whitbread, who rapidly showed him the door with advice to cease engaging 'in such visionary pursuits' (quoted in Hornsey 2006:426). He was more successful at Thrale's brewery, later Barclay Perkins, the first big producer to adopt it commercially. Richardson used it to report gravities for the first time in 1784, and from this we gather that common porter was around 7.1% ABV, compared to 6.7% for common ale.

The saccharometer confirmed something many brewers already knew empirically: that brown malt yielded much less sweet extract, and therefore much less alcohol, for the same weight of grist than the paler alternatives. Brewers began introducing pale malts into porter recipes in the 1780s, requiring further steps to retain the beer's deep colour, initially by adding agents like liquorice, caramelised sugar or concentrated wort. A better solution arrived in 1817, when Daniel Wheeler adapted coffee roasting techniques to produce heavily roasted black or patent malt. It had no diastatic power but imparted sufficient colour and roasted flavour when used in small proportions alongside pale malt and perhaps a small residual dose of brown. This was no doubt the point when porter became the black stuff we know today.

In the 17th century the adjective 'stout' was applied generically to stronger beers, so it's no surprise to find London brewers in the following century referring to stronger porter as 'brown stout'. From early in the 19th century stronger versions of porter, perhaps of 8% or more, were increasingly referred to as 'stout porter', sometimes shortened simply to 'stout'. The subsequent evolution of the term to designate beers that were anything but stout was shaped by the declining strengths and contracting repertoires of 20th-century brewing, discussed in more detail in Chapter 7.

At the other end of the colour spectrum, commercial pale ales were also matured in wood, like their country house cousins, and undoubtedly shared with porter the distinctive character and flavour of a mixed fermentation. They were also exported, giving rise to perhaps the most famous beer style of all.

British brewers shipped to India, at least on a small scale from the 1710s, when British interests were limited to coastal trading posts. The spoils of empire moved in the inward direction, so beer was a useful ballast for outbound ships with largely empty holds. As the British presence expanded aggressively from the 1760s, supplying the East India Company's staff and private army became big business. Hodgson's of Bow was the most prominent brewery in this trade, active by 1784 and probably earlier. Hodgson's exported a range of styles, mainly porter, but became particularly associated with the sort of fine, strong pale ale dubbed East

Supplying the East India Company's staff and private army became big business for British brewers

India pale ale by the 1830s and later known simply as India pale ale (IPA). But Hodgson's never had a monopoly, and to frustrate its attempts at securing one, the Company encouraged competitors. The most successful of these emerged from Burton upon Trent, helping transform the small Staffordshire market town into one of the most celebrated and prolific international brewing centres.

Burton's brewing history, as we've seen, can be traced back to the medieval abbey brewhouse, but improvements to navigation on the river Trent in the early 18th century gave it easy access to the port of Hull and not only the coastal but also the Baltic trade, with oak for casks and other brewing vessels returning on the inward journey. By 1780 the town's brewers were exporting over 30,000 hl a year of Burton ale of the older, darker kind, much of it ballasting ships bound for Gdansk and St Petersburg to pick up timber and iron. By the end of the century, war, political instability and import duties had sabotaged this trade, leaving the surviving brewers desperate for new markets, so companies like Allsopp and Bass were keen to take up the call for more pale ale for India in the 1820s.

According to one account, Samuel Allsopp was specifically invited by an East India Company board member to clone Hodgson's pale ale (Bushnan 1853:100–102). Serendipitously, Burton water provided an ideal basis for hoppy pale ale, prompting brewers from elsewhere to set up satellite sites in the town, beginning with Ind Coope of Romford (then Essex, now London) in 1856. By then IPA was a well-known style both at home and abroad.

Despite Hodgson's and others claiming their export pale was 'brewed for this climate' from at least 1809 (quoted in Brown 2009:167), the basic recipe already existed in the form of country house-style October ale: Hodgson's advertised 'prime picked pale ale of the genuine October brewing' in Kolkata in 1822 (quoted in Cornell 2010a:105). The beer proved an ideal export product: the hop and alcohol content that equipped it for ageing also helped it travel well, and, even more fortuitously, the sea voyage seemed to accelerate maturation. Casks in the ship's hold for perhaps four or five months were subject to constant motion and slow but extreme changes of temperature, fluctuating between 11–28°C, and arrived in a condition that would otherwise take two years to achieve in the cellar of an English mansion.

Wild and mixed fermentation once more took a hand, particularly as brewers were keen to avoid casks exploding during shipment, so took pains to ensure export beer was fermented out as far as possible and was flat and completely bright before it was racked. Booth (1852:106) advised maturing it for one season and leaving the vat open for three to four weeks, 'as the heat and motion of the ship are apt to render the beer very brisk, and endanger the casks'. Such treatment was applied to other styles too: 'It is imperatively necessary,' instructs Tizard on preparing porter for export (1857:463), 'that all extraneous vegetable matter that forms the yeast, lees, etc, be removed; because the agitation during the voyage would otherwise provoke extreme fretting, leakage, and premature acidity.' Such treatment was only suitable for beer 'of superior gravity or strength,' as 'weaker beer or ale would not bear such long flattening.' (Shannon 1805:283.) But by the time the beer reached the quayside at Kolkata, it was by all accounts delightfully sparkling. Maturation would also round out hop aroma and bitterness, something not grasped by the craft revivalists of the style in more recent years.

Quality pale ales intended for domestic consumption continued to undergo long maturation throughout the 19th century. The celebrated Scottish brewing engineer James Steel, writing at a time when vatting was 'going out of fashion', notes that in Burton beer was still kept for many months outdoors, with casks 'piled up many tiers high, in acres of horizontal extent' as 'chilling or freezing in winter is held to be beneficial', helping beer last 'in safety far into the summer.' (1879:78.) Early 20th-century US brewing chemists Robert Wahl and Max Henius (1902:810) noted that 'Burton beers, in former days, were exposed by day to the heat of the sun, and by night to the frost, and, by this treatment, they became so hardy that they retained their condition and brilliancy under the most adverse influences.'

When beer writer Pete Brown attempted to recreate IPA's journey to Kolkata in 2008 with two pins brewed with Steve Wellington at the Museum Brewery in Burton, he assumed they should be cask conditioned like modern beer. Then he read Tizard. 'True IPA,' he realised with a shock, 'was not technically real ale. And that means that Steve Wellington and I had packaged our beer wrong, following a tradition that wasn't even invented in IPA's heyday.' (2009:235.) As if to prove the point, one of Brown's pins exploded long before reaching the Indian Ocean.

Nothing but mild

By no means all 18th-century beers were vatted and aged: significant amounts were still drunk 'mild', meaning young and not sour, soon after fermentation, particularly the cheaper, lower alcohol varieties like small beer. Some drinkers got the best of both worlds by asking pub staff to blend stale and mild at the point of dispense, just as they mixed strong and small beer to adjust the alcohol content. Mild porter was still produced, and by the start of the 19th century it was customary to drink a mix of both, in proportions determined by the customer's taste. According to an 1812 encyclopaedia, porter is:

> compounded of two kinds, or rather the same liquor in two different stages, the due admixture of which is palatable, though neither is good alone. One is mild, and the other stale porter; the former is that which has a slightly bitter flavour, from having been lately brewed; the latter has been kept longer. This mixture the publican adapts to the palates of his several customers, and effects the mixture very readily, by means of a machine containing small pumps worked by handles (Rees 1972).

The writer goes on to describe two pump handles, one drawing stale and the other mild, which feed a single outlet, allowing the operator to vary the blend 'by dexterously changing his hold'. By then, bar staff were returning more frequently to the mild than the stale pump as tastes shifted away from the old vinous flavours. A Covent Garden licensee giving evidence to a House of Commons committee in 1817 recalled that 25 years previously, 'we never thought of drawing our beer under twelve months old…but if we had that beer now the people would not drink it… the public have their palate so vitiated, that they will not drink beer which is more than a month or six weeks old.' (Barrett 1817:213.) The following year, porter brewery owner Charles Barclay confirmed to another Commons committee that 'beer which was formerly kept a twelvemonth would not be drunk by the public, their taste is for mild beer' (1818:527). Only 10% of his brewery's product now shipped in stale condition. These were the first signs of what became a thoroughgoing transformation of British beer flavour over the course of the century, towards lighter, younger, fresher, sweeter, more clean-tasting ales.

Drinkers' growing rejection of stale porter was fuelled by suspicions that brewers were routinely adulterating it, a practice that was harder to conceal in a mild than a stale beer. German chemist Friedrich Accum, then resident in London, published a sensational book in 1820 purportedly exposing such practices across the food and drink industry. He dated the problems with porter from the adoption of pale malt, when the use of colouring materials 'became in many instances a pretext for using illegal ingredients' (1820:163), including quassia and wormwood as a substitute for hops. Further, the most unscrupulous were cutting costs by reducing malt content and covering up the resulting lower strength with dangerous psychoactive substances like the poisonous herb *Cocculus indicus*, also known as Spanish fly (*Anamirta cocculus*). Other alleged adulterants included gentian root (a bittering ingredient), nux vomica (*Strychnus nux-vomica*, which contains strychnine), opium, potassium aluminium sulphate, sweet flag (*Acorus calamus*, another psychoactive plant), tobacco and a variety of more innocuous herbs and spices. Brewers allegedly even added sulphuric acid for instant acidity in young porter.

Concerns about additives had already prompted the government to ban anything other than malt, hops and water in beer from 1802, with a small concession between 1811 and 1817 when burnt sugar was permitted as a colouring agent in porter. The parliamentary Committee on Public Breweries in 1818 echoed concerns about adulteration by smaller brewers and individual licensees while largely exonerating the big porter brewers, though subsequent examinations of private correspondence reveal some of them 'at least experimented with additives' (Sumner 2016:113). Perhaps just as worrying was the legal and widespread but decidedly insalubrious practice of adding slops and ullage returned from pubs, and waste beer from the brewery itself, back into the porter tuns, where it was found to prompt acidification and hasten the staling process.

Besides damaging porter's image, the scandals raised the spectre, not for the last time, of what historian of technology James Sumner terms 'chemical beer', which 'was, by implication, drugged or doctored, undoubtedly fraudulent and probably poisonous' (2016:107). Such perceptions dogged the progress of brewing science, the very discipline that could do most to improve the quality and consistency of beer without resort to adulteration. Horace T Brown, chemist at Worthington's in Burton in the 1860s, was denied a laboratory 'due to the fear that the display of any chemical apparatus might suggest to customers… the horrible suspicion that the beer was being "doctored".' When he was finally granted a small lab, it 'had its windows carefully obscured so that no one could see what was going on inside' (quoted in Sigsworth 1965:538).

Changing public tastes were doubtless influenced by wider dietary trends. Beer writer and campaigner Tim Webb points to the increasing availability of cheap sugar, refined from raw materials grown initially under the appalling conditions of slave labour in Britain's Caribbean colonies. Annual sugar consumption per head in England increased from 1.8 kg in 1700 to 8.1 kg in 1800 and was approaching 30 kg by 1900. Tea and coffee, luxuries when first imported, became increasingly everyday beverages through the 19th century: these non-intoxicating drinks were bitter rather than sour in flavour, and often sweetened with sugar. Sparkling mineral waters, initially considered health tonics, were marketed in the form of sweetened, flavoured soft drinks by the mid-19th century. The growing numbers of workers in heavy industries were also more likely to favour lighter, sweeter, fresher beers, offset with a drying, moreish finish, for their refreshing and replenishing qualities.

Licensing considerations also played a part. Responding to concerns about emerging brewing monopolies and a possible return of the gin craze, the government passed the 1830 Beerhouse Act, allowing any ratepayer in England and Wales to buy a license allowing them to sell beer, and brew it if they wished, on their own premises for a mere two guineas (£2.10, about £190 today). Within eight years the number of licensed premises had almost doubled, with the addition of nearly 46,000 new beerhouses. Such places were more likely to use their slender resources for brewing mild rather than stale beers. Ultimately, although they remained a force into the 20th century in certain regions, like the West Midlands, they never accounted for much more than 10% of the industry's output, though they doubtless contributed to changing trends.

Improvements at pubs helped too. Crude beer pumps were installed in some busy outlets from the late 18th century. The modern beer engine is usually credited to Joseph Bramah, who patented a design in 1797, though it seems the simple handpump we know today is a subsequent early 19th-century refinement by an unknown engineer: manual pumps were in any case already familiar from applications like pumping bilge water from boats. Whoever was responsible, it was now easy to pump beer from the cooler and more favourable environment of a cellar rather than constantly fetching it in jugs, or, as was often the case, simply pouring from casks in the bar area itself.

Finings of various kinds were used by brewers for centuries as a trouble-shooting dodge for beer that refused to drop bright before the London porter brewers universally adopted isinglass as the ideal material in the mid-18th century. They initially used it as a shortcut for clarifying vatted beer, but early 19th-century

A large pub cellar in the early 20th century. Note the rigid lines, which may have been made of lead.

sources confirm its extension to mild products. Beer could be fined at the brewery, but the process was more often accomplished in the pub cellar. An early edition of *Encyclopædia Britannica* says fining mild beer is a practice common in London, 'where beer is sent out quickly' (Thomson 1824:482), while the *Lancet* credits Burton water for the fact that ales from that town 'speedily become bright and clear, that they never require finings' (quoted in Marchant 1888:257).

By the 1920s fining had largely become the responsibility of the brewer, as it is today, though manuals for licensees still included instructions on how to fine if necessary. Early 20th-century brewer Julian Baker (1905:122) is one of several commentators from the period to recognise how finings helped facilitate the growth of fresher styles: 'A good beer will become bright if stored long enough. But, in these days of quick consumption, sufficient time cannot be allowed for natural clarification.'

The pursuit of brightness was intimately connected to the increased availability of drinking vessels that revealed it. For millennia, people drank from everything from animal skins and wood to ceramics and metal, all of them opaque. Although glass has a long history, and glasses specifically for beer are known from the 1630s, these were initially individually hand-blown and substantially taxed luxury items. Mass production of cheaper pressed glass began in the USA in 1825 and spread to the UK by 1833, though sales didn't really take off until taxation was abolished in 1845, just as brewers were getting more adept at making fresh, bright, lively ales in attractively light shades. Even so, it wasn't until the 1890s that glasses largely supplanted pewter and ceramic mugs.

The emerging tied house system in England and Wales, where pubs were owned by breweries and obliged to stock their products, extended brewers' reach into cellars. Tied houses originated with breweries making cheap loans to licensees, helping them buy out the leases on their premises or carry out improvements in exchange for exclusive supply rights. If licensees defaulted, their property often ended up with the brewery. 'From the beginning of the eighteenth century, and earlier,' says Peter Mathias (1959:119), 'public houses were falling into the hands of brewers by the accidents of trade and bankruptcy, and tending to remain there.' Complaints that brewers were more intent on seizing control of outlets than improving the quality of their products go back at least to the 1760s, and by 1817 nearly half London licenses were tied, with the practice gradually spreading to the provinces. The following year, the parliamentary Committee on Public Breweries noted the 'disgraceful' practice of breweries compelling tied pubs 'to take an inferior beer at a higher price' (1818:10).

At the same time, licenses became harder to obtain as, by the end of the 18th century, increasing concern for the potential social harms of alcohol prompted magistrates, who were responsible for licensing, to flex their muscles in restricting pub numbers and imposing conditions on management. In these circumstances, comments historian of alcohol George Wilson (1940:81), 'it was natural … that brewers should seek these outlets, and the very licensing laws played into their hands.' The 1830 act did little to halt the trend, with breweries eventually acquiring substantial numbers of beerhouse licenses.

From the 1880s breweries began to incorporate as limited companies, generating cash through share flotations. Together with further pressure on licences inspired by an increasingly influential temperance movement, this unleashed a fresh scramble for property. Even the Burton brewers, who had previously relied on selling through agents, now went shopping for pubs, often paying hugely inflated prices. By 1900 around 90% of retail outlets in England were brewery owned. With tied outlets increasingly key to market share, breweries spent considerable sums on building and rebuilding them, in the hope of securing custom and undermining the criticisms of temperance campaigners who caricatured pubs as squalid dens of iniquity. The grandiose late Victorian and Edwardian buildings that resulted have left lasting marks on today's streets, though few of their spectacular interiors – riots of engraved glass screens, massive carved wood back bars, marble pillars, mosaic tiling and textured ceilings – have survived. Purpose-built pubs, unlike the converted cottages of the past, routinely incorporated underground cellars, providing a better environment for beer.

Improvements in transport extended the speed, frequency and ease with which beer could be delivered to consumers. The dramatic expansion of Burton's output from 82,000 hl in 1831 to around 5 million hl in 1888 would not have been possible without the arrival of the railway in 1839. Both railways and improved roads made it easier to deliver fresh beer on a more frequent and regular basis. Smaller cask sizes became more common: porter was traditionally delivered in giant butts holding almost 500 l, but by the 1850s these were replaced by 36-gallon (164-l) barrels, still large by today's standards but better suited for rapid turnover.

All these changes occurred against the wider background of a world that looked increasingly like the one we know today. The growth of mass literacy and the spread of print media facilitated commercial advertising, the beginnings of the consumer society, and the emergence of what we now recognise as brands. The inaugural registration under the Trade Mark Act of 1875 was famously the red triangle logo of Burton brewer Bass. New pubs acted as bricks-and-mortar advertisements for their owning breweries, with plentiful space for large and prominent signage. Marketing encouraged consumers to differentiate products and develop preferences and brand loyalties, which in turn required more consistency and control in the production process, increasingly facilitated by a scientific understanding of fermentation.

With demand for beer still strong, the brewing process was transformed across the board in terms of scale, efficiency, and technological sophistication. The quality of ingredients improved through innovations in both breeding and cultivation. The Select Committee on the Hop Industry concluded in 1890 that one of the reasons why hop acreage had shrunk was improved utilisation in the brewhouse. This was the age of that Victorian industrial and architectural marvel, the 'tower brewery', a custom-designed building where grain store, mill, grist case, liquor tanks, mash tun, copper, fermentation vessels, racking hall and cask store were arranged vertically to take best advantage of gravity during the process. Examples can still be admired at, among others, Batemans, Harvey's, Hook Norton,

Hook Norton brewery, rebuilt to a classic tower design in 1890s

199

Theakston and, on a smaller scale, Sarah Hughes. There's a large and handsome 1930s brewhouse based on similar principles at Greene King.

The turn towards fresher products suited breweries economically. Improved ingredients, more efficient production methods, and quick consumption favoured lighter beers with reduced malt and hop content. Cashflow eased as costs were recouped more quickly. There was no longer a need to reserve capital, space and maintenance expenses for gargantuan vats occupying vast halls, which, following an infamous incident in 1814 when the explosion of a London porter tun resulted in eight deaths and numerous demolished houses, were increasingly recognised as a health and safety hazard. By the end of the century, the great tuns had been almost entirely dismantled. When late-Victorian brewery chronicler Alfred Barnard visited Mann's Albion brewery at Whitechapel in the late 1880s, he saw iron columns surmounted by beams on which vats once stood, but:

> Their occupation is gone, for now there is nothing but a blank space between them and the roof, 40 feet [12 m] above us...[The vats] have all been removed within the last five years, not from decay, because we were shown some of the staves of which they were composed, 22 feet [6.7 m] in length, as sound and trustworthy as the best English oak ever was; but simply because the fickle public has got tired of the vinous-flavoured vatted porter and transferred its affections to the new and luscious "mild ale" (1890:378).

The changes brought further shifts in terminology. As the old distinction between unhopped ale and hopped beer was now redundant, 'ale' came to mean lightly hopped beer for quick consumption. Brewers, who continued to make ales that underwent maturation, like export pale and stock ales, distinguished the fresher types as 'running ales' by the mid-19th century. Even in London in porter's pomp, there were common brewers that made only ales, though still only a fraction of the porter brewers' size. But they were about to shift into the vanguard of the industry, with the porter houses scrambling to catch up by switching to ale.

'Porter triumphed in the 18th century,' says Mathias (1959:12). 'The 19th century proved to be the century of ale.' It's in this 19th-century ale that we can recognise the emergence at last of cask beer as we know it today. In some ways, ale was a continuation of the lower strength, quick turnaround beers that had always been available for rapid consumption, but now transformed by technological advance and customer preference into a thoroughly modern product for a new age.

Mild and bitter

The first of the improved running ales to achieve widespread success was known to most brewers as 'X ale', a simple recipe at a relatively low strength, racked soon after fermentation and intended to be drunk long before any wild yeasts or bacteria had a chance to express themselves, thus requiring only a modest hop addition. By the mid-19th century beer like this was rapidly supplanting porter's role as the default choice in cities and may already have supplanted it in the country. Its spread prompted another specialisation of terminology: as the most familiar mild, as opposed to stale, beer, it was tagged by some drinkers simply as 'mild ale', a term that appeared in brewery advertising from the 1860s. It was also known as 'fourpenny' or 'four ale' after its early 19th-century price per quart (4d, 1.7p), and so ubiquitous did it become that some drinkers simply knew it as 'ale'.

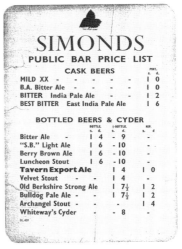

Simonds of Reading
1926 price list

The dark, lower alcohol style we associate with mild today is the result of further evolution. Typical mid-19th century recipes contain 100% pale malt, though the colour obtained would likely have been a little darker than the straw or gold yielded by today's pale malt. One of George Amsinck's mid-century London X ale recipes (1868: no 19) contains 0.3% black malt, suggesting a light amber shade, while all his other examples are 100% pale. Strengths would raise eyebrows today: 5–6% was a session beer by Victorian standards. As often, the same basic recipe was made to different strengths, often distinguished with multiple X's: while 1830s X ales might go above 7%, by the 1860s standard X was around 5.5%, XX about 7% and XXX about 8%, though a quantity of the strongest versions might be vatted as a stock ale.

Quite when bitter as we now understand it appeared on the bar is less clear. The standard explanation is that it evolved sometime in the mid-19th century as a lighter, running version of the classic export pale ale discussed above. The term 'bitter beer' was in regular use in the 1850s, distinguishing the drink from mild by its comparatively higher hop rate. This also made it more expensive, lending a fashionable, upmarket image. Martyn Cornell (2010:16) quotes various sources on its popularity with 'swells' – well-dressed middle-class young men – and Oxford undergraduates. Many brewers certainly referred internally to what drinkers called bitter as PA or pale ale and a few old-school ones still do. But classic pale ales remained long matured for some time.

The answer may well lie in the mysterious 'AK', a designation that appears in brewery advertisements since at least the 1840s, particularly in southern England, in connection with a light and refreshing bitter beer at around the same strength or a little weaker than mild but with more of a hop character. According to brewery historian Ronald Pattinson, AK was the original 'running bitter, that is, a pale ale which was intended to be drunk young' (2022). Initially it seems to have been more popular in private homes than pubs, in the days when middle-class households, with their busy social life and teams of servants, could empty a pin or firkin on a regular basis. In some sources it's referred to as 'family ale'. Burton brewer James Herbert (1872:54) describes AK in the 1860s as 'a light tonic ale' used 'mostly for private families', but also insists it should

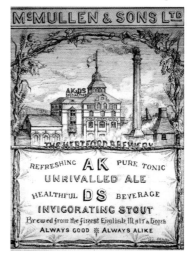

be a quality product, using the best malt and hops: any deficiency in ingredients would be cruelly exposed in a beer like this. The McMullen brewery in Hertford, still brews a heritage AK, a light (3.7%) cask pale ale which likely retains something of its late-Victorian character, though confuses the issue by subtitling it a mild.

Drinkers used the term 'bitter' approvingly, acknowledging an appreciation for its hop character, which in a young beer with undiminished aromas and bitter acids would be much more focused and identifiable than in an aged product. Previously, hop rates had been largely determined by concerns for shelf life; a new-style bitter or AK, in contrast, didn't need to last significantly longer than a mild, so extra hops were added primarily for flavour. Herbert (1872:55) acknowledges the need to grapple with the capricious preferences of drinkers when he advises that, when making AK, 'brewers must be guided to their own discretion as to the quantity of hops to be used, to suit the palates of their different customers, which is no easy task'.

By the end of the 19th century most brewers offered a selection of cask AK, bitter beers and running pale ales at various strengths, separate from the IPAs and 'stock' pale ales intended for keeping. Other styles were now available as running ales too, including porters, stouts and the older, sweeter style of Burton ale. As early as the 1850s, David Booth (1852:106) voiced brewers' increased desire for consistency of the finished product by advising that porter was sent out ready-blended, warning that if the task was left to publicans, 'by inattention, it will be drawn either too mild or too stale, and endeavours to maintain a uniform flavour and strength will be frustrated'. Half a century later, most porter and stout was made in the same way it is today, as a modestly hopped, non-vatted running ale made mainly with pale malt, and small proportions of speciality and roasted malts for colour and flavour.

How similar were these beers to today's cask products? Detailed descriptions of both beer flavour and cellar management are sparse, but mild and running ales were expected to be 'brisk' when served, meaning lively and carbonated. 'Ale is light-coloured, brisk, and sweetish,' says *Britannica* (Thomson 1824:485), 'while [porter] beer is dark-coloured, bitter, and much less brisk.' Stale vatted porter would be near-flat, rather like unblended lambic today. Classic pale ales aged in a bunged cask would retain the carbonation from their mixed fermentation for some time and would likely pour well-carbonated, a quality retained when they became largely bottled products in the 20th century. Obtaining sufficient condition with a mild or running ale required more careful management, and I suspect that in the early days of the mild era, at least, condition varied, though was typically at least higher than the average vatted beer. Today's few surviving

traditional farmhouse beers from Scandinavia and the Baltic tend to be relatively low in carbonation, and drinkers are used to them that way. But as understanding and control of fermentation, conditioning and cellaring progressed, cask beers became more consistently lively.

We can learn something from the fermentation methods of the day. Main fermentation times were typically short: after pitching, beer was kept in a fermentation vessel, or 'gyle tun' as they were known, for only two or three days, after which it was considered ready for 'cleansing' or separating the beer from the yeast. Continuing the practices of country-house breweries, this was accomplished in smaller vessels, often casks or 'pontos', a larger upright vessel arranged over wooden troughs called 'stillions'. These cleansing vessels were left unbunged for perhaps three more days, with the yeast continuing to work out of the top, pushing out quantities of beer which ran down the sides and into the stillions.

It was, originally, customary simply to tip this overflowing beer back into the vessel. The microbiological nightmare of recycling part-fermented beer that has trickled down sticky staves in the open air and through a wooden trough must have yielded widely varying results. As hygiene awareness increased, some, but by no means all, brewers discarded the expelled beer and topped up the vessels with unfermented wort kept back for the purpose. Still-familiar systems like Burton unions, Yorkshire squares and open fermenters equipped with cooling

coils and parachute skimmers, as described in Chapter 1, were designed as much-needed improvements to this procedure. Though most bigger breweries had shifted to these by the 1880s, older methods persisted for a surprisingly long time: Batemans in Lincolnshire was still cleansing beer in stillions and returning it to the casks in 1953, and the equipment can be seen in photographs displayed at the brewery.

After fermentation subsided, the beer might be racked to fresh casks for storage or delivery or put into vats for ageing. But some breweries simply cleansed their

Cleansing beer in stillions at Batemans

running ales in trade casks which were then bunged and sent out to pubs and other customers. 'There are a great many brewers who cleanse their ales in firkins, kilderkins, and upwards,' says Herbert (1872:27), 'and are sent out without racking; and the ales probably have not been out of the gyle tun more than two days.'

As explained in Chapter 2, a beer's ability to continue to ferment and condition in cask depends on the yeast count and viability and a supply of residual sugar, helped along by movement and temperature changes during shipping. Cleansing in trade casks was not the most effective way of separating out the yeast, so we can assume plenty of cells remained, though their viability might be variable. The 1870s manual writer Frank Faulkner says most beer in London is supplied to pubs 'in very fresh, and what I may term, yeasty, condition' (1884:253), while breweries elsewhere delivered cleaner beer in tightly bunged casks. Residual sugar levels are likely to be haphazard if relying on visible signs that fermentation has subsided, but more skilful brewers could obtain greater precision with the aid of a more scientific approach, as David Booth wisely recommended in the 1850s:

> The attenuation is generally supposed to cease when the beer is cleansed: this is not the case, however; for if, after a lapse of weeks, or sometimes months, we apply the saccharometer, we find a reduction of gravity…Hence we see the necessity of keeping a quantity of this fermentable matter unattenuated, in order to support the natural consumption, in proportion to the time we intend keeping the beer. This is a point requiring extreme accuracy, and especially in beers intended for immediate use; here, if we attenuate too low, we deprive the beer of its natural energy, and it cannot recover itself, but remains sickly, and becomes sour (1852:31–32).

In 1847 brewers were once again permitted to use refined sugar, and in 1880 the previous duties on malt and sugar were replaced with a new duty on beer, removing restrictions on ingredients in the process. Following this 'Free Mash Tun Act', as it was known in the industry, the practice of including a proportion of sugar in the grist was widely adopted, not primarily for cost-cutting but to create lighter bodied products without reducing strength, which brewers considered desirable in the newer, lighter styles. Caramel and other dark sugars could once again be used for colouring, beginning the shift to the darker milds we know today: 'mild ales are in most localities brewed of a higher colour than pale ales,' noted E R Southby five years later (1885:217). Quite what drove the shift to darker milds is unclear: perhaps simply the need to distinguish them more clearly from bitters and pale ales, or perhaps because a darker, sweeter character was more suited to the increasingly industrial lifestyle of many drinkers.

Adding a dose of unfermented wort to ensure fermentation after racking is an old brewer's dodge: Thomas Poole (1781: 79) mentions the practice in country-house breweries. Various 19th-century sources say it was common in Irish porter breweries, where the practice of blending stale and mild porter at the bar evolved into one of blending beer from 'high casks', which had been dosed with wort and were therefore more highly carbonated, and less lively 'low casks'. Guinness was served like this in Ireland until the introduction of nitrokeg in 1959. The national custom of pouring stout in two stages is a vestige of the high and low system reduced to beer theatre.

Sugar provided an even simpler method of priming, as the technique is known. Chemist C O'Sullivan, who had worked at Bass for 30 years and confirmed practices had hardly changed during those times, described to the government's Departmental Committee on Beer Materials in 1899 that, in Burton, for beers made for quick consumption:

> The fermentable matter is reduced down to almost the smallest possible point... When the beer is put into the casks, it has a tendency to remain flat, and in that condition it is practically unconsumable. This small quantity of sugar revives the yeast and sets up a fresh fermentation, bringing the beer thereby into condition, and, further, it helps to carry on the fermentation afterwards.

An 1890s textbook (Moritz and Morris 1891:403–404) identifies invert sugar as the favoured priming agent, though glucose is sometimes preferred in pale ales 'where a dry flavour is more desired than the sweet fullness of invert sugar'.

But while priming is an effective way of ensuring a continued fermentation in cask, it isn't strictly necessary if the beer is still sufficiently sweet when racked. Henry Stopes, writing in the same decade, decries 'the increasing use of priming, the fictitious and deceptive appearance of strength of "fullness" that is given by the addition of raw wort or dissolved sugar of high gravity to the finished and fermented beer just prior to delivery.' He considers it a shoddy practice intended to cover up for cost savings in malt and is amazed that the excise authorities haven't taken more interest, remarking that 'weak beer fortified with syrup satisfies the consumer and enhances the brewer's profit very appreciably' (1895:59–60).

Priming has never been a universal practice, and certainly isn't today, though it likely became much more common when strengths of cask beer were reduced still further following World War II. Brickwoods in Portsmouth, for example, finally started priming its cask mild in 1953 following a reduction in strength (Dye 2021:23). At Hook Norton, the mild is still the only cask beer that's primed. However, continuing fermentation is achieved, though, its effect is not just to infuse the beer with an attractive sparkle. Yeast activity extends the period of freshness and helps keep oxygen and bugs at bay – important as draught beer became more widely distributed.

Brewers have also long known how to regulate carbonation in cask using shives and spiles, though early references are mainly about managing mixed fermentation during storage and transport. For some time, it seems, casks were simply bunged, then broached for tapping, which would make achieving the best condition rather a hit-and-miss process. This may have been offset by more opportunity for fermentation at the brewery before shipping than is typical today. Prominent brewing chemist Edward Moritz (1899:190–191) told a government committee that light pale ale or AK is kept for two to four weeks before delivery, while X or XX mild is sent out after only four to 10 days – much shorter times than for the vatted ales of the past.

As the 19th century approached its end, several commentators applied *fin-de-siècle* hindsight to recognise the major changes both in brewing and public taste witnessed in the preceding decades. E R Southby notes that the taste for old-fashioned vatted ales remained only in 'a few remote districts', commenting that these were also cider-drinking areas where drinkers were used to acidity. 'Strong, heavy, rich ales were believed in both by the public and private brewer,' he says, but 'the public taste has become more exacting as to the condition and flavour of the lighter and newer ales which have replaced them' (1885:iii–iv). A Birmingham brewer interviewed by Henry Pratt, a temperance-inclined journalist, in the early years of the new century, marvels at the technical, scientific and hygiene advances of the bigger common brewers, which, over the course of the century, progressively displaced small, pub-based producers in the region. Such brewers, he says:

> have succeeded in producing beers containing 25% less of alcohol than the beers formerly retailed… Those now produced are more wholesome, less intoxicating, lighter in character, more palatable, more nutritious, of lighter and better condition, and more suitable for general consumption. Such beers have gradually won the public taste, and are produced and sold at a much lower cost than the heavy and intoxicating ales of the past (1907:298).

Moritz summed up the emergence of modern cask beers in the *Brewers' Almanack* of 1897, noting that even in the past 10 years, 'lighter ales, both of pale and mild character, have come especially to the front. The public in this period has come to insist more and more strongly upon extreme freshness of palate with a degree of brilliancy and sparkle that our fathers never dreamt of.' (Quoted in Protz 1995:73.) Brewers' increasing ability to satisfy such public insistence was, in part, the fruit of an unprecedented advance in biochemistry that finally unlocked the secrets of fermentation.

From gods to genomes

The story of how human understanding of fermentation progressed 'from alchemy to biochemistry', as brewing historian Franz Meussdoerffer puts it (2009:31), is a lengthy one. For many millennia, we utilised yeast to produce pleasant and intoxicating beverages without any deeper understanding of the process. It's sometimes said that the reason the much-cited Bavarian beer purity law or *Reinheitsgebot* of 1516 specified only 'Gersten, Hopfen und Wasser' (barley, hops and water) as permitted brewing ingredients is because its drafters didn't acknowledge the existence of yeast. But there is plenty of evidence to the contrary. Though yeast cells themselves are invisible to the naked eye, collectively they manifest as a distinct, semi-solid substance: the thick barm that floats on the surface of a liquid fermenting in an open vessel, or the sediment that sinks to the bottom. In pre-scientific days, the term 'yeast' and its various synonyms and translations referred to this substance, which was readily managed and manipulated by brewers, bakers and others and even dried for long-term storage.

Though the first alcoholic drinks were likely fermented 'spontaneously' by wild yeast, this is a haphazard process that can even produce toxic results. Long ago, it seems, brewers learned that if they reserved the residue of previous successful fermentations and deliberately repitched it into fresh wort, or added it to dough for bread, they increased the likelihood of a successful result, beginning empirically to domesticate yeast and select for particular strains without realising what they were doing. There are references to 'making' and pitching yeast from the 1st century CE. Walter de Bibbesworth's 13th-century account of English brewing includes yeast among the ingredients, and 16th-century German herbalist Tabernaemontanus implies pitching is optional when he writes that 'many [brewers] throw a little leaven' into the wort. 'In this way,' he continues, 'a snappy and prickling taste is soon achieved, so that the beverage produced is a delight to drink.' (Herz 1964:112.)

Even so, the nature of this substance and the transformations it effected were long regarded as miraculous, a munificent gift from the likes of Ninkasi, Osiris or the biblical God. The synonym 'godisgood', used by Andrew Boorde in the 1540s, once had a wide currency. A direction to Norwich brewers in 1468 to make their surplus yeast available to other citizens explains that barm is 'otherwise clept [named] godisgood … because it cometh of the great grace of God' (quoted in Salzmann 1913:193). Lack of understanding, however, allowed for only the most basic degree of control. As historian and brewing scientist Gregory Casey

(1990:66) describes it: 'variable product quality and frequent incidences of microbial spoilage have been the trademarks of brewing for most of its existence'.

Dutch scientist Antonie van Leeuwenhoek was the first person to record observations of yeast cells in beer using a microscope in 1680, but didn't realise they were alive, assuming they were a by-product of the grain starch. Early brewing scientist John Richardson considered a theory that yeast is simply carbon dioxide (CO_2) 'enveloped in the mucilaginous parts of the fermenting liquor'. Why, then, he wondered, do yeasts from different breweries behave differently, concluding pessimistically that the answer may be 'beyond the reach of philosophical investigation to ascertain' (1798:117–120). French chemist Antoine Lavoisier tightened up the science in 1790, building on his ground-breaking work on the role of oxygen in combustion by suggesting alcohol and CO_2 resulted from the simultaneous oxygenation and deoxygenation of different components of sugar, 'incited' by yeast.

Another piece fell into place with the isolation of diastase enzymes in malt by Anselme Payen and Jean-François Persoz at a French sugar refinery in 1833, a confirmation that there were substances in living matter capable of facilitating chemical changes without being changed themselves (Teich and Needham 1992:30). Aberdeen brewer William Black was the first to discuss the new discovery in a brewing context in 1835 (1849:222), though his beliefs about fermentation were curious: he regarded it as the result of electricity and recommended for this reason that fermentation vessels weren't earthed.

Two researchers independently followed up van Leeuwenhoek's work with better microscopes in 1837 and realised yeast was a living organism. Frenchman Charles Cagniard-Latour concluded that yeast was 'a mass of little globular bodies able to reproduce themselves, consequently organised, and not a substance simply organic or chemical'. These bodies 'belong to the vegetable kingdom… [and] seem to act on a solution of sugar only as long as they are living' (Teich and Needham 1992:25). German Theodor Schwann, observing yeast growth, noted 'it has great similarity to many organised moulds, and is without doubt a plant'. He believed this 'sugar fungus', as he called it, was most probably the cause of fermentation (27–28).

The view of yeast as an independent living organism wasn't immediately accepted. Some still clung to the theory of 'spontaneous generation' from dead matter dating back at least to Aristotle in the 4th century BCE , which had once been used to explain phenomena like the presence of maggots in rotting meat. More credibly, the German chemist Justus von Liebig, following Lavoisier, explained yeast particles in 1848 as non-living solids precipitated by the action of oxygen on nitrogenous compounds. He was outspokenly dismissive of claims these were living cells, later declaring that 'the form and nature of this insoluble precipitate has misled many physiologists to a very peculiar view about fermentation' (33).

That peculiar view ultimately prevailed thanks largely to the work of Louis Pasteur. Persuaded by the observations of Cagniard-Latour and others, Pasteur experimented in 1857 with swan-neck flasks that allowed the ingress of air but not dust or other particles. Boiling a broth in a flask to sterilise it, he noted it wouldn't ferment spontaneously but only if he tipped the flask so the liquid came into contact with particles, and therefore microorganisms, trapped in the neck. He also demonstrated fermentation was possible without oxygen and distinguished both alcoholic and lactic pathways.

Pasteur developed his ideas in his books *Études sur le vin* (Studies on wine, 1866) and *Études sur la bière* (Studies on beer, 1879/1928, first published 1876), both aimed at improving manufacturing processes by eliminating what he called 'diseases' of wine and beer. Visiting numerous breweries, including in the UK, he found rogue microorganisms everywhere, both wild yeasts and bacteria, and identified them as the main source of brewers' fermentation headaches. 'Every unhealthy change in the quality of beer coincides with the development of microorganisms foreign to brewers' yeast,' he concluded. 'The absence of change in wort and beer coincides with the absence of foreign microorganisms.' (Quoted in Chapman 1912:72.)

The unruly eukaryote was finally tamed by Emil Christian Hansen at the laboratories of the Carlsberg brewery in Copenhagen, Denmark, in 1883. Looking for ways to distinguish between helpful and unhelpful yeast strains, Hansen was able to isolate a single lager yeast cell from a sample originating at the Spaten brewery in Munich and propagate an entire population descended from it. This was soon profitably put to work, laying the foundation for the 'pure culture'

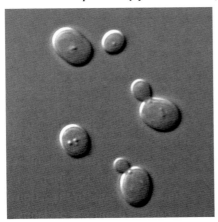

S.cerevisiae ale yeasts   Louis Pasteur in his laboratory

single strain techniques now taken for granted. The same lab identified many other strains, and Hansen's colleague, Niels Hjelte Claussen, isolated a different genus from an English stock ale in 1904. He named it 'British fungus' or *Brettanomyces*, sparking a discussion about the role of secondary fermentation in British brewing, which I'll return to below.

Meanwhile, German chemist Eduard Buchner showed his predecessors were partly wrong and partly right by demonstrating in 1897 that the individual stages of fermentation were carried out with the help of enzymes produced by yeast cells. Though he assumed rightly that sugar conversion normally took place within the cells, he was able to extract the enzymes and replicate their effect chemically (Teich and Needham 1992:47).

After millennia of mystification, the riddle of fermentation was finally solved in a mere four decades. This was an unprecedented leap forward that delivered immediate benefits in managing fermentations more efficiently, producing more consistent beer that could remain clean and palatable for longer without large doses of hops or alcohol. The benefits of these discoveries have stretched far beyond brewing, not only to other branches of industry but to medicine and public health, in areas like the understanding and prevention of microbial infections and the development of antibiotics. Following the discovery of DNA in the 1950s, yeast, with its rapid reproductive habits, found a role in genetic research, culminating in the breakthrough decoding of its complete genome in 1996.

> *The beers of England, as of France, and for the most part Germany, become sour by the contact of air. This defect is absent from Bavarian beer.*
>
> JAMES MEW and JOHN ASHTON (1892:199)

Lager

Lager is at base another solution to the problem of alterability. Lagering, or storing, beer fermented with an appropriate yeast at near-freezing temperatures for long periods enables a slow continued fermentation while keeping unwanted bacteria and wild yeast at bay. The result is a product which is more stable even when relatively low in alcohol. Pasteur noted lager 'is less alterable, less subject to contracting diseases… Manufacture at high temperatures, on the contrary, yields beers that must be consumed quickly.' (1928:16.) This is one of the crucial reasons why lager-style beers went on to dominate international brewing from the later 19th century onwards, almost to the exclusion of other styles, except in a few territories, notably Belgium, Ireland and the UK.

The earliest clear evidence of lager fermentation is found in the 1325 brewing ordinances of Nürnberg (Nuremberg) in Franconia, now the northern part of Bavaria. The difficulty of year-round brewing was acute in the continental climate where (at least until very recently) summers were reliably sweltering, often 30°C or more, and winters reliably frozen. Conveniently, the region is also noted for natural cave systems where beer brewed in the cooler months might be stored in cold conditions even in summer, with the temperature reduced further if required using ice cut from frozen rivers and lakes in winter. These conditions favoured the emergence of the distinct species of yeast now known as *Saccharomyces pastorianus*, 'a special yeast which is capable of vigorous growth and fermentative action at a temperature so low that the ordinary ferments of disease such as the bacilli, bacteria, etc, cannot develop,' as E R Southby (1885:355) describes it.

Lager worked its way south: city records from Munich in 1420 confirm that brewing it was briefly banned. But its increasing dominance in the region was boosted in the next century when concerns about cross-contamination from infected beer in summer prompted the Bavarian state in 1553 to ban brewing completely between St George's Day on 23 April and Michaelmas on 29 September. The prohibition remained in place until 1850. As Bavarian beer regulation goes, though the 1516 *Reinheitsgebot* is more trumpeted, the summer ban had a much greater impact on subsequent brewing history, as it ensured most Bavarian beer was cold fermented so it could be stored for drinking in the warmer months.

The spread of lager beyond its homeland didn't start until well into the 19th century. English brewer David Booth noted in 1834 that *Untergährung* ('bottom fermentation') was 'almost universal in Bavaria, where the beer is most famed; but it is scarcely known in any other quarter' (quoted in Dredge 2019:57). Booth was aware of the practice through an encounter with two German-speaking heirs to brewing dynasties who had made a fact-finding visit to Britain the previous year: Gabriel Sedlmayr of Munich's Spaten brewery and Anton Dreher of Klein-Schwechat, just outside Vienna in Austria.

The two young men were impressed by the size and level of organisation of British breweries, the technical sophistication of devices like saccharometers, and the use of pale malt. The beers they knew at home were still dark, made with malt kilned over direct heat. On their return, both used what they'd learned to improve the output of the family businesses. In 1837 Spaten launched a lager made with a new 'Munich' (Münchener) malt kilned with indirect heat, lighter in colour than the typical local lager of the day but still darker than a pale ale. Dreher meanwhile introduced Bavarian-style lager production in what was previously an ale brewery, and in 1841 began marketing an amber-coloured lager made with a lighter 'Vienna' (Wiener) malt.

The next year, the citizens of Plzeň, then a bilingual Czech and German-speaking city in western Bohemia (now the Czech Republic), acted to improve their local beer by switching to lager production with the help of a Bavarian brewer, Josef Groll. Inspired by Sedlmayr and Dreher's adoption of British malting techniques, Groll used an even paler malt to create what's usually regarded as the first true golden lager, very different from the brown ales then popular in the region. Although there's some evidence that paler beers were brewed in Munich in the 1820s, the Czech version was certainly the first example of the style to achieve widespread fame and was extensively exported in subsequent decades. The descendant of this beer today, though now owned by Asahi, still names itself Plzeňský Prazdroj, or Pilsner Urquell in German, the 'original source' from Plzeň.

The combination of stable and clean-tasting lager fermentation with lighter malts and the classic 'noble' hop flavours of Bavaria and Bohemia attracted ever-widening attention, particularly as ongoing technical innovations made them easier to brew. Besides the microbiological discoveries described above, there was artificial refrigeration, pioneered by Bavarian engineer Carl von Linde, who successfully installed the first working mechanical refrigeration system at Spaten in 1873. Bavarian brewing grew in the years that followed, with output near-doubling from 8.6 million hl in 1871 to 17 million hl in 1897, and German unification in 1871 facilitated the spread of lager throughout the country. 'For many people, unless they worked in a brewery, the first clean-tasting beer they had was probably a lager beer,' says yeast specialist Chris White (White and Zainasheff 2010:9).

One of the earliest adopters abroad was J C Jacobsen in Copenhagen, who, inspired by tasting a bottled Bavarian beer, began producing dark lagers at the brewery he'd inherited from his father in 1838. In 1847 he opened a purpose-built lager brewery named Carlsberg, using yeast obtained from Spaten. In 1876 the brewery added a pioneering laboratory, and it was here that Hansen isolated single strain yeasts in 1883. Remarkably, Carlsberg didn't brew its first pale lagers until 1904, by which time it already had a healthy export business.

Lager spread to the Netherlands in 1854 when the Nederlands Beijersch Bierbrouwerij (NBB, Dutch Bavarian Beer Brewery) opened in Amsterdam. Soon, established ale breweries were converting to lager production, most famously fellow Amsterdammer Heineken, which switched to lager in 1870 under the guidance of a newly recruited German head brewer, laying the foundations for its later international success. Producing lager required major investment in brewhouse, fermentation and refrigeration facilities: the NBB had a starting capital of a million guilders, or around €10.2 million in today's prices.

One of the places where there were plenty of confident investors ready to support ambitious and innovative new industrial enterprises serving a growing consumer base was the expanding economy of the United States of America. The so-called Gilded Age of post-Civil War reconstruction between 1870 and 1900 overlapped with an extended period of German immigration boosted by the failed revolutions in Europe in 1848. The first US lager brewery was likely founded in 1840 with a yeast sample carried from Bavaria by Johann Wagner to Philadelphia, Pennsylvania. His success was limited, but others were more fortunate: the names of Pabst (founded 1844), Schlitz (1849) and Miller (originally Müller, 1855) in Milwaukee, Wisconsin, Anheuser-Busch (1852) in St Louis, Missouri, and Coors (1873) in Golden, Colorado, are still familiar today.

From the 1870s American lager crossed over from the immigrant market into the mainstream, not in the form of the brown beer then still popular in Bavaria, but as a light and sparkling beverage based on the pilsner style. Historian Maureen Ogle (2006:72) speculates this was better suited to the tastes of an increasingly mobile, dynamic and prosperous society than the dark, nourishing brews of the 'old country', associated with memories of overcrowding and scarcity. 'Americans preferred a beer that sat lighter on the stomach,' she writes, 'a beer more suited to the American way of life.'

Initially, brewers struggled to achieve a sufficiently light body with a Germanic-style 100% barley malt grist using protein-rich US barley, but soon perfected the technique of including unmalted grains like rice and maize in the mash. Adolphus Busch of Anheuser-Busch, who as a fluent French speaker was familiar with Pasteur's work, was one of the first brewers to pasteurise beer in the early 1870s. US brewers subsequently applied other technical innovations to ensure a completely bright, consistent and easy-drinking result, distributed in fleets of refrigerated railcars, rendering 'beer production and distribution … standardized and independent of seasonal and climatic variations' as Meussdoerffer (2009:36) characterises it. This new way of brewing inspired another shift in terminology, as ale, made with old-school ale yeast at warmer temperatures, was distinguished from lager, made with lager yeast at cooler temperatures.

As with hops, Britain proved a late adopter of lager, though its history here goes back further than many drinkers realise. It was first brewed experimentally at the Calton Hill brewery in Edinburgh in 1835 using yeast supplied by Sedlmayr in gratitude for a brewery tour, but there were problems with propagating the culture. Beer from Klein-Schwechat was first imported in 1868, and the UK's first Austrian-themed pub-restaurant, the Wiener Bierhalle, opened in London's Strand the same year. William Younger's brewed lager in Edinburgh from 1880, though ceased in 1885 following poor results. The first purpose-built British lager brewery, the Austro-Bavarian Lager Beer Company, in Tottenham, London, opened in 1881, but its fortunes proved uneven and it closed in 1903.

More enduring was the Wrexham Lager Beer Company, also opened in 1881 by German immigrants to the North Wales town: this survived until 2000, latterly as part of Carlsberg, and was revived as an independent in 2011. Tennent's Wellpark brewery in Glasgow is arguably one of Scotland's oldest businesses, claiming a foundation date of 1556, and is certainly Britain's oldest continuous lager producer. Hugh Tennent started brewing with lager yeast in 1885 following a trip

to Bavaria. Historic London porter giant Barclay Perkins installed a lager brewery under the direction of a Danish brewer in 1921, which remained active until Courage wound down the site in the early 1970s. All were initially noted for dark as well as pale lager.

Despite these investments, lager remained a niche drink in Britain, and in England and Wales in particular, for a very long time, an upmarket novelty mainly familiar in bottled form and at least as likely to be imported as domestically brewed. It wasn't until the 1960s and 1970s when the newly formed Big Seven brewing groups put their capital investment and marketing muscle behind the style that sales grew significantly, as explained in Chapter 7. Lager didn't overtake ale until 1989, long after it had triumphed in practically every other market.

In the 20th century lager faced obvious obstacles. During the two world wars, expressing a liking for anything German was deemed unpatriotic and there are numerous examples of this extending to beer. Britain's beer halls rapidly changed their names and themes in 1914, with the most famous, the Olde Gambrinus in Regent Street, London, rebranding as a French-style café-brasserie. Economic problems in the first half of the century dissuaded breweries from significant investments in lager brewing hardware. The view of it as primarily a bottled style among customers who preferred draught beer may have contributed. It took the creation of large brewing combines to overcome the resource problem, at a time when growth in disposable income and more affordable overseas travel were widening the tastes of the public of large.

But why wasn't lager successful in Britain earlier? It's no coincidence that the international spread of lager coincides with the growth of cask. Dreher and Sedlmayr visited Britain in 1833 because at that stage it had the biggest, most technologically advanced, and most professionalised breweries in the world. There's some irony in the fact that what they learned ultimately helped displace Britain from the industry's cutting edge, shifting the centres of innovation from Burton, Edinburgh and London to Amsterdam, Copenhagen, Milwaukee and St Louis. But in the closing decades of the 19th century, British brewers applied all their skill, resources and improved scientific understanding to perfecting their own version of a light, refreshing, easy-drinking beer suited to the modern industrial world, and through the tied house system created an infrastructure to deliver it to drinkers at its best.

Some brewers even promoted the lightest and most refreshing of their cask ales by comparing them to lagers. One example is Hereford Golden Sunlight Ale, a 'light pale golden ale of wonderful value', which in 1888 was advertised with an endorsement by a Dr Wallace claiming that it 'resembles in composition the lager beer of Germany' (reproduced in Boak and Bailey 2020). Brewing chemist Alfred G Salamon, giving evidence to the Committee on the Hop Industry in 1890, explained declining demand for hops as follows:

> The public taste is not in the direction of actual lager beer, because the conditions of lager beer brewing do not adapt themselves to the requirements of the English brewer; but the English brewer has been striving during the last ten years to approximate his product to the Continental lager beer by making it less in gravity, less intoxicating, and less narcotising. He has produced his beer more quickly; he does not store it; the public have acquired a taste for a sweeter and less sub-acid product; and the result is that the brewers...do not need to add so much hop to it (1890:116).

Having converted to a system based on fresh beer, brewers were understandably reluctant to return to one requiring long storage. There were practical limitations too: 'the instability of the British climate, even in winter, was much less favourable for making natural ice,' observes economist E M Sigsworth (1965:542), so would-be lager brewers 'would have to install special refrigerating plant in addition to providing underground storage chambers', a particular challenge on their typically cramped urban sites.

But there was in any case no crying need for such disruptive reconfiguration. Cask beer was already Britain's lager.

Bottled beer

For almost its entire history beer has been a bulk product first and foremost, measured out from larger containers into drinking vessels immediately prior to consumption. At domestic and smaller commercial breweries, 'small pack', as modern brewers say, was very much a secondary format, hand-filled from a cask to take beer out into the fields, say, or on a journey. Suitable containers of various kinds have been around since at least 1500 BCE, and in various materials including leather and ceramics as well as glass. By the 17th century, though, at least some bottled beer was shipped commercially over comparatively long distances: diarist Samuel Pepys shared 'several bottles of Hull ale' with friends in 1660. Gervase Markham provides English housewives with advice on packaging at least 20 gallons (91 l) in 'round bottles with narrow mouths, and then stopping them close with cork'. They should then be placed 'in a cold cellar to the waist in sand, and be sure that the corks be fast tied in with strong pack-thread, for fear of rising out, or taking vent, which is the utter spoil of the ale' (1623:238).

The need for such precaution is echoed in a much-cited story reported by Thomas Fuller in 1662. Churchman Alexander Nowell, who went on to became Dean of St Paul's in 1561, took a bottle of ale out fishing with him, most likely filled from a cask at home. He forgetfully left the bottle behind, and 'found it some days after, no bottle, but a gun, such the sound at the opening thereof' (Fuller 1840:204). Fuller claims this is 'the original of bottled ale': it's not, but the description of what's clearly carbon dioxide pressure building up to dangerous levels is only too credible. The weather isn't mentioned, but we can assume it was warm enough to prompt residual yeast to further activity, and if the bottle was left for long enough, a wild fermentation would set in too. Today, bottle-conditioned beer is often kept in a warm room before dispatch to promote carbonation.

Until the mid-19th century, glass bottles were individually hand-blown or crudely moulded. Ceramic bottles were also used, thrown on a potter's wheel. Before the invention of the screw top in 1879, bottles were sealed with cork and tied down, as in Markham's instructions, or, later, wired. As Nowell's experience demonstrates, both bottle and fastening had to be strong enough to withstand considerable pressure, so bottled products were expensive luxury items. William Tizard skips over bottling in his 1850s brewing manual as 'a subject too devoid of art or interest to deserve any peculiar attention' (1857:15). Following the invention of the chilled iron mould in 1866, beer pre-packed in mass-produced glass or stoneware bottles became cheaper and more commonplace, primarily for home consumption and for export. Its popularity was undoubtedly boosted by a marked decline in beer consumption from the 1860s and the increasing popularity of lower-strength beers.

Bottled beer was brewed strong and allowed to undergo a complex mixed fermentation with wild yeast for some time after such practices went out of fashion for the draught equivalent. A late-Victorian manual notes the 'pleasantly pungent' results of this classic process:

> Beer destined for bottling...should be permitted to go through the ordinary cask fermentation, and then flatten. When thus flattened (but still just about saturated, though not supersaturated, with gas) it should be bottled, and the bottles stored in a warmish place (about 65°-70°F [18-21°C]). The warmth of the bottle store will soon resuscitate the residual yeasts, and the beer will then come into the required degree of briskness. Bottle fermentation induced in this manner produces the pleasantly pungent flavour characteristics of bottled beer (Moritz and Morris 1891:414).

Beer intended for export was allowed to go completely flat before corking. 'In all probability,' observes historian H S Corran, 'the beer came into condition, i.e. became sparkling, not by the fermentation of its brewing yeast, but by "secondary fermentation" by a similar organism called *Brettanomyces*.' (1975:152.) This was what brewers once meant by 'bottle conditioning'.

Demand for lighter beers in bottle as well as cask, and the economic arguments for shortcutting this lengthy process, drove brewers to seek other methods. Bottled beer requires a longer shelf life than draught because of the time it typically spends in the distribution chain, particularly when exported, and, often, in storage once bought. This wasn't a problem with a stronger beer that underwent a proper secondary fermentation, but lighter styles were much less robust. 'Bottle conditioning', observes E J Jeffery, is 'usually only given to pale ales, stouts and strong or old ales. It would be useless to attempt to produce a light gravity beer by this process, as it would be difficult to give sufficiently long maturation periods to give the necessary bottle condition, and the keeping qualities would be poor.' (1956:366.)

Brewers had long known how to reawaken the original fermentation in a bottle by priming it. Richard Bradley advises in the early 18th century: 'Into every bottle put a piece of loaf sugar, about the quantity of a walnut, which will make the drink rise and come to itself.' (1727:54.) Heat could also be used in a technique known as 'forced bottling'. Beer for bottling was fined while it still contained some fermentable material or, alternatively, primed. After packaging it was kept in a warm store for a few days to reinvigorate fermentation, then sent out to trade, where it had a shelf life of a week to ten days. 'The flavour of such beers is very variable and frequently far from pleasant,' comments Frank Lott (1901:195).

A refinement of this practice, sometimes involving fining or filtering, priming and perhaps reseeding with a little fresh yeast before bottling, allowed for a longer and more predictable shelf life while still retaining a fresh flavour, even with products relatively light in alcohol. The few bottled conditioned beers that survived into the 1970s were largely prepared in this way, as are many examples today. If care and strict hygiene are applied, the results can be excellent, though in my view successful results are much more likely at 5% ABV and above. The old practice of mixed fermentation in bottle is now almost completely obsolete: the few arguable exceptions include Harvey's Imperial Extra Double Stout and the Belgian Trappist ale Orval, both of which are packaged to encourage the eventual development of signature wild yeast flavours. In Harvey's case, a wild yeast species is present in the house culture but doesn't get an opportunity to show itself except through long maturation.

Filtration began with the ancient practice of running beer through rush matting or shrub branches to remove larger solids. The first paper filters appeared in 1879, with cellulose and asbestos versions following in the 1890s. Unfortunately, though these removed brewer's yeast, they were less effective against unwanted microorganisms, which may have prompted brewers to investigate pasteurisation. More effective methods of yeast separation were adopted after World War I in the form of centrifuges and finer diatomaceous earth filters. Rather than relying on yeast to produce carbon dioxide naturally, condition could be adjusted with force carbonation, using gas either captured from closed vessels during the initial fermentation or manufactured by methods such as mixing sulphuric acid with calcium carbonate.

British brewers began applying such techniques to bottled products in the late 19th century. 'The public taste is tending toward a newly bottled beer rather than its old friend the fully-matured aged pale ale,' noted Lott (1895:189). 'The modern method of bottling comparatively newly brewed beers, rapidly forcing into condition, and distributing for what is practically immediate consumption, is unfortunately growing far too rapidly, as, I believe, such beers are far less healthy to the consumer than the old-fashioned, fully matured, naturally fined, stock bottled ale.'

Despite concerns about impacts on flavour, it seemed to many brewers that new bottling technology promised a future in which the problem of alterability was solved at last. In 1916 the much-respected brewing chemist Horace T Brown, reflecting on his 50-year career, conceded that 'a certain quality of flavour… can only be attained by maturing in a bottle,' and that 'connoisseurs of bottled ale who still retain a preference for beer treated in the old way regard with disfavour these modern innovations.' But he nevertheless believed that:

> One of the most important developments of brewing practice which has taken place within my recollection is the comparatively recent introduction of a process of chilling, filtering and carbonating ales. It has already practically revolutionised the bottled trade of this country… and bids fair to have an equally wide influence on the cask trade in the near future… The future has much in store in the way of improvement in this process of chilling and filtering beers… There is no branch of the operations of a brewery that is more promising for scientific investigation [and] more educative of the brewer (1916:331–334).

In the event, the spread of such treatments to draught beer took much longer than Brown foresaw.

Rare historic Bass bottles, which would have been bottle conditioned with a mixed fermentation

Scotland

So far we've largely focused on English brewing, but the broad sweep of the story applies to other parts of Britain. There are significant differences in detail, though, in Scotland, which has its own distinct traditions in brewing as in so many other aspects of life.

As we've seen, some of the earliest traces of brewing in Britain have been found in Fife and Orkney. The various peoples who occupied what's now Scotland in ancient and early medieval times – Picts, Celtic Britons, Scots, Anglo-Saxons and Vikings – were all grain farmers, brewers and beer drinkers. There's a well-known folk tradition that the 'pechs' were 'great people for ale, which they brewed frae heather… an extraornar cheap kind of drink; for heather… was as plenty then as it's now.' (Chambers 1869:80.) The story goes that the last two people who knew how to make heather ale chose to die rather than give up the secret to the conquering Scots. In some versions it was heather wine, or mead, or a Viking rather than a Pictish secret, and we don't know how much older the story is than when it was first written down in the early 19th century. But, while you certainly couldn't make an alcoholic drink just from heather without an additional source of carbohydrate for fermentation, the fragrant moorland plant was one of many used as a beer flavouring, as it still is today in Fraoch (Gaelic for 'heather'), the modern interpretation made by Williams Brothers in Alloa.

Barley, oats and wheat have long been grown throughout Scotland: as in neighbouring countries, oats, which are particularly hardy, were once the more popular brewing grain. By the mid-18th century, swathes of the Borders, Fife, Lothian and elsewhere had become the highly productive barley producers they remain, and close family links between farmers and brewers drove the continued expansion of both industries.

Barley malt has also long been in demand among distillers of Scotland's other national drink, whisky. Given the challenges of the environment, particularly in the Highlands, converting grain starch into spirit was a foolproof way of extending its shelf life, and the warming qualities of the drink suited the climate, placing the extremities of the country into the northern European 'spirit belt'. Though made on private stills since at least the 15th century, Scotch whisky didn't start to become the global leader it is today until the introduction of the continuous still, blending, and a more practical duty and regulation framework in the early 19th century, and its rise overlapped that of Scottish brewing.

Contrary to widespread assumptions, hops grow in Scotland: a hop tax introduced in 1710 makes separate provision for home-grown and imported hops and in the 1860s there were hop gardens as far north as Aberdeen. But commercial cultivation proved uneconomic in the less favourable climate and was abandoned in 1871. The craft beer boom has sparked renewed interest, with experimental crops grown in Perthshire since 2014. Hops were widely adopted by Scottish brewers in the 17th century and have long been imported from England and elsewhere. Until the early 20th century they were used with equal generosity on both sides of the border: the modestly hopped ales later associated with Scottish brewing evolved in response to 20th-century challenges that also saw hop rates reduced elsewhere in Britain.

As in England, beer in medieval and early modern times was brewed in monasteries and other institutions, country houses, and commercially in smaller home breweries and alehouses, largely under the direction of female brewers. Traquair House at Innerleithen, in the Scottish Borders, claims to be the oldest inhabited house in Scotland, dating back at least to the 12th century, and likely brewed from the start, though the first records date from a visit by Mary Queen of Scots in 1566. Four centuries later, her distant descendant, Peter Maxwell Stuart, then the laird and house owner, rediscovered the 18th-century brewhouse, which had fallen into disuse sometime after 1800, and revived it as a commercial operation. Launched in 1966, it was the first new UK brewery since the 1930s and arguably the first modern microbrewery, despite the storied history of its site.

A Company of Brewers was established in Edinburgh in 1596, by which stage common brewers were not only active in the capital but in other larger towns, cities and ports. There were sufficient domestic brewers that in 1625 Parliament banned 'the hamebringing of foreign beer' (quoted in Donnachie 1979:3), which at that time included English products, though it seems the prohibition was largely ignored as imported beers were considered better than domestic ones.

Peter Maxwell Stuart
using a saccharometer
to measure gravity

Industrial-scale brewing developed a few decades later than in England, in the second half of the 18th century, with significant exports by 1765: port cities like Aberdeen, Dundee, Glasgow and above all Edinburgh were well-placed for this trade. By 1825 there were 233 breweries in Scotland: Edinburgh and its surroundings were particularly favoured, with around 50 breweries in 1850. The capital was now Britain's third main brewing centre after London and Burton upon Trent, and the home of internationally renowned names like Campbell, Drybrough, McEwan's, Usher's and Younger's. Its success rested not only on its concentration of population and favourable transport links via the port of Leith but on its water supply, the 'charmed circle' of wells which provided particularly pure water with useful levels of carbonates. The Forth valley around Alloa, Falkirk and Stirling was a fourth major centre, with the Forth and Clyde Canal, opened in 1790, increasing access to the growing markets of Strathclyde.

The main products in the 18th century were strong and small beer, made by mashing the same grist several times as in England. The former evolved into the celebrated strong Scotch ale, a long-matured beer originally pale to amber in colour, which was exported from early in the 19th century. It became an internationally recognised premium product, popular in London and throughout the empire, including in India. Small beer, also known as 'twopenny', was more affordable for ordinary people but regarded as an inferior brew: 'thin, vapid, sour stuff', according to a Stirling clergyman quoted by brewing historian Ian Donnachie (1996:113), which was so unpalatable it was driving the working classes to drink whisky instead. Milds made by more modern methods became increasingly popular as a superior but still affordable alternative.

Loading drays at McEwan's Fountain Brewery, Edinburgh, c1890s

Scottish brewers also cloned English styles. London-style porter was brewed from the 1750s, often with English brewers recruited to ensure success. The charmed circle was a source of good pale ale too: the Edinburgh and Leith brewery launched the first example, Edinburgh Pale Ale, in 1821, and by the 1850s the city's brewers were supplying IPA to India and the Caribbean.

Traditionally, fermentation was managed differently, with mashing temperatures higher, fermentation temperatures lower and times longer than in England: although ale yeasts were used, the methods are curiously reminiscent of lager. In a classic manual, brewer William Roberts (1837:157–160) describes a 100% pale malt Scotch ale made in 1836 that was pitched at only 10°C and fermented for 13 days in a square at a maximum temperature of 17°C. It was then cleansed using the double drop system and the next day put into a cask but left unbunged for a few more days, before being shived down and left to mature for what we now know is long enough for a mixed fermentation. Another brew underwent 15 days fermentation at similar temperatures, and some beers might take 21 days to attenuate fully. Applied to weaker ales designed to be served mild, this would likely yield a cleaner tasting result with less yeast-related flavour compounds than the English ales of the day.

Roberts points out that such methods were already associated with 'the system which obtained in former times' (xi), as brewers increasingly adopted English techniques, making English-style milds and pale ales at lower strengths, fermenting them fast at higher temperatures and selling them quickly for rapid consumption. In Scotland as in England, by the end of the century most beers drunk domestically were cask running ales – a variety of milds and twopennies at various strengths, pale ales on the Edinburgh model and porters and stouts now made with pale and roasted malts and poured mild. Such beers benefited from the introduction in the 1870s of air pressure dispense that presented them in particularly lively condition, as described in Chapter 2.

One major advance that English brewers learnt from their Scottish colleagues was sparging: spraying hot water onto the mash during lautering to rinse out as much sugar as possible, replacing the former practice of multiple mashes from the same grist. According to brewing scientist John Richardson (1798:375–376), 'leaking on', or continuously sprinkling hot liquor on the mash by hand, was a common practice in English country breweries in the 18th century: he disparaged it, but in the early 19th century a more reliable mechanical method involving a rotating sparge arm, manufactured by a Leith coppersmith, was widely adopted in Scotland. Given the evident deficiencies of small beer, the ability to make a lower-alcohol beer efficiently from a single infusion with the aid of a sparger, thermometer and saccharometer was a major step towards a better and more

Open fermenters at Dryburgh brewery

Brewhouse at Hook Norton, Oxfordshire.
Mash tun in foreground with sparge arm visible, copper in background.

consistent product. The device was championed by Roberts, who claims that 'the great proportion of the more scientific and experienced brewers in England have adopted it' (1837:83). Two decades later, the method was 'tolerably known in England' (Tizard 1857:172), and soon became the standard practice it remains today.

Scottish engineering and technological prowess made many other significant contributions to brewing. Those breweries that used steam engines to boost their productivity from the 1780s relied on the innovations of James Watt, a Greenock native. The Burton union fermentation system was actually invented by Peter Walker, originally from Ayr, in Liverpool in 1838. Glasgow brewer James Steel, whom we've already met on a Burton visit, patented a mechanical method of thoroughly mixing grist and hot water on their way to the mash tun in 1853: the Steel's masher, little changed from the original design, is still used today. Heriot-Watt College in Edinburgh began serving an important local industry by teaching brewing courses in 1903, and the International Centre for Brewing and Distilling at what's now Heriot-Watt University is today one of the best known and most respected brewing schools in the world.

Scotland proved more receptive to the initial spread of lager brewing than England. I've already mentioned the Edinburgh experiment of 1835 and Tennent's enduring participation from 1885. Others at the time were less successful, but the 1920s and 1930s witnessed considerable growth in lager brewing. The most significant example was Graham's Golden Lager, launched in 1927 at the Shore brewery, Alloa, using equipment transplanted from then-struggling Allsopp in Burton: owner John Calder had an interest in both breweries. By 1937 the brand was one of the most widely distributed Scottish beers. The Alloa plant became a dedicated lager brewery in 1951, and in 1959 rebranded its flagship product as Skol, one of the notorious brands of the years of 'merger mania' described in Chapter 7.

It's tempting to suggest that the old tradition of low fermentation temperatures helped pave the way for lager in Scotland, but the combination of light flavour and strength with stability was useful in a country which, outside a few cities mainly concentrated in the 'central belt' linking the firths of Clyde and Forth, is rural and remote, with populations dispersed over difficult terrain. The tied house system also worked differently. A royal commission concluded in 1899 that, unlike in England and Wales, it did not 'generally prevail' (quoted in Donnachie 1996:194). Instead, brewers partially controlled outlets through a system of loans to licensees, without tying up so much of their capital in licensed property, which may have enabled them to invest more in product development in the 20th century when English brewers were falling behind.

The best-known traditional Scottish styles today are the various 'shilling ales' popular in the later 20th century, as described above, but their origin turns out

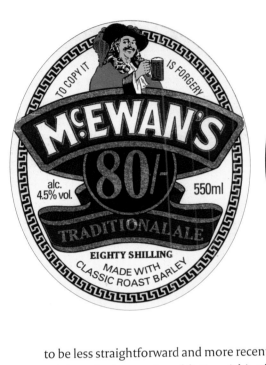

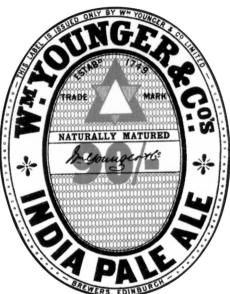

to be less straightforward and more recent than is often assumed. The names originate in the practice of distinguishing beers by their price per 36-gallon (164 l) barrel in the now-obsolete currency denomination of shillings (s or, more often, /-). Some English brewers also referred to their beers in this way, but the practice was particularly prevalent in Scotland, and the range was very wide: historian John Alexander (2022:126) lists 17 price points in use before 1880, from 28/- to 200/- (£1.40 to £10), depending on the strength and quality of the brew.

You may wonder why brewers didn't denominate in pounds instead. In fact, some of them did where this resulted in a whole number, but the shilling terminology was more flexible for intermediate amounts: for example, it was neater to talk about a 28/- ale than a £1 8s ale. After 1880, shillings became a trade jargon used internally by brewers and licensees for particular beers independent of their actual cost: as Alexander (129) says, '60/- ale in the 1880s remained 60/- ale in the 1940s, although the gravity was significantly attenuated and the price greatly inflated'. It wasn't really until the 1970s when brewers began using shilling terminology to brand what were essentially the descendants of 19th-century milds in a range of different strengths as 60/-, 70/- and 80/-, with 90/- applied to modern examples of the traditional strong Scotch ale. By then, the designations were arbitrary as shillings as a unit of currency were abolished with decimalisation in 1971.

'No true secondary fermentation'

The term 'secondary fermentation' is widely used today by brewers, licensees, beer writers, educators and informed drinkers to describe what happens to a cask beer between being racked into casks and drunk. Nearly all the brewers I consulted while researching this book used it this way. Until CAMRA updated its definitions in 2020, its policy described real ale as having 'undergone secondary fermentation in the container from which it is dispensed', and asserted that this was 'an essential and indispensable characteristic of real ale' (CAMRA 2015:3.1). Its current definition of cask beer as 'a live beer that continues to mature and condition in its cask' (CAMRA 2022) is a little less specific and would sound much more comfortable to brewers and brewing scientists of the early 20th century. For them, secondary fermentation meant something quite different, and indeed was one of the last things they wanted in a typical cask beer for quick consumption. Even in the 1870s, brewing writer James Herbert regarded secondary fermentation as a 'complaint… caused partly by bad management, and partly by using inferior materials' (1872:57).

It's easy to see how the change in meaning has come about. Originally, secondary fermentation described what we now call a mixed fermentation, taking place in a strong beer left to age, like a vatted porter or a well-matured pale ale. The relatively clean palate and refreshing sparkle desired in a light cask beer, in contrast, was and is simply a continuation of the primary fermentation with brewer's yeast. As British brewers shifted towards fresher beers, the term was freed up for reapplication. Its older meaning nonetheless captures a useful distinction, one that I've tried to retain in this book.

Julian Baker (1905:114) is one of the early 20th-century writers to distinguish between running and keeping beers in terms of yeast activity: in the former, he says, 'there is no true secondary fermentation'. Walter Sykes (1907:540) concurs that 'running comparatively quick-draught beers' don't undergo 'a true secondary fermentation, but … a survival of the primary fermentation which invariably occurs to a greater or lesser extent in all beers after racking, and may be increased by the addition of priming or by racking at higher gravities.' US writers Wahl and Henius (1902:793) say that in Britain mild beers 'are called such as undergo no secondary fermentation, but are marketed about seven days after the principal fermentation is finished,' while the great Belgian brewing scientist Jean De Clerck (1957:363) believes that 'little or no secondary fermentation' can take place after a cask has been fined.

The distinction was illuminated by Emil Christian Hansen and N Hjelte Claussen's work in isolating pure single yeast strains at the Carlsberg laboratory.

Though lager brewers were already reaping the benefits of their results, some British brewers doubted they applied to ale styles, believing that traditional multi-strain yeasts were essential in achieving both the long maturation of keeping beers and cask conditioning of running ones. Some 17 years after Hansen's breakthrough and 11 years after he presented his pure yeast system to British brewers, the Country Brewers' Society (1900:77) editorialised that 'nothing so far has been proved as to its successful application to English brewing under normal conditions of fermentation, and under conditions that ensure that both the primary and secondary fermentations are carried out with one single race of yeast… We ourselves do not know of any brewery in the United Kingdom in which pure yeast, cultivated from a single cell, is being systematically and continuously used.'

When Claussen isolated the species we now know as *Brettanomyces claussenii* a few years later, he showed that this very different yeast, already resident in the brewery environment, was responsible for 'the luscious winey character', as John Shimwell puts it (1947:22), of English stock ales and porters. The yeast pitched by the brewer had nothing to do with it. This 'state of affairs in which the success of a process is dependent on fortuitous infection' would be much improved, Claussen suggested, by pitching a suitable pure ale yeast for primary fermentation, then inoculating keeping beers with a pure Brett strain, after which they will 'assume *an unmistakable English character*' (his italics). In contrast, a pure ale yeast by itself would suffice for 'all sorts of running beers', which 'do not get sufficient time to go through a secondary fermentation, and consequently

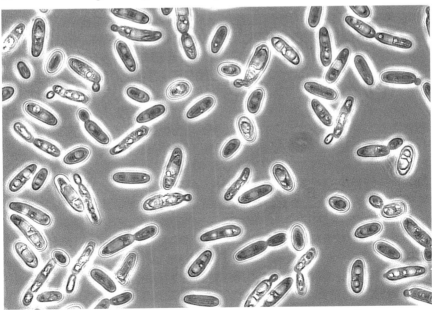

Brettanomyces yeast cells, their shape contrasting to the rounder *Saccharomyces* cells.

Brettanomyces will hardly be able to influence upon them to an appreciable extent.' (1904:312–314.)

As it happened, Claussen made his discovery just as the last beers that depended on Brett were falling out of production. Beamish and Whitbread brewer Shimwell, who once isolated a Brett strain himself, recounts that:

> The strength of British beers, owing largely to increase in taxation, began to decline, and the British brewers, instead of welcoming Claussen's distinguished work as it deserved, began to state that after all the type of flavour produced by *Brettanomyces* was not desired any longer... *Brettanomyces* species are still very common organisms in top fermentation breweries. But they no longer fulfil their function as the maturers of good strong beer, but have descended to the ignominious role of spoilage organisms (1947:22).

Another 1940s technical authority, H Lloyd Hind, confirms that the British fungus was increasingly no longer welcome at home:

> Equally uncontrolled infections so constantly accompany the pitching yeasts or are derived from the plant, producing condition during storage or sought-after flavours, that there has been a tendency to regard them as normal partners in the production of certain types of beer and refer to them as "secondary yeasts". It is difficult to justify this view, on account of the liability of these yeasts to get out of hand, and their help in producing cask condition is not required in most modern ales (1940:890).

Rather than disappearing with the process it named, though, the term 'secondary fermentation' was simply reapplied to modern cask conditioning. E J Jeffery in the mid-1950s distinguishes 'two kinds of secondary fermentation. One is a healthy one, due to the breaking down of the sugars passed on from the primary fermentation by healthy yeast. The other is the result of wild yeast', by implication unhealthy (1956:236). By the 1970s J G Miles has no need to advise pub staff of old-school secondary fermentation. In the brewery, he says, 'casks are rolled... to encourage a slight secondary fermentation to be set up by the very small quantity of yeast left in the beer after racking' (1972:14).

British brewers also remained slow to take up pure yeast fermentation for their cask running beers. While Claussen's science was spot on, he betrayed his background in lager brewing by underestimating the flavour contribution in ales of house yeast cultures, some of which, according to Hind (1940:795), had not been changed in living memory. Today, as we've seen in Chapter 1, many traditional cask brewers assiduously retain multi-strain house yeasts as an important component of house character, though they benefit from the work of Hansen,

Claussen and others in better recognising and understanding the way these cultures work, keeping them free of contamination and repropagating them when necessary. But many newer breweries happily use pure single strains supplied by labs to make excellent cask beers. Brett, meanwhile, has reclaimed something of its former role in contributing to specialist products, often added in the form of a laboratory culture, as Claussen recommended.

Peak cask

I once asked brewing historian Ronald Pattinson where he would go if he could take the ultimate beer trip in a TARDIS. He immediately answered London at the beginning of the 20th century, when 'you could walk into a pub and have a choice of five or six draught beers such as bitter, mild, Burton and porter, all completely different in character and with strengths ranging from 3 to 7 or 8% ABV' (quoted in de Moor 2010:13). Researching this book, I can see what he meant.

Though bottled beer was growing in importance, cask running beers were a clear majority of production and consumption. The scientific and technological advances of previous decades had significantly improved quality and consistency, and though turnover was falling, it was still sufficiently high to ensure fresh beer. With the widespread adoption of sugar, all-malt brews were rarer, but the large reductions in strength and cost-cutting practices of future years were still to come. There were 1,520 breweries producing over 1,000 barrels (1,600 hl) a year in the UK in 1901, and many more smaller ones (Gourvish and Wilson 1994:111), so plenty of competition and choice.

Julian Baker confirms:

The varieties of beers brewed at the present day are exceedingly numerous. Roughly speaking, they may be divided into strong, medium, and light. In the strong, we may include stock or old ales, and the heavier stouts. The medium, comprises the lighter stouts, superior bitter beers, mild or four-ale, which latter is still the beverage of the working classes, and porter. The light beers, of which increasing quantities are being brewed every year, are more or less the outcome of the demand of the middle classes for a palatable and easily consumable beverage (1905:11–12).

Based largely on Ron Pattinson's investigations of 1909 recipes (2009), we can summarise Edwardian cask beer styles as follows: these are English, and to some extent Welsh, styles, except where Scottish origins are clearly indicated.

Designation	Style	Colour	ABV	Notes
X	Mild ale	Pale amber to near black, with darker versions becoming more popular	5–6%	Still the default beer, accounting for half the output of major London breweries. Comparatively low hop rate.
K, KK	Burton, old ale	Dark brown	6–7.5%	Both denser and more heavily hopped than mild, coloured with brewing sugar.
Porter	Porter	Near-black, black	4–5.2%	All now in 'mild' form, as cheap as X ale, made with some black and brown malt
Oatmeal stout	Oatmeal stout	Near-black, black	5–5.5%	English versions contained only a small proportion of oats.
Stout	Strong porter	Near-black, black	6–7%	Comparatively sweet.
Double, triple stout	Strong porter	Near-black, black	7–9%	A few stronger examples were still aged.
IPA	Pale ale/ bitter	Gold, amber	3.5–5%	Weaker but more heavily hopped than typical pale ale.
AK	Light bitter	Gold, amber	4.5–4.8%	Rivalling X ale in popularity for some brewers.
Pale ale	Pale ale/ bitter	Amber	4.5–6.5%	Variety of strengths, still niche compared to X ale.
Strong ale	Strong pale ale	Brown	7–9.5%	Variety of strengths, some still matured, stronger ones popular in bottles.
Scottish mild	Shilling ale	Brown	3–5.5%	Variety of strengths, known internally by 'shilling' terminology.
Edinburgh pale ale	Pale ale	Amber	3–5.5%	Variety of strengths, known internally by 'shilling' terminology.
Scotch ale	'Wee heavy', 90/-	Very dark brown	6–9%	Variety of strengths.

Both pale and dark lager were also available if you looked for them, though almost always as bottled beers.

One notable feature of British brewing was its high hop usage. While UK brewers used 27,850 tonnes of hops to brew 55 million hl of beer a year, their German counterparts used only 13,000 tonnes to brew 65 million hl. That's 5 grams per litre on average, compared to 2 g/l in Germany and 2–3 g/l in other brewing countries (Barth and others 1994:11). As a comparison, a best bitter today might use 1.5 g/l, while only modern hoppy styles and strong beers climb above 5 g/l.

But there were gathering clouds beyond the deteriorating diplomatic relationships between the European Great Powers. The issue that focused brewery directors' minds as the 1910s began was falling sales and profits. Despite commercial brewers picking up business from the decline of domestic and pub brewing, consumption fell over 18% between 1900 and 1908, and dividends to shareholders shrank accordingly. The number of bigger breweries declined from 1,520 in 1901 to 1,111 in 1914; output went down from 56.4 million hl in 1900 to 51.1 million in 1910 (Wilson 1940:59); the overall figures, including smaller breweries and brewpubs, reduced from 6,447 to 4,512. Profitability was further squeezed by the creaking tied house system, on which the breweries were now dependent for market share. Having paid overinflated prices in the scramble to secure outlets, they were now saddled with large estates of overvalued property and mounting bad debts from struggling licensees.

Brewers worked in a less favourable social and political context, as hardening attitudes to alcohol misuse were increasingly influential on tax and licensing regimes. For most of the 18th century excessive drinking had been so common-place that some laws even specified that trials were to be heard before dinner so there was a reasonable chance that magistrates were sober. The gin craze and middle-class concerns for social order changed the terms of the debate. The first temperance society was formed in Glasgow in 1829. Following a parliamentary select committee investigation into the 'increasing evil of drunkenness' in 1834, magistrates began to tighten up on licenses. Early temperance campaigners mainly targeted spirits, and even promoted beer in preference, but the more radical sections of the movement increasingly advocated teetotalism – total abstinence. Support for temperance grew rapidly in the second half of the 19th century and solidified its political affiliations, with the National Temperance Foundation, an umbrella organisation established in 1884, formally linked to the Liberal Party.

A series of new laws, beginning with the Licensing Act of 1872, strengthened the hands of magistrates and local authorities in regulating alcohol sales, after which the number of licensed premises stopped growing and began to fall. The act imposed a global closing time for the first time – 11pm in rural areas and midnight in urban centres – and empowered local authorities to restrict hours further, or even to go totally dry if enough electors wished it; the so-called 'local option'. An 1891 court decision confirmed magistrates' right to withdraw licenses without compensation for reasons other than the misconduct of a licensee, including to reduce the number of pubs in their jurisdiction. In some places, brewers participated in 'surrender schemes' where they at least received compensation for voluntarily giving up licenses.

A duty increase in 1900 prompted breweries to reduce strengths, and therefore materials, to avoid increasing prices, and the Liberal government's 1909 budget imposed hefty increases on duty for both breweries and pubs. Three districts of Scotland voted to go dry following the Temperance (Scotland) Act of 1913. The country also saw the rise of not-for-profit 'Gothenburg' pubs run by temperance-influenced cooperatives, particularly in Fife, inspired by the example of the Swedish city where all pubs had been brought into public ownership.

By no means all temperance campaigners were religiously motivated puritans: some were socialists and liberals who saw alcohol abuse as a barrier to the emancipation of working-class people, and decried the profits made by wealthy brewers and distillers. And, stepping back from the ideology, broader shifts in society were changing the way people drank. While a Georgian ticket porter may have been able to tolerate several litres of 7% beer over the course of his working day, such consumption patterns were less advisable for the operators of blast furnaces, power looms, mining equipment, railway locomotives and similar features of an industrialised society. Clean water, other non-intoxicating drinks and improved nutrition removed the practical rationale for beer drinking. Alternative leisure pursuits now competed for the time and money previously spent on drinking. 'Your old toper who would sit in the public house until closing time is gradually dying out and not being replaced,' observed David Faber, chair of Hampshire brewery Strong's, in 1912. 'Popular amusements such as picture shows have multiplied.' (Quoted in Gourvish and Wilson 1996:307.) The same forces that helped shape the character of cask beer as we know it were robbing it of its status as an everyday drink.

7 Cask at bay: 1914–2020

Beer at war

The troubles of the brewing industry pale into insignificance beside the greater horrors of World War I. Nevertheless, the war 'came to be regarded as an unqualified misfortune by Britain's brewers' (Gourvish and Wilson 1996:317), with a particular and enduring impact on brewing and beer culture that helped shape the way the British drink today. Alongside other industries, breweries had to contend with blockages on exports, shortages of ingredients and materials, and mass mobilisation of workers and customers. But the war also marked the peak of the temperance movement's influence. The tone was set by Chancellor of the Exchequer and future Prime Minister David Lloyd George, who was convinced that drunkenness was a major cause of absenteeism in the munitions industry. In early 1915 he opined in a speech that 'drink is doing more damage in the war than all the German submarines put together', then told shipbuilding executives that 'we are fighting Germans, Austrians and Drink, and as far as I can see the greatest of these deadly foes is Drink' (quoted in Rowland 1975:301).

Alcohol was never banned entirely, unlike in some other countries, but its production and consumption were increasingly taxed and regulated. The war budget of 1914 hiked excise duty on beer from 7s 9d (38.5p) to 24s (£1.20), and further rises followed. The following year the government appointed a Central Control Board for the liquor trade which began imposing unprecedented restrictions. Pub opening hours were limited to short lunchtime and evening sessions with an enforced closure in the afternoon, an arrangement that persisted to 1977 in Scotland and 1988 in England and Wales. Licensees were banned from serving overgenerous measures, the so-called 'long pull' which had become a common way of attracting customers, and from offering credit. Buying rounds, or 'treating', was outlawed as it was considered to encourage people to stay later and drink more. The government investigated the feasibility of nationalising the entire alcohol industry and piloted a state-owned monopoly of brewing and pubs in parts of northwest England and southwest Scotland where there were large munitions factories – the 'Carlisle Experiment' – which continued into the 1970s.

Limits on beer production were imposed from 1916, with pre-war output reduced by 65% by 1918. Reductions of beer strength through limits on original gravity (OG), begun in 1917, had a more enduring effect. While the average OG before the war was around 1.051° in England and Wales, with ABV around 4.5–5%, by 1918 it was down to 1.030°, or an ABV of perhaps 2.8–3%. Price limits followed in 1918, with beers under 1.036° capped at 4d per pint (1.7p, or about 76p in today's prices) and those up to 1.042° at 5d (2.1p or 94p). Temperance newspaper *Alliance News* claimed that the total absolute consumption of alcohol in the UK decreased by 60% between 1913 and 1918 (quoted in Hornsey 2003:588). Interestingly, many brewers managed to increase their profits in this artificially restricted and controlled market, but at the expense of customers antagonised by beer shortages, increasing prices and poor-quality products.

Towards the end of the war, the government began back-pedalling a little, as food and drink shortages and high prices, including for beer, became a widespread source of popular discontent. 'The beer shortage is causing considerable unrest, and is interfering with the output of munitions,' home secretary George Cave told the House of Commons in 1917, listing 'unrest, discontent, loss of time, loss of work' and even the threat of strikes as attributable to lack of beer (quoted in Glover 1996:3). The Commission of Enquiry into Industrial Unrest (1917:8) suggested that some relaxation of beer

restrictions might 'be made with advantage in cases of prolonged and exhausting labour, especially where men are exposed to great heat'.

Though some restrictions were lifted once peace was made, others were tightened further. Duty was quadrupled, and the price of a pint had doubled to twice the pre-war level by 1922. In 1933 the link between duty and beer strength was formalised by calculating it based on OG, with stronger beers taxed more steeply. Although the precise mechanism has changed several times since, the principle persists, with duty per hectolitre currently incrementing by every percentage point of alcohol by volume, with premiums for stronger beers and discounts for weaker ones. The trend towards fewer, bigger breweries continued, with 5% of breweries responsible for 65% of output by 1920 (Wilson 1940:49).

The Great Depression of the early 1930s exacerbated these economic woes. Although average OG recovered a little to 1.041° in the later 1930s, it was never to regain its pre-war heights. Milds, once brewed to strengths of 6% or more, came down to around 2.5% at the height of wartime restrictions, before stabilising in the 3–3.5% band they usually inhabit today. Porter, in strength if not in colour, was a pale shadow of its former self: with original gravities in the 1.030s, it was now one of the weakest and cheapest beers available. While prices remained relatively steady in cash terms, at around 6d or 6½d per pint throughout the 1920s and 1930s, they increased in real terms. A pint in 1920 cost the equivalent of about 90p today; by 1938, it cost over £1.30. Unsurprisingly, annual consumption per head almost halved from 95 l in 1920 to 49 l in the depths of the depression in 1932, and only recovered to 63.6 l by 1938 (Gourvish and Wilson 1994:340). For comparison, the 2020 figure was 60.9 l (Fish 2022:91).

Nonetheless, beer continued to account for a considerable proportion of expenditure. Based on 1935 figures, alcohol researcher George Wilson calculated that:

> Hundreds of thousands of wage-earners consume two pints of beer a day, or 14 pints a week, which at 5½d [2.3p, £1.48 today] a pint amounts to £16 14s [£16.70, £951] per annum. Many thousands of those do not earn more than £3 [£171] a week; and therefore every year each such a man works 5½ weeks to pay his beer bill (1940:227).

Though conditions weren't favourable for large-scale technical innovation and improvement, the interwar years were not without progress. Brewing textbooks now explained how to set up laboratories, and in 1933 brewers teamed up to back an industry-wide promotional campaign for the first time under the slogan 'Beer is best'. H Lloyd Hind's detailed manual, published in two volumes in 1938 and 1940, shows how cask beer production now followed a method for the most part familiar today. Hind emphasises the importance of cask cleaning; describes systems for racking directly from fermenting vessels; explains how to carry out a yeast count to ensure ongoing fermentation; covers fining, priming and dry hopping in cask; specifies storage temperatures at both brewery and pub cellar (13–14.5°C for the latter, a little warmer than is typically preferred today); and describes spiling to regulate pressure (1940:859–877).

When work is done

Over his pint of beer in the evening the average man puts away the cares of the day; restores his toil-spent energy; revives his flagging spirit. Having your talk out in your inn, then, you're actually making good a hard day's wear and tear.

beer is best

MALT · HOPS · SUGAR · YEAST

But Hind's description hints at issues to come. Colouring is included alongside priming and fining as an option during the racking process. By then, it was a common dodge to make a cheap light pale ale that could either be sent out as an AK or ordinary bitter or dosed with caramel for an instant 'mild', not exactly a sign of a commitment to quality and distinction. And he mentions the use of carbon dioxide pressure systems in dispensing cask beer.

British brewers became proficient in the techniques of filtration, pasteurisation and force carbonation through bottling, which grew from less than 5% of output in 1900 to 25% in 1939 and 34% by 1954. Bottles had also become the favoured format for exports by the end of the 19th century, with new techniques avoiding the need for an unpredictable mixed fermentation in bottle or cask while in transit. Canned beer made its UK debut at Felinfoel brewery in Llanelli in 1936, though there's some evidence Tennent's in Glasgow got there slightly earlier. Though increasingly popular for exports, it remained an insignificant format in the domestic market until the later 1950s.

The pursuit of brewery conditioning was increasingly driven by a perceived public demand for crystal-clear 'bright' beers, and by falling strengths and lighter styles, which made traditional conditioning challenging due to the scarcity of residual sugar. Even in draught beers 'the gravity is often so low that anything approaching reasonable condition is difficult to develop', laments E J Jeffery. 'Artificial condition is introduced into bottled beers and makes them palatable.' (1956:330.) Brewers were keen to promote bottles; though more complex to produce, they commanded higher prices and higher margins. Looking to the USA, where small pack overtook draught following the repeal of Prohibition in 1933, some even contemplated a future in which they'd render cask beers obsolete.

The old habit of blending returned in a new form as pub customers increasingly used bottled beers to 'liven up' draught, creating prosaic cocktails like light and bitter, light and mild, brown and mild, black and tan (bottled stout and cask bitter) and others, a practice that persisted into the later 20th century. Once again, it was a way of getting the best of both worlds, combining a cheap but weak and perhaps under-carbonated and past-its-best half of cask with a more expensive but livelier and more consistent half-pint bottle. Unsurprisingly, brewers began to consider how best to apply the technology of bottling to the draught product.

The use of air pressure to force beer to the bar had been known since the 1870s, but like more traditional methods it still required a quick turnover as oxygen was allowed to enter the cask. The unknown authors of One Hundred Years of Brewing (1903:86) confirm that in the US at the turn of the century, 'the use of carbonic acid gas pressure ... is now becoming quite general' to dispense beer from 'keg'. Pressurised pure carbon dioxide (CO_2) protected the beer against infection, oxidation and loss of condition, but also increased carbonation, favouring refrigerated dispense. The system was first used with wooden kegs but became easier to implement as more rigid containers were introduced.

Martyn Cornell (2015b) suggests Watney's in London pioneered a system of dispensing beer from large cellar tanks pressurised with CO_2 in 1913, and a decade later a trade manual mentions beer from glass-lined tanks as a small but significant peculiarity of the north of England (Greenway 1923:63). Using CO_2 to dispense, and likely extend the shelf life of cask-conditioned beer – what's now known as 'top pressure' – was reasonably familiar by the late 1930s. Once again, it was Watney's that took the concept further by creating what was likely the UK's first draught equivalent of a brewery-conditioned bottled beer.

In 1930 the company installed a German-built bulk pasteuriser at its Mortlake brewery and began experimenting with pasteurised beer and pressurised dispense from metal containers. The original intention was to create a draught beer suitable for export, and indeed it seems other UK breweries applied the idea to similar ends in the mid-1930s, with Whitbread sending 'keg' beer to Palestine. But another obvious application was in domestic outlets where cask wasn't practical because of limited cellar facilities, opening hours or turnover, like the East Sheen Lawn Tennis Club where the new Watney's Container Bitter was first served to UK customers in 1935.

Many of the familiar challenges returned during World War II, with shortages of materials and labour, increased taxation and the disruption of air raids and rocket attacks. But the social and political context was much more comfortable for the industry. Breweries and pubs were seen as important contributors to the war effort and to the way of life the war was being fought to protect.

'It is a national duty that every brewer should do his utmost to supply beer for troops in their messes, many of which are a long distance from the nearest licensed premises,' declared the industry's Beer for the Troops committee in 1942 (quoted in Glover 1995:126).

Despite grain shortages and further inflated duty rates, the government resisted forcing output restrictions on the industry. 'A reduction in beer output sufficient to save any considerable amount of grain would mean closing the public houses, say, two days a week, or in effect, rationing beer,' reported The Economist in 1943 (quoted in Vaizey 1960:39). 'From this prospect, the Lord President's Committee unanimously recoiled.' So strengths were reduced again, with the average original gravity (OG) reaching 1.035° by 1944, and oats and maize were used to supplement barley. To save fuel, breweries moved to a weekly rather than twice-weekly delivery schedule, which inevitably compromised freshness and quality for vulnerable low-strength cask beers (Pattinson 2013:310).

Rationing and austerity continued for some time after the war's end and beer grew weaker and more expensive than ever before: average OG was down to 1.033° in 1948 and stayed in the 1.030s for the rest of the century. The style repertoire was visibly contracting with the focus increasingly on bitter and mild – the term IPA had essentially become interchangeable with best bitter (Drinker 1933:23).

'The price of beer today seems fantastic,' comments writer and broadcaster Maurice Gorham (2011:18) in his anecdotal but revealing guide to London pubs in 1949, 'but there is no way of knowing whether before this book comes out it will have gone up again.' By then, a typical pint of bitter cost around four times what it had 30 years earlier, at around 1s 4d (6.7p, or £1.88 today). Even more significantly for what was to follow, he observes:

> The war has ironed out many differences and narrowed the field of choice… The weakening of beer all round has taken the edge off many fine distinctions. Personally I find that I can drink brews that I could not drink before, partly because their rivals have got worse too and partly because the weakening has taken away the worst of the taste. The merging of breweries goes on, and it takes some time to realise that the name you see over the house is not always the name that goes on the casks. But if the brewery is less important, the landlord is all the more so. The keeping and serving of the beer make almost more difference now than the brewing, and the quality in any pub can change with a new landlord or even a new girl behind the bar (1949:16–17).

Gorham mourns the decline of Burton ale and declares porter obsolete: Whitbread brewed its last example in 1941 and the style was extinct in the UK by 1958. Its cousin, stout, underwent something of a resurgence after the war due

to the increased availability of draught Guinness, increasingly served from
pressurised 10-gallon (45.5 l) 'metal containers' standing on the bar. 'Mackesons
are doing the same thing,' Gorham notes, 'and I have even seen Simonds bitter
served this way. Anything that makes for more variety, and especially for more
draught stout, is all to the good, but I do hope that the trade will soon evolve
some nicer name for the novel device.'

Brewers have long been concerned that drinkers tend to blame them for
deficiencies in the pub: 'Any malt liquor may be truly brewed, yet it may be
spoiled in a bad cellar,' observes 18th-century farmer and brewer William Ellis
(1759:60). Despite improvements in hygiene, cellar quality issues persisted in the
mid-20th century, doubtless exacerbated by declining turnover and strength.
E J Jeffery strongly advises brewers to condition cask beer as far as possible in the
brewery as 'very few licensees know how to manage a cask fermentation. Some
are even alarmed at it, and at once imagine that the beer is defective.' He recalls
occasions when he was 'urgently summoned during the heat of summer for
assistance, to find the cask standing on end in some terribly hot outhouse,
the heads bulging and straining under heavy internal pressure of gases, and
threatening at any moment to burst' (1956:249–250).

Decrying the practice of returning stale beer from lines to the cask, an
anonymous licensee concludes in a trade manual that 'it has often given rise
to comment how the same brewed beer in two different houses varies, and in
many instances that has been the sole cause.' (1950:29.) Martyn Cornell (2010:40)
claims that by now most mild wasn't properly conditioned but racked bright
with the intention of serving quickly, and since it therefore didn't have too
much of a troublesome sediment to stir up, the mild cask became the receptacle
of all the slops from the drip trays. The now generally darker colour and the fact
that, following the extinction of porter, it was the cheapest and least prestigious
beer, must have made that conveniently large shive hole even more tempting to
a publican with a large jug of leftovers. Much as I'd prefer not to believe this was
the general practice, I've heard the story repeated enough times by brewers,
hospitality staff and drinkers old enough to remember the tail end of the bad
old days that I've sadly concluded it has the ring of truth.

Here was cask essentially as the early beer campaigners found it in the 1960s
and 1970s: beer in a restricted range of styles, flavours and strengths, nearly all
3–4% ABV. At their best, they could be subtle, delicate and characterful in a way
that fizzy bottled beers, or, increasingly, their draught equivalents weren't,
which may explain Gorham's curious point about the 'weakening taking away
the worst of the taste'. But declining strength brought increasing 'alterability',
rendering them easily spoiled by poor handling, inadequate storage or low

turnover. Without all the economic, practical, political and social challenges of the previous decades, the industry might have achieved Horace Brown's vision and got rid of them long ago, as happened pretty much everywhere else.

Merger mania and the rise of keg

At the dawn of the 20th century the UK (at that stage including Ireland) boasted almost 6,500 licensed commercial breweries of all sizes. By 1980 there were just 142, and 81 separate brewing companies, several of them brewing on multiple sites. As Maurice Gorham mentions, brewery closures and mergers were already very much a feature of the pre-war period, but large-scale concentration accelerated in the 1950s, which began with 305 companies owning 479 breweries (Gourvish and Wilson 1996:448). By 1977 seven large brewing groups between them produced 89% of UK beer (Protz 1978:41).

The drivers of this 'merger mania', as it's often called, are obvious in retrospect. As we've noticed before, brewing is a process that readily scales up, with numerous opportunities for economies of scale, but there were several more specific factors at work. British brewers had long since lost their technological edge, with chronic underinvestment in brewing kit, and laboratories still mainly limited to larger businesses. Brewery sites that were once on the edge of town now found themselves struggling with restricted space and traffic congestion in densely populated suburbs. Declining sales resulted in overcapacity, while rising property prices made sale and redevelopment financially attractive. Overall production reached a new low in 1958, at just under 39 million hl, down from the 1944–45 figures by more than a quarter (Spicer and others 2012: 1).

The increasing popularity of keg beers, although they have not yet reached 20% of the market, is due to consumers finding them consistent in quality. Originally they were conceived to serve clubs, ships and other outlets without proper cellars and without continuous trade. Their advantages to both consumer and the Trade are clear... They are universally obtainable beers with a standard palate for the mobile public wherever they may be.

J G MILES (1972:3)

The tied house system exacerbated the process: though a drain on investment, pubs were the key to market share, making struggling breweries attractive to predatory rivals purely for their tied outlets. Mergers, economist John Vaizey observed, were 'the only possible method of growth … [in] an industry with a persistent tendency towards excess capacity and high fixed expenses.' (1958:421–422.) Then there was the long tradition of 'gentlemanly' management of businesses that were largely still family-owned and controlled, a culture of 'restraints against commercial pushfulness, and an emphasis on dealing "properly" with employees and the public' (Vaizey 1960:151). Though admirable in many ways, this undoubtedly made old-established breweries vulnerable to more aggressive and unscrupulous rivals.

The puff of carbon dioxide that ultimately blew down the house of cards arguably emerged from a bottle of a Canadian lager known as Carling Black Label. The Carling brewery in London, Ontario, founded in 1840 and brewing lager since 1877, was bought in 1930 by a colourful and ambitious Toronto businessman, E P 'Eddie' Taylor. In his hands, it became one of the building blocks of Canadian Breweries, and by the end of the 1940s one of the biggest brewing groups in the country. Exploring opportunities for international expansion, Taylor spotted the notable underdevelopment of lager in the UK, and in 1952 signed a deal with a small Sheffield brewery, Hope and Anchor, to brew Carling under license. He quickly encountered the obstacle of the tied house system and realised that the simplest way of getting more pubs to stock his lager was to buy the breweries that owned them.

Watney's merged with fellow big London brewer Mann's in 1958, attracting the attention of property magnate Charles Clore of Sears Holdings, who launched an ultimately unsuccessful hostile bid for the combined company the following year. Taylor made his first move in 1960, buying out Hope and Anchor and adding another Sheffield brewery, Hammonds, and John Jeffrey in Edinburgh to created United Breweries. Both men were outsiders with little patience for 'gentlemanly' industry traditions, and their actions provoked much disquiet, with other breweries making similar moves to protect themselves.

To mention just a few key developments: Scottish Breweries, which had combined Edinburgh giants McEwan's and William Younger's since 1931, almost immediately merged with Newcastle Breweries to form Scottish & Newcastle (S&N). Courage, which had taken over Barclay Perkins in 1955, now combined with Simonds of Reading, while Watney's acquired breweries in Manchester, Northampton and Trowbridge. When Taylor went after George's in Bristol in 1961, the company sold itself to Courage instead. In the weeks that followed, Ind Coope merged with Ansells in Birmingham and Tetley in Leeds, while Bass took over another Birmingham brewery Mitchells & Butlers. Taylor was more successful in acquiring London's Charrington in 1962, and by 1967 had added both Bass and Glasgow's Tennent's to create Britain's largest brewing company. Whitbread developed a different strategy, the 'Whitbread umbrella', taking minority shares in smaller breweries for their 'protection' while keeping them nominally independent – for a few years at least, as nearly all were subsequently taken over. Mergers invariably triggered a shakeout of capacity, with many bought-up plants closing, their pub estates now supplied by their new owners.

These developments prompted the government to ask the Monopolies Commission to examine the industry. Its report (1969) found that on the eve of the 1970s, seven national brewery groups between them now brewed 73% of the UK's beer. Moreover, six of these groups also owned 56% of the pubs. The seventh was Guinness, which had opened what was briefly the world's biggest brewery in west London in 1936: it never pursued pub ownership, but concentrated on a distinctive, consistent and well-marketed product that became a must-stock in other firms' outlets. Despite the commission making various recommendations, including limiting pub ownership, its report was shelved, the big brewers continued to swell and the overall numbers to fall.

The first professionally produced edition of the *Good Beer Guide* in 1974 (Hanscomb 1984:96–97) boasts 108 entries in the breweries section, some operational on multiple sites, all of them with a history stretching back to at least the early part of the 20th century and in many cases much longer. Today, only 38 of these can arguably be said to survive. The impact on Scotland has been particularly harsh: John Alexander (2022:35–36) lists 24 major breweries closed between 1958 and 1999. Since then, Caledonian in Edinburgh has joined the casualties, leaving Belhaven in Dunbar, founded in 1719 and now owned by Greene King, as the country's only continuing historic brewery, with the marginal exception of Traquair House. Though there are now over 1,800 breweries in the UK (SIBA 2023), the vast majority are more recent creations, most dating from the 21st century.

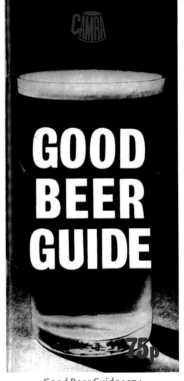

Good Beer Guide 1974

THE BIG SEVEN IN 1990

Name	Selected brands	Pubs	2023 status
Allied Lyons (formerly Allied Breweries, Ind Coope)	Allsopp, Ansells, Benskins, Friary Meux, Graham's, Ind Coope, Skol, Taylor Walker, Tetley	6,600	Most brands owned by Carlsberg UK, Burton brewery by Molson Coors, Allsopp owned privately.
Bass	Bass, Carling, Charrington, Mitchells & Butlers, Stones, Tennent's, Worthington	7,300	Bass brand owned by AB InBev, Tennent brewery by C&C, most other brands and Burton brewery by Molson Coors. Successor pub company renamed Mitchells & Butlers.
Courage (Elders IXL, formerly part of Imperial Tobacco)	Barclay Perkins, Courage, Fosters, George's, Harp (with Guinness, S&N), John Smith's, Simonds	5,100	Bought by Scottish & Newcastle 1995 to create Scottish Courage, UK interests bought by Heineken 2008, Courage brand owned by Carlsberg.
Guinness	Guinness, Harp (with Courage, S&N)	0	Merged with Grand Metropolitan to create Diageo 1997.
Scottish & Newcastle	Harp (with Courage, Guinness), Matthew Brown, McEwan's, Newcastle, Theakston, Younger's	2,300	Took over Courage 1995 to create Scottish Courage, UK interests bought by Heineken 2008, McEwan and Younger's brands owned by Carlsberg, Theakston restored to family ownership.
Watney's (Grand Metropolitan)	Mann's, Phipps, Truman, Ushers, Watney's, Websters	6,100	Grand Metropolitan sold off breweries in 1991 and later merged with Guinness to create Diageo. Most brands eventually passed to Heineken but are now in independent ownership.
Whitbread	Boddingtons, Campbell, Flowers, Lacon, Mackeson, Nimmo, Rhymney, Stella Artois, Strong's, Whitbread	6,500	Brands owned by AB InBev, company still active in chain restaurants and hotels.

The newly bloated brewing groups had unprecedented resources at their disposal, and not only in terms of marketing and the power to limit choice through their control of pubs. They were at last able to invest seriously in new technology and formats. Inevitably their attentions turned to cask beer, which was already in a sorry state. The style repertoire shrunk still further throughout the 1950s and 1960s, focusing almost entirely on bitter and mild: as mentioned in Chapter 4, the *Good Beer Guide* required only three symbols in its 1976 brewery listings. Mild still outsold bitter in 1959, but by the early 1970s, struggling with an unhelpful image and a reputation for poor quality, it had dropped to claiming only a sixth of draught beer sales. The time was ripe for reconsidering Horace Brown's vision of applying bottling techniques to draught beers by putting a filtered, pasteurised and force carbonated beer in a metal container and serving it under pressure.

Green's of Luton supplied such beer from 1946, if not before. One story is that it began experimenting during World War II when USAF airmen stationed nearby expressed the customary complaints about flat and warm cask beer. Green's merged with Flowers in Stratford-upon-Avon in 1954 and adopted the latter's branding, soon afterwards launching Flowers Keg Bitter, likely the first British beer to use the designation 'keg' in the domestic market. This became the generic term, although alternatives such as 'container' and 'canister beer' persisted for a while.

Thanks to backing from Whitbread, which later bought out its brewery, Flowers Keg became the first such beer to be marketed extensively. Former employee Ivar O'Brien (1992:32) recounts that, like Watney's 1930s product, it was initially aimed at free trade outlets where there was a prohibitively low turnover for cask:

> Keg was not at this time ever intended, and I stress this point, for sale in the tied trade…All the plant for brewing, racking and dispensing keg beer, plus the kegs themselves, were expensive and only justified if new draught sales were gained, usually, it was hoped, to be followed by orders for bottled beers. From our customers' point of view, here was a beer with a good profit margin which was easy to look after and dispense in small free houses and clubs. In spite of the future views of CAMRA supporters, Flowers Keg Bitter proved immediately popular and gained a constantly widening circle of consumers. In the course of time individuals…came to ask for it also in their locals. For several years the brewery resisted this demand except in a few smaller pubs that were unable to keep small quantities of bitter in good condition. Eventually, however, increasing production reduced overhead costs and by 1960 keg bitter was on sale in many tied houses.

The 'views of CAMRA supporters' were ultimately even more damning on what became the most notorious keg brand of all. Watney's Red Barrel, named after a longstanding element of the brewery's branding, first appeared as a premium bottled pale ale in 1950, and in 1956 became the heir to the 1930s experiments with 'container bitter'. Once again it was initially marketed as a premium brand to non-pub outlets, even served on luxury ocean liners, and brewed at around 4.2% to a reasonably decent recipe. But it reached the same economic tipping point as Flowers' entry and was soon being marketed aggressively in pubs. Reformulated to an inferior specification and rebranded as Red in the early 1970s, it became a byword for a poorly brewed and characterless national brand foisted on an unwilling public, its reputation cemented by the *Monty Python's Flying Circus* TV sketch quoted below that portrayed it as the ersatz-Brit beverage of choice in the average Spanish package holiday resort. It was all but withdrawn in the late 1970s, but its poor reputation has proved curiously enduring.

Postwar Watney's pub

And spending four days on the tarmac at Luton airport on a five-day package tour with nothing to eat but dried BEA-type sandwiches and you can't even get a drink of Watney's Red Barrel because you're still in England and the bloody bar closes every time you're thirsty.

Monty Python's Flying Circus, 16 November 1972,
quoted in Wilmut (1989:116–118)

Beers like these multiplied through the 1960s and into the mid-1970s, when pioneering beer writer Richard Boston listed the best-known as 'Allied's Double Diamond, Courage's Tavern, Bass Charrington's Worthington E, Scottish and Newcastle's Tartan, Watney's Red and Whitbread's Tankard,' adding, 'There's little to choose between them, and personally I don't care for any of them.' (1976:64). By then, brewery-conditioned draught beer in both keg and tank, which had accounted for only 1% of draught production in 1959, was up to 63% (Protz 1978:51). Cask-conditioned beer was also increasingly dispensed under 'top' carbon dioxide pressure, a practice made easier by the switch to metal containers, making it gassier than it might otherwise have been and perhaps inhibiting flavour development.

Merger mania had been triggered by an ambition to sell lager in the UK, and the big brewers were finally able to crack this nut too. Social factors were increasingly favourable: as in the US many years before, pale lager seemed clean, modern and aspirational, and was increasingly familiar through overseas travel. Allied, which had acquired Graham's via Allsopp, relaunched it as Skol in 1959, deliberately marketed at younger drinkers. Guinness developed Harp in Ireland in the late 1950s and marketed it in Britain in partnership with Courage and Scottish & Newcastle from 1961. In the early 1970s these were supplemented by well-known mainland European names brewed under licence, like Carlsberg and Heineken. Boosted further by the hot summers of the mid-1970s, lager grew from a market share of 1% in 1961 to 25% in 1976. It finally became the majority beer style in 1989, when its share of sales by value reached 50.3%. A seemingly new-style beer suited a new-style package: in 1966, cans accounted for only just over 1% of overall beer sales, but the proportion was increasing, especially in Scotland where 70% of consumers said they preferred cans for take-home beer (Monopolies Commission 1969).

Sadly, most British lagers were poor examples of the style, low in alcohol with a high proportion of unmalted grains and ruthlessly truncated lagering times. Harp was around 3.4%, as was Heineken as brewed by Whitbread, much lower than the 5% Dutch original. Despite the corner-cutting, they sold at premium prices. In 1973, Carlsberg, brewed by Watney's at an OG of only 1.030°, cost 18p a pint (£1.79 today), 22% more than Red, with an OG of 1.037°, at 14p (£1.39). As brewers weren't required to declare the strength of their beers until the implementation of European Union rules in 1989, ordinary drinkers couldn't make informed comparisons, so existing beers too fell prey to the old dodge of shrinkflation in the mash tun, reducing strength while retaining price.

The lid was lifted by the *Daily Mirror* and *Sunday Mirror* newspapers and *Which?* Magazine in 1971. Laboratory tests showed, for example, that Watney's Special had reduced from an OG of 1.043° in 1960 to 1.038° in 1971 and 1.036° a year later. Future CAMRA chair Christopher Hutt (1973:41) worked out that the first reduction saved the brewery £2.64 per barrel in duty, and the second a further 44p. Worthington E went down from 1041.8° to 1036.8° (164 l) over the same period. The strongest beer sampled was Young's Special at 1.050°, followed by Marston's Bitter at 1.046°. Not only were keg beers often weaker than the cask beers they replaced but on average 2p a pint more expensive. *Mirror* investigator Richard Sear (1971:24) wrote that beer:

> is generally weaker and dearer than at any time (except possibly during the last war)… Some brews are so weak they could have been sold legally in America during part of the Prohibition era… Keg beers, gassy, highly-priced and much loved by the husky manhood of the TV commercial are, in fact, among the worst value. Modern beer has been so chemicalised, synthesised, pressurised and filtered by the time it reaches the cellars of many of Britain's 75,000 locals that any resemblance to the natural brew of yesteryear can be virtually coincidental (1971:24).

Appreciating quite what these beers were like is difficult due to the lack of detailed observations of flavour and character made at the time. The 1970s beer writer Frank Baillie, in his ground-breaking consumer guide *The Beer Drinker's Companion,* laments the decline of 'good bitter, well-hopped, and what can best be described as "beery" beers' (1973:65). Baillie has an issue with increasing sweetness, but I suspect he is also missing malty body and perhaps yeasty characteristics in the increasingly light and smooth beers of the period. Certainly, hop rates had already dramatically declined from early 20th-century levels. In 1969 the industry consumed 9,454.5 tonnes of hops to make just under 54 million hl of beer, a mere 1.75 g per litre. Though the reduction was partly explained by declining strengths and more efficient utilisation, it was undoubtedly exaggerated by brewers becoming increasingly convinced that making beers less bitter would broaden their appeal.

Some drinkers saw kegging as a way of disguising unscrupulous cost-cutting: when 'taste is governed by coldness and fizziness,' wrote Hutt, 'it becomes less important for the brewers to use good quality malt and hops, because the body and the bitterness that these products contribute cannot be detected anyway.' (1973:21.) Even some industry executives had misgivings about keg quality. When Bass began producing keg bitters in 1960, its declared intention, as with Flowers and Watney's previously, was not to replace cask but to supply outlets where cask was impractical. But a mere four years later, chair Percy Grigg reported to shareholders on the 'spectacular growth in the sales of our canister beers although this to a certain extent has been at the expense of the traditional Bass and Worthington qualities' (quoted in Cornell 2012).

Outwardly, the brewers insisted such developments were in response to public demand, and indeed it's more than likely significant numbers of drinkers preferred more consistent keg products in comparison to poorly kept cask, which, as Spicer and others put it (2012:1), in an echo of Maureen Ogle's observations about lager in the US, was 'evidently not to the taste of the newly affluent British consumer'. Increased levels of carbonation, together with a trend towards sweeter beers, may also have appealed more to consumers weaned on soft drinks. Both brewers and retailers told the Monopolies Commission that 'keg beers are especially popular with the younger generation' (1969:8).

The challenges of serving cask beers so low in alcohol at their best in the face of declining turnover and uneven cellar skills were, and are, entirely genuine. A 1970s manual for bar staff depicts keg as the saviour of draught beer and communal drinking:

> The days when a dozen hogsheads of ale were seen being delivered to the corner pub have long since passed, but the brewers, aware of current trends, developed Pressure Beer in the shape of 'keg' or 'canister' beer, which has maintained and even strengthened the premier position which draught beer has always held (Coombs 1982:1).

Similar sentiments from the same period are expressed in the quote from J G Miles above, and even real ale campaigner and journalist Roger Protz admitted that 'in the days before keg came to dominate the market, an awful lot of sour and cloudy beer was served up in pubs throughout the country and the filthy habit of pouring the slops back into the cask was widespread' (1978:50). That last bad practice was rendered impossible with a sealed and pressurised keg. A late 1970s microbiological survey of pubs duly found a fabulous menagerie of wild yeasts and bacteria in cask dispense systems, noting that in some cases the 'mild had too many contaminants to count'. On the other hand, 'the number of contaminants in both keg and cellar tank beer were much lower than in the traditional draught beer, some samples not containing any organisms at all' (Harper 1980:3-4).

But the bigger breweries increasingly took a firmer hand in shaping demand. By 1977 they were spending £20 million a year (over £108 million today) on advertising and sponsorship (Protz 1978:35). More powerfully, they could now restrict choice through their increasing grip on the tied house system, replacing local beers in the pubs they took over with national keg brands and thereby achieving further economies of scale. In some areas, a single big brewer owned nearly all the pubs: Courage dominated Bristol and Bath and Allied presided throughout much of Buckinghamshire and Hertfordshire. Watney's, which had a near-monopoly in Norfolk and Northamptonshire, was deliberately phasing out cask to brew exclusively keg, bottled and canned products.

Protz, who estimates the number of different beers more than halved from 3,000 to under 1,500 between 1966 and 1976, provides telling examples:

> When Watney took over Tamplins of Brighton and Henry and Constable of Chichester in 1953 and 1954, they replaced the two distinctive beers brewed by the firms with one new beer called Sussex Bitter. Complaining customers were mollified by the fact that at least Sussex Bitter was preferable to the national Watney beers… But Sussex Bitter was withdrawn in 1970 and replaced with Watney's Special… When Bass Charrington brought in a new beer, Brew Ten, in the north of England, landlords were told they could no longer have supplies of Stones Bitter from Sheffield, a Bass subsidiary. A spokesman commented, in the style of George Orwell's Newspeak: "It is not true that Stones is being discontinued, merely that Brew Ten is being promoted" (1978:52).

Where the big brewers went, the increasingly vulnerable smaller regional and local brewers often saw no alternative but to follow. Numerous listings for independent brewers in the first *Good Beer Guide* include warnings like 'many pubs on pressure', 'nearly all pressurised', 'too much gassy beer', 'sometimes hard to find real draught', and among those that earned the *Guide*'s unqualified approval, this was often through want of resources rather than a positive choice. True cask champions, like John Young of Young's brewery in Wandsworth, London, which eventually closed in 2006, were very rare and regarded by their peers as aberrations. When during a Brewers' Society meeting a hearse went by, one of Young's fellow members quipped, 'There goes another of your customers, John.' (Quoted in Protz 2006.) And in purely economic terms, the industry was doing rather better than it had in years. Annual UK production grew from its 1958 nadir of 38.93 million hl to 44.35 in 1960, 56.23 in 1970 and 63.81 in 1980 (Gourvish and Wilson 1996:630).

Looking back, the problem wasn't so much keg as bad keg, enervated, overpriced, over-carbonated, lacking in character and foisted on drinkers, whether they liked it or not, through control of retail and ever-swelling marketing budgets. At the same time, the established alternative, cask, was also often weak, poor quality and limited in variety. But for a significant number of drinkers it was at least locally distinctive and less aggressively carbonated and chilled. If the big brewers had made better keg beers and sold them on their quality rather than ubiquity and brand recognition, things might have turned out differently.

Cask fights back

Beer has always been appreciated by its drinkers, but the sort of detailed treatment represented by, for example, the book you're now reading is a very recent development. The first writing on wine appreciation aimed at the informed consumer appeared in the early 19th century; beer, long regarded as a more prosaic drink appealing to a less prosperous and educated class of drinker, had to wait considerably longer.

With few exceptions, the pre–1970s literature on beer comprises technical manuals aimed at brewers or licensees, academic studies on historical, economic or social topics, discussions on alcohol as a social and political problem, or anecdotal material. Though a tiny handful of independent venues offering what we might now call a 'curated' selection of beer existed in the 1950s, like Becky's Dive Bar in London, it wasn't until two decades later that some pubs grasped the opportunity to sell themselves on their beer range in a manner analogous to wine bars. Only when good beer was under threat, it seems, did drinkers begin to take it seriously. The obligation to defend something still colours the thinking of beer advocates today.

The consumer movement that rose to defend cask and, later, other beers of quality and distinction emerged from a current in society increasingly critical of consumerism, advocating authenticity and naturalness over pre-packed, homogenous, mass-marketed products. The 1960s and 1970s witnessed an upswing of interest in topics like wholefoods, self-sufficiency, traditional crafts and environmentalism. The economic critique of mainstream attitudes to industrialisation and wealth was expressed in 1973 by economist E F Schumacher in the influential *Small is Beautiful*, which argued that limitless growth was neither economically sustainable nor the best way to enrich human experience. 'What is at stake,' says Schumacher, 'is not economics but culture: not the standard of living but the quality of life' (2011:220). To help rebalance growth, he advocated small-scale businesses using 'intermediate technology...to which everybody can gain admittance and which is not reserved to those already rich and powerful' (127).

One self-sufficient craft, homebrewing, received a boost in the 1963 Budget, which dropped the requirement for non-commercial brewers to hold a licence. By the mid-1970s malt extract-based brewing kits were readily available on high streets, sold mainly on their price as compared to the ever-inflating costs of commercially brewed beer. There were more serious practitioners too, including historical recreationists the Durden Park Beer Circle, formed in 1971 (Harrison 1991). The interest in reviving vanished beer styles was very much in line with another dissenting theme of the times: the preservation of elements of the past, as reflected in everything from campaigns to save historic buildings to projects to reopen axed railway lines with steam traction. Small business, homebrewing and heritage conservation met in the revival of brewing at Traquair House in 1966, mentioned in Chapter 6.

Most ordinary disgruntled drinkers struggling to articulate what was going wrong with their beer faced a knowledge gap that's hard to imagine today, when detailed information about practically every aspect of the subject is at the finger-tips of anyone with an internet connection. In these circumstances, it's not surprising that the UK's earliest organised campaign for better beer, the Society for the Preservation of Beers from the Wood (SPBW, 2006), focused on one of the most obvious changes, the replacement of wooden casks with metal ones, for which there was visible evidence stacked up in every pub yard. It helped that wood was the more 'natural' material with the longest heritage. At the time of the Society's inaugural meeting in 1963, while not all beer in metal containers – or 'sealed dustbins' as SPBW literature labelled them – was pasteurised and pressurised, anything still delivered to pubs in a wooden cask was almost certainly cask conditioned. As its membership became better informed, and perhaps as its first field of battle seemed increasingly lost, the Society broadened to encompass cask in general, but still aims to 'support and encourage' the use of wooden casks today.

The SPBW was, and is, a small and relatively light-hearted organisation mainly focused on social drinking activities, but in the mid-1960s its concerns resonated more widely, resulting in press coverage disproportionate to its size. Encouraged, it began demonstrating against brewery closures and lobbied to restrict the description 'draught' to unpressurised beers that had been drawn from the cask rather than pushed by gas. Though this latter argument was also ultimately lost, the debate was reflected in the Monopolies Commission's 1969 report, which spent some time making clear that it regarded all beers supplied in bulk as 'draught' and preferred the term 'cask' for 'traditional draught' – unpasteurised, unpressurised beer. Beer historians Jessica Boak and Ray Bailey identify this as the origin of the use of the term 'cask' in the sense employed in this book.

Disputes about terminology can seem petty and obscure, but well-chosen words have power. In 1973 a newer, more ambitious and better-organised group with similar aims to the SPBW not only came up with a rather more sophisticated set of criteria for beers it considered worth preserving and promoting, but also a new name for them: 'real ale'. The term was snappier, unencumbered by existing baggage, and, most importantly, resonated with the cultural climate. Following a precedent already set by the movement for 'real bread' in response to comparable concerns, it was an exemplary exercise in guerrilla branding at a tiny fraction of the big brewers' marketing budget.

As with the SPBW, the four young journalists (Michael Hardman, Graham Lees, Jim Makin, Bill Mellor) who founded the Campaign for the Revitalisation of Ale, as it was initially known, first publicised their idea as 'a bit of a joke' but were overwhelmed by the response. Formally constituted in 1972 and renamed the Campaign for Real Ale (CAMRA) the following year, it attracted attention and support from the press and from writers like Frank Baillie and *Guardian* journalist Richard Boston, whose pioneering beer column debuted in the paper in 1972. With the help of keen and able volunteers, CAMRA had, by 1976, 30,000 members and numerous local branches. Its enduring annual publication *The Good Beer Guide* was first circulated as a set of typewritten sheets in 1972, followed by a professionally printed version in 1974, and its flagship event the Great British Beer Festival (GBBF) was first held in 1975.

CAMRA's original four founders: Jim Makin, Bill Mellor, Michael Hardman and Graham Lees

Following some research and discussion at a special general meeting, CAMRA newsletter *What's Brewing* officially set out the conditions under which beers would be considered as real ale in November 1972 (CAMRA 1972:3): 'living beers, kept in their natural condition and not pasteurised'; dispensed by handpump, beer engine, electric pump or air compressor without extraneous carbon dioxide; and tasting 'pleasant and wholesome'. This last requirement, reflecting wider contemporary concerns with naturalness and wholesomeness, was a welcome acknowledgement that quality and flavour mattered beyond the technicalities of dispense, though it was imprecise and subjective in contrast to the rest of the definition and was ultimately dropped.

Good Beer Guide 1972

CAMRA and its fellow travellers initially took the industry by surprise: while brewers and licensees were used to defending themselves on alcohol-related issues, they were unaccustomed to reasoned but passionate criticism of the quality, strength and presentation of their products from a consumer's point of view. Their initial response was hostile, with trade publication the *Morning Advertiser* at one point banning its writers from using the term 'real ale'. But they eventually recognised the business logic of meeting the obvious demand for cask beer that CAMRA's growth reflected.

Several independent brewers on the point of ditching cask hastily revised their plans, and the big brewers began reintroducing cask brands. Head brewer Miles Jenner told me that by 1968 half the output of Harvey's of Lewes, now one of the most revered traditional producers, was in keg and bottle. Then, unexpectedly, 'CAMRA appeared and suddenly cask beer came back into vogue, growing by 10% a year, and keg and bottled beer just fell away.' Gaskell and Chambers, the main supplier of handles for beer engines, announced in 1976 that it could no longer keep up with demand. By the early 1980s, though the ascent of lager continued apace, the much-reviled big brand keg bitters had largely been consigned to the drain. Cask, it seemed, had been saved, and CAMRA was considered a victim of its own success, struggling with a membership slump and a lack of direction, as 'drinkers saw no reason to continue in membership' (Protz 1995:122).

Growing interest in cask also heralded the first significant cluster of brewery startups in the UK since the early 20th century, as a new wave of microbreweries and brewpubs, founded mainly by refugees from big brewing and enthusiastic homebrewers, swept in to target an increasingly discriminating public: exemplars of Schumacher's small-scale businesses whether conscious or otherwise. The defunct Selby (Middlesbrough) brewery relaunched in 1972, the Miner's Arms restaurant in Somerset added a brewery in 1973, and former Watney's employee Bill Urquhart opened the Litchborough brewery, arguably the first entirely new standalone microbrewery, in 1974. Sixteen new breweries opened in 1979, 18 in 1980, and 31 in 1981 (Boak and Bailey 2014a:113).

Bill Urquhart

A handful of the 1970s generation are still around today, including Butcombe just outside Bristol, founded in 1978 by a Courage executive made redundant by the closure of the city's major brewery, and Ringwood in Hampshire, opened the same year though since acquired by Carlsberg (and currently up for sale). Ringwood's influence spread internationally through its founder Peter Austin, who went on to set up 140 other breweries as a consultant in Britain, the US and several other countries. Austin was a co-founder of the Small Independent Brewers Association (SIBA, now the Society of Independent Brewers although it uses the same acronym) in 1980, by which time there were enough potential members to render such an organisation viable. By 1987 the UK had 220 breweries, a number that more than doubled to 450 by 2001 (HM Treasury 2021).

Peter Austin

Many of the newcomers struggled with quality and consistency, and with securing outlets when most pubs were tied. One obvious solution to the latter problem was to combine production and retail in a single package, triggering a revival of what used to be called brewing victuallers, or, in more modern terms, brewpubs. Only four historic examples were still operational when CAMRA was founded, but their numbers had doubled by 1979, the year that Austin helped unemployed entrepreneur David Bruce install a brewery at a long-derelict south

London pub, which was reopened as the Goose and Firkin. By 1987, when Bruce sold off the business, it had expanded to a chain of 11 brewpubs and two non-brewing venues. At its peak, before being wound up by eventual owners Allied in 1999, the Firkin chain had 150 pubs in the UK, France and the Netherlands, including 19 that brewed.

Old-established brewers and new micros alike began to widen their repertoire of styles, though largely remaining within the low-strength bands that now prevailed, with the first porters brewed in England since the 1950s appearing in 1978. Mild continued to struggle in competition with bitter, 'which many can now afford and consider much better value for money', as a 1970s trade manual puts it (Coombs 1982:17). 'In most public houses,' the author continues, 'mild ale is not even on sale and apart from a few elderly old-timers who will stick to their pints it is more often sold mixed.'

Despite the adoption of 'shilling' branding to give them a more traditional gloss, distinctively Scottish session ale styles also struggled. CAMRA was active in Scotland by 1974 and helped spur renewed growth in cask there too. The biggest developments were in the more populated areas, as remote pubs continued to struggle with transport and turnover. Scottish microbreweries followed – Broughton Ales in the Scottish Borders, founded in 1979, is one of the early survivors – but increasingly brewed in broadly the same style as their colleagues south of the border, and the near-extinction of air pressure dispense, as described in Chapter 3, also helped elide the distinctiveness of Scotland's beer culture. Today, Edinburgh remains Scotland's main cask centre, with a few hotspots elsewhere. 'The further you get out from the city,' says Mark Hyson, 'the less you see cask.'

A wholly new cask style, golden or summer ale, emerged in the second half of the 1980s to cement the turn to paler beers. The founding example is usually considered Exmoor Gold, launched in 1986, though Burton Bridge Brewery for one produced a very pale 'summer ale' as a seasonal for a pub chain in 1985. Co-founder Bruce Wilkinson told me that, once it became evident there was a year-round demand, it was renamed Golden Delicious. The breakthrough brand, though, was Summer Lightning from Salisbury's Hop Back, which also originated as a seasonal special, in 1988. With their golden hue, fragrantly refreshing character and relatively robust strength of 4.5–5%, these beers positioned themselves as a cask alternative to premium lagers – Summer Lightning was originally conceived as a cask lager – or maybe even to popular white wines: Exmoor's website proclaims Gold as 'the colour of Chardonnay' (2023). Soon, other brewers were launching their own examples, and by the 1990s golden ale was vying with bitter as the most popular cask style.

Perhaps the most striking example of how such beers have changed the cask landscape is at Adnams, where the classic and still excellent Southwold Bitter has been decisively overtaken as the best seller by Ghost Ship (4.5%), a Citra-hopped pale ale with a dab of rye which originally appeared as a Halloween special in 2010. The most successful example is Carlsberg's Wainwright, at a more modest strength of 4.1%: according to the *Morning Advertiser*, it was the 7th best-selling UK cask beer in 2022. In 2005, in response to concerns that the newcomers were elbowing out the generally darker and more full-bodied traditional bitters, CAMRA introduced a new golden ale category in the Champion Beer of Britain competition.

Though they marked a welcome uptick in hop rates that finally began to reverse the post-war trend, the first generation of golden ales showcased English and other European varieties like East Kent Golding, First Gold and Styrian Golding. But they paved the way for a second wave of pale beers influenced by developments in US craft brewing and foregrounding the distinctively fruity and piney notes of Cascade and other hops imported from the Pacific Northwest. Sean Franklin first tasted these when visiting as a wine professional in 1980, inspiring him to set up a microbrewery and experiment with using them in English cask styles. That brewery, simply called Franklin's, closed in 1986; his second attempt, Rooster's, in 1993, proved more enduring and still operates today in Harrogate, though under different ownership. Its inaugural brew, Yankee, was arguably the first successful UK cask beer to feature Cascade. It was soon joined by beers like Oakham JHB, Kelham Island Pale Rider (both 1993), Dark Star Hophead (1996) and many more, presaging the American influence that became increasingly important in the 21st century, as we'll shortly see.

Meanwhile, and perhaps against expectations, CAMRA continued to grow, both through activities like festivals and publications targeting the growing numbers of beer enthusiasts, and through campaigns, reaching 30,000 members in 1991. Though cask was once again more widely available, it only accounted for 16.8% of overall volumes in 1980 (Fish 2022:13). The structural problems with the big breweries persisted in the absence of government action on the 1969 report: they were still buying up and closing historic breweries and using local monopolies to restrict choice and raise prices. The campaign provided key evidence to yet another investigation by the expanded Monopolies and Mergers Commission (MMC) in 1989. The final report echoed several CAMRA contentions, concluding that the Big Six operated a complex monopoly through their control of 75% of production and 74% of tied pubs, and recommending limits on tied pubs and giving brewery tenants the right to stock a guest beer. This time the government responded with new regulations known as the Beer Orders, forcing the big brewers to remove the tie from 11,000 of their pubs and allow at least one guest cask in the remaining 20,000.

The consequences of this were transformative, but not entirely in a way that advocates of greater choice and competition had hoped. The new rules prompted breweries to question the time-honoured logic of combining production and retail. A few shed their pub estates and focused on their brewing businesses, but many more, including numerous well-established independents, cashed in their brewing sites for redevelopment and focused on pubs, contracting their production out to others. A new wave of consolidation followed, and, as shown in the table on page 245, the old Big Seven have since been succeeded by five multinationals, only one of which still owns pubs. A similar process swept the retailing side of the industry, with a handful of big pub-owning companies or 'pubcos' eventually emerging. These were often streamlined around a limited range of beer, much of it sourced from the successors to the Big Seven.

Although they no longer brewed and were therefore exempt from the numerical restrictions of the Beer Orders, the pubcos retained the right to enforce the tie on their leaseholders, placing the biggest ones in a powerful position. They negotiated aggressively for substantial discounts from the brewer, while selling on to the licensee at as much as double the price the brewery would charge a free house, while progressively hiking up rents. Now divorced from brewing, they began acting more like property management companies, sometimes deliberately running down sites that might realise more value when sold off for non-pub use. Combined with other issues such as changing patterns of consumption, one result was a 27% decline in the number of UK pubs from 64,000 in 1990 to 47,000 in 2019. Of those that remained, 21% were still tied to brewers, with another 29% tied to pubcos, leaving half in independent hands (Foley 2021).

In response, CAMRA's focus has increasingly widened to pubs campaigning, recognising that, as mentioned in Chapter 2, the cask format depends on communal drinking spaces. It was partly because of such lobbying that a new Pubs Code in 2016 gave leaseholders of the bigger pubcos a right to move to a 'market rent only' option, paying a higher rent in exchange for freedom from the tie, with an independent Pubs Code Adjudicator to settle disputes. But the slow and piecemeal implementation of these arrangements has frustrated many licensees and campaigners, and a long-running review of the regulations is still in progress.

Nonetheless, the changes have unarguably widened choice, bolstered by another legal change in 2003 which simplified alcohol licensing regulations and shifted responsibility for issuing licences from magistrates to local authorities. This has made it much easier to sell alcohol in places that weren't previously licensed, partially offsetting the loss of traditional pubs in longstanding or purpose-built premises with a range of new social drinking environments, usually free of tie, including micropubs and specialist bars in shopfront sites, large bars in conversions of buildings like banks and cinemas, and brewery taprooms (of which more shortly).

In 2002 SIBA achieved its long-held campaign aim of persuading the government to ease the duty burden on smaller producers through Small Brewers Relief (SBR, sometimes called progressive beer duty), further extended in 2004. The new arrangements provided a 50% duty discount to the smallest breweries producing 5,000 hl a year or less, with progressively smaller discounts as production rose to 60,000 hl, when the full rate was payable. Combined with an ever-broadening market for speciality beer and a burgeoning and ever more serious homebrewing scene, the changes triggered an explosion in UK brewery numbers in the first decades of the new millennium, exceeding 1,000 for the first time since the 1930s in 2012, and reaching 2,000 in 2019 (Fish 2022:70).

This may be a peak, as the UK total had fallen back to 1,824 by March 2023 (SIBA 2023), but the brewing scene has nonetheless been irrevocably transformed and a contraction of variety and choice on a 20th-century scale is unlikely in the foreseeable future. Importantly, though, these new breweries are, on average, much smaller than those of the past, reflecting reduced production and consumption which, though they initially increased thanks to the renewed interest in cask in the 1970s, have since returned to their historic downward trend. Significant numbers of the more recent openings make little or no cask, a point I'll return to below.

UK annual overall beer production and average consumption

YEAR	PRODUCTION (million hl)	CONSUMPTION (l per head)
1970	55.1	103
1980	64.8	118.3
1990	61.8	113.9
2000	55.3	88.4
2010	45	68.5
2015	44	67
2020	32.2	60.9

Sources: Fish (2022:92, 95), Brewers of Europe (2017:7, 11)

Increased choice doesn't necessarily mean increased average quality, particularly with a vulnerable product like cask. The loosened links between breweries and pubs following the Beer Orders contributed to further declining conditions in cellars and increasing knowledge gaps in the trade as neither pub companies nor brewers were taking direct responsibility for cask quality. An ad-hoc partnership of family brewers investigated the problem by testing cask beer temperature, appearance, aroma and flavour in 1,000 pubs in 1998, finding that these parameters were too often not up to brewers' expectations, particularly temperature. Out of this emerged Cask Marque, now a not-for-profit trust that also involves industry bodies and pubcos. It's best known for its accreditation scheme based on twice-yearly independent assessments of subscribing pubs, but importantly it also offers training and support to help address problems identified during inspections (Cask Marque 2023).

The subject of quality brings us back to the development of beer appreciation and the question CAMRA posed when it included the requirement to be 'natural and wholesome' in its initial definition of real ale. The persistent reluctance to consider flavour in detail perhaps reflects a British reticence about acknowledging sensory enjoyment for fear of being labelled self-indulgent or pretentious. While aficionados of wine have long waxed lyrical about the sensory aspects of their favoured drink, some still find such analysis incongruously comical or infuriatingly inappropriate when applied to beer. Frank Baillie alludes to this with an extended quote from *Pantaloons and Antics or Doodling with a Hermes*, a 1964 comic novel by Australian writer and beer drinker Cyril Pearl, in which a 1961 Foster's is compared favourably with a 'tolerable' 1962 Melbourne Bitter as being 'brut, mon, charnu, pettilante fino, pizzicato and faintly amerture … urbane but quietly persuasive and with a notable wet finish' (1973:286).

Baillie wonders whether such conversations about beer will ever become commonplace, but the rest of his book, though it provides a valuable and admirably comprehensive survey of the breweries of the day, tells the reader more about pub liveries than beer flavour. 'Some draught beers,' we read, 'are distinctly "malty", and others "nutty". Some are extremely sweet and lack the *characteristic taste of beer.*' (83, my italics.) A few beers, mainly bitters, merit the briefest of tasting notes: Arkell's has 'a pleasant nutty flavour', Brains and Everards are 'well-balanced', Hook Norton offers a 'draught bitter with the smack of hops', while Theakston Old Peculier is merely 'of distinctive flavour'. Many milds are simply listed as 'a darkish mild' or 'a light mild'. Even Michael Jackson's seminal *World Guide to Beer*, published a few years later in 1977, is surprisingly sparse on tasting notes, though richly detailed on many other aspects of international beer culture.

Michael Hardman's 1976 book *Beer Naturally*, accompanied with beautiful black and white photographs of historic breweries by Theo Bergstrom, also lacks detail on how beer should taste. Instead, Hardman expands on contemporary concerns by considering the production of 'beer unnaturally'. He lists 'unmalted barley, wheat flour, flaked maize and even potato starch' as well as malt extract among the unwelcome additions to contemporary mash tuns. Also decried as 'unnatural' are hop extracts, which 'generally make uninspiring beer', the use of anti-foaming chemicals during fermentation, and the familiar bugbears of filtration, pasteurisation and force carbonation that yield beers 'missing the taste of the barley field and hop garden', as if it can be taken for granted that readers have extensive sensory experience of such environments.

While some of what Hardman describes can indeed have a negative impact on flavour and character, not all of it is so self-evidently undesirable, especially when considered alongside other practices common in cask production such as the use of refined sugar, colouring and finings, which are left unquestioned. As is evident from Chapter 1, brewing at any scale is an involved and sophisticated industrial process, so it's hard to condemn certain beers for being 'processed' without being able to demonstrate where the acceptable processes end and the unacceptable ones begin, especially if the results taste acceptable.

CAMRA eventually grappled with the issue of taste following motions at a 1983 Annual General Meeting condemning increasing blandness and mediocrity. The discussion noted the importance of being 'able to talk intelligently about the taste of beer. If the customer wants to persuade breweries to produce a beer he likes, he has to be able to say what they should taste like' (Hanson 1983:10). The Campaign finally set up members' tasting panels in 1989, but the subsequent inclusion of tasting notes in the *Good Beer Guide* triggered an angry motion at the

1990 AGM from members concerned that 'flowery language and the wine bar image' were 'the hallmark of Southern middle class beer snobs', and would result in CAMRA being 'laughed out of the public bar' (Protz and Lawley 1990). Thankfully, the motion was rejected, and intelligent conversations about beer flavour have since become as commonplace as Baillie speculated.

Craft brewers since 1874.
Current Batemans slogan

The age of craft

'We weren't actually opposed to keg beer,' says CAMRA co-founder Graham Lees of the early days of the campaign. 'Right from the start our view was people should have choice.' (Quoted in Hadland 2021:25.) Nonetheless, several generations of drinkers took away the simplistic message of unpressurised cask good, pressurised keg bad, bolstered perhaps by the naming of CAMRA's flagship publication, a guide to cask pubs, as *The Good Beer Guide*. In the context of UK brewing in the 1970s, the simplification was understandable, as the good beers, or at least the most characterful and interesting ones, were by and large cask beers, many of which were threatened by merger mania.

Beer in bottle and can had fallen to only 22% of production in 1978 (Harper 1980:2), and most discerning drinkers preferred draught. 'Back then cask ale stood out as the only beer worth drinking,' current chair of CAMRA's real ale campaigns committee Gillian Hough told me. 'We always recognised bottle-conditioned beers as being special, and supportable, but there were only five of these.' And there were few other points of comparison, as beer writer Jeff Evans points out: 'These were the days when beer was highly parochial. British people drank British beer – even the "foreign" lagers they were acquiring a taste for were mostly brewed in the UK.' (2011:6.)

But even at the time, a blanket insistence on the superiority of cask, particularly when justified by arguments that ignored the science, infuriated some commentators, among them Richard Boston. Following a debate on electric pumps, Boston remarked:

The more doctrinaire members of CAMRA...have at times shown the fanaticism of religious dementia...They consider anything that in any way uses extraneous CO_2 to be non-kosher. This can involve questions of an almost philosophical nature, since a living beer is giving out carbon dioxide on its own the whole time... At times it has seemed that CAMRA's sole interest was in means of dispense. It has been said that some of their members would drink castor oil if it came from a handpump, and would reject nectar if it had no more than looked at carbon dioxide (1976:66).

Ironically, CAMRA went on to play a significant role in creating an expanding beer scene in which nectar was fully embraced by carbon dioxide, by introducing British drinkers to the exotic delights of imported beers and by inspiring brewers outside the UK whose influence ultimately returned to these shores.

The cultural shifts of the 1960s rippled through the fermentation vessels of other countries too, initially in a small way. In 1965, the same year commercial brewing began at Traquair House, Fritz Maytag, heir to a washing machine dynasty, took a majority share in the historic but decrepit Anchor brewery in San Francisco, California, an extremely rare survivor of an earlier brewing age, buying it out four years later. His priority was to improve the quality and consistency of the brewery's distinctive Steam Beer, the last remaining example of the 'California common' style. But when he eventually added other lines, he looked to British brewing heritage for inspiration, creating likely the first porter of the modern era in 1973 and introducing a barley wine in 1975. Pierre Celis revived an extinct local spiced wheat beer in Hoegaarden, Flemish Brabant, in 1966, a year after Maytag's intervention. Celis later helped Frank Boon establish a new young presence in the apparently terminally declining industry backwater of traditional lambic production in 1975.

Though some new UK brewers were initially inspired by Belgian styles, developments in the US ultimately turned out to be the most significant. Though homebrewing remained illegal following the repeal of Prohibition, there was enough of an underground community by 1973 that the Treasury Department issued an official warning to 'leave the beer-making to the brewers' (quoted in Ogle 2006:278). Interest in imported beer was also growing, and there was briefly a Committee for Real Ale, inspired by the British model, in California in 1976. The first new US microbrewery was likely New Albion in Sonoma in the Bay Area, launched by Jack McAuliffe in 1977. It was named after Elizabethan explorer Francis Drake's designation for California, conjuring a significantly transatlantic image. The following year the federal government bowed to the inevitable by legalising homebrewing and Charlie Papazian co-founded the American Homebrewers Association in Boulder, Colorado, two months later.

New Albion struggled with quality and sales, closing in 1982, but others proved more enduring, including fellow Californian Sierra Nevada, established in 1979, the first to make a big success of a pale ale hopped with Cascade. In 1978 there had been only 42 brewing companies in the entire country: a few years later there were over 50 more, including brewpubs. Keen to present themselves as alternatives to the macro lager producers that completely dominated the country's industry, the newcomers initially followed Maytag in looking to Europe for inspiration. But they weren't beholden to any tradition and were free to mix, match and innovate as they saw fit, while applying a healthy dose of their native entrepreneurial flair.

A catalyst in all this was Yorkshire-born journalist Michael Jackson, now widely regarded as the founder of modern beer writing. Though he was inspired by CAMRA and later contributed to its publications, Jackson's interests were always broader and more international, as exemplified by 1977's *World Guide to Beer*, his first major work on the subject, and his consistent championing of Belgian beer, which is widely recognised as having helped maintain the country's remarkable brewing diversity. The *World Guide* inspired numerous brewers, including Papazian, who befriended Jackson and invited him to the US, prompting the latter to write in more detail

Michael Jackson

about the developing scene there in later books like his series of pocket guides, launched in 1986, and the *Beer Companion* (1997). In 1981 the two friends visited the Great British Beer Festival (GBBF), that year held in Leeds. Papazian recalls:

> When I walked into the hall and saw all those people enjoying beers and the beer culture everywhere... I wonder[ed] if we could ever have something called the Great American Beer Festival in the United States. And I proposed the idea to Mike and he said, "that'd be a great idea, Charlie, but where are you gonna get the beer?" (Quoted in Hadland 2022:119.)

They got the beer, nonetheless, with 24 breweries pouring 47 brews at the inaugural Great American Beer Festival (GABF) in Boulder in 1982. Today, the event, now resident in nearby Denver, stands alongside GBBF as one of the biggest in the international beer calendar, and every year a giant portrait of Jackson, who died far too young in 2007, hangs over the bars like a patron saint. In 2022, 40,000 drinkers enjoyed over 2,000 beers from 500 breweries. Even this represents only a fraction of the US industry, which in 2021 numbered 9,247 breweries. Some 9,118 of these are classified as craft, and although they contribute only 13.1% of production, at 28.7 million hl, the premium prices of their products secure almost 27% of the total spend, or $26.8 billion (Brewers Association 2022a, 2022b). It's a big country.

Some new American brewers were, and are, passionately interested in cask, but it's hard to build a cask beer business from scratch where the containers themselves, and all the associated cellar and dispense paraphernalia, have to be imported, bar staff lack the knowledge, skills and facilities to manage them and sufficient turnover is by no means guaranteed. US craft beer, though often unpasteurised and unfiltered, developed predominantly as a keg, bottled and, later, canned product, meeting established expectations of higher carbonation and lower serving temperatures and evolving bold flavours to suit.

Meanwhile, British cask drinkers who ventured to explore the diverse and flavourful traditions of closer neighbours soon discovered cask was not among them. The first imported beer bar, a table with a few bottles, debuted at the 1979 GBBF. It has since grown into one of the major attractions of the event, offering many hundreds of imported beers from several bars under the banner of *Bières sans frontières* (BSF, 'beers without borders'). Throughout the 1980s and 1990s writers like Jackson, Roger Protz and Tim Webb celebrated traditional Belgian and German beer culture and the rising US craft scene in features in the *Good Beer Guide* and other CAMRA publications, with Webb publishing the first edition of his influential *Good Beer Guide to Belgium and Holland* (since limited just to Belgium) in 1992. 'World' beers began to appear at local festivals, and a small community of specialist bottle shops and bars sprang up to cater for the curious. For some, including me, they became as much the destination of a special trip as a particularly celebrated cask pub.

For a long time, though, British microbreweries almost exclusively focused on cask beer. It could be produced on relatively basic and affordable equipment: beer could be racked with a simple hose, with no need to package under pressure as with keg. There was a clear market for cask and drinkers and the trade expected microbrewed beer to appear in the format. Keg and canned beer remained the domain of mass-produced lager, stout and the remaining unremarkable brewery-conditioned ales from established producers. Though bottling slowly expanded as interest from specialist retailers increased, it remained a secondary activity. Bottled beers were practically all filtered and force carbonated, and many were pasteurised: retailers, including the big supermarket chains, which became increasingly important in the 'off trade' after they were allowed to sell alcohol in 1962, insisted customers used to bright draught beer regarded the sediment left by bottle conditioning as a fault.

Smaller breweries, whose customers might be more understanding, often turned to bottle conditioning as it required minimal investment in hand-operated equipment. This turned out to be a mixed blessing: packaging in this way is a skilled operation requiring scrupulous attention to hygiene, and failings rarely become apparent until the bottle has sat on the shelf for a while. Reviewing small pack for *BEER* magazine since 2002, I've encountered far too many undercondi-tioned beers, unplanned acidic and wild yeast infections, and 'gushers' that explode on opening. But the numbers multiplied nonetheless. Jeff Evans included 180 bottle-conditioned beers in the first edition of *CAMRA's Good Bottled Beer Guide* in 1998. By the most recent edition in 2013, this had grown to over 1,700 (2013:4).

The first modern keg beer targeted at the discerning drinker was likely Newquay Steam Lager, launched by since-defunct family brewer Devenish in 1987. It wasn't a 'steam beer' in the Anchor sense but one of a range of cheerfully branded upmarket offerings also available in swingtop bottles. Ultimately more influential were the various projects of maverick brewer Alastair Hook, who developed a love of lager as a postgraduate at Bavaria's celebrated Weihenstephan brewing school and worked in Californian breweries. He began brewing authentic German-style lagers at the Packhorse brewpub in Ashford, Kent, in 1991, then helped create the Freedom lager brewery, still around today, and several US-style brewpub-restaurants before establishing his own Meantime brewery in southeast London in 2000 (sold to SABMiller in 2015 and now owned by Asahi).

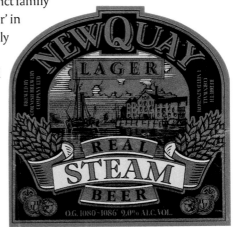

Though all Hook's beers were unfiltered and unpasteurised, and sometimes bottle-conditioned, the Meantime-branded cask beers that occasionally appeared were contract-brewed elsewhere, while the brewery itself concentrated on keg and bottle. It did, however, raise the bar of British lager by several notches. It broke with tradition too in initially targeting restaurants, upmarket bars and bottleshops rather than pubs, and supplying premium own brands to supermarket chains. Several other non-cask microbreweries followed over the course of the decade, initially mainly fellow lager enthusiasts. But some began to dabble in keg speciality ales too, like Lovibonds, founded in Oxfordshire in 2006, and family brewers Adnams and Fuller's.

Meanwhile, US influence on British brewing grew through imports, the country's increased affordability as a tourist destination, and the growing quantities of US hops in British beer. The early milestones already mentioned were cask beers, as was, initially, Punk IPA, the flagship of a brewery founded in 2007 at Fraserburgh in Aberdeenshire. BrewDog was the brainchild of homebrewer James Watt and ex-Thornbridge brewer Martin Dickie, two young men heavily influenced by the brash, hop-led style of West Coast breweries like Stone in San Diego, California. Their creation has become one of the most influential and successful of all UK breweries, with sites in Australia, Germany and the US, and well over 100 bars across the world, though its progress has been marked by controversy due to its provocative communications strategy and more recent accusations of an unhealthy workplace culture. It made much of phasing out cask in 2012, stating that most of its beers benefited from a higher level of carbonation. Though it's since reintroduced the format on a small scale, its initial withdrawal undoubtedly inspired others to follow suit.

When CAMRA Books first invited me to compile a London beer guide in 2010, I insisted it couldn't be limited to cask brewers and venues, as it was already clear that interest in specialist beer was broadening both among drinkers and brewers. I was thinking in particular of the Kernel brewery, opened in 2009 as the first on the now-famous Bermondsey 'beer mile' and today, though still modestly sized, one of the most highly regarded of its generation. Its founder, former cheese-monger Evin O'Riordain, underwent his beer epiphany in Brooklyn, New York City,

Evin O'Riordain at his
Kernel brewery in 2010

but as a homebrewer became interested in heritage London porters and stouts alongside pale ales and IPAs with single US hops. His brewery initially produced only bottle-conditioned beers and marketed them to bottleshops, delis and restaurants. It also joined neighbouring food and drink specialists in selling directly to the public on Saturday mornings, and soon added an on-licence so customers could drink on site.

This 'taproom in the brewery' model was already familiar in the US but was a novelty in the UK: though historic breweries traditionally had brewery taps, these were separate pubs, and most micros were on unattractive industrial estates with no footfall outside business hours. Drinking in at the Kernel generated considerable excitement among the capital's growing band of beer enthusiasts, homebrewers and aspiring commercial brewers, and prompted other startups to provide similar facilities, to the extent that an on-site taproom is now widely considered a prerequisite of any new brewery. Following early and unsuccessful attempts at cask, the Kernel added regular draught beer exclusively in keg which, as at East Sheen Lawn Tennis Club in the 1930s, better suited the limited hours. But, like the bottles, the quality and character were outstanding. The brewery only began producing modest amounts of cask on a regular basis in 2022.

The US influence was also obvious in the increasing adoption of the term 'craft beer' to replace mouthfuls like 'microbrewed', 'speciality' and 'artisanal'. This was extended in the UK to label newly flavourful keg beers as 'craft keg'. In sporadic use since the 1980s, 'craft' was officially adopted by the US Brewers Association in 2004 to define a 'craft brewery' as one that produced less than 2 million US barrels (2.38 million hl) a year and was independently owned. The output threshold was subsequently tripled to 6 million barrels as the Association's biggest members got close to breaching it.

With no such official definition in the UK, where few breweries even approach that level of production, the term provoked much argument. One question was whether cask beer could be 'craft'. Of course it could, within any sensible definition of the term, but some thought otherwise, like pubs writer Robin Turner (2012):

> Craft beer isn't real ale. In fact, in some ways it's the antithesis of real ale. Where real ale might be (fairly) represented by scenes of beer festivals populated by lovable old Gandalfs, craft beer might be two demented blokes driving a tank up Camden High Street to promote a bar launch [as Dickie and Watt did to publicise London's first BrewDog bar in 2011] … Where real ale is cask and handpull, craft beer will proudly pour from the keg or the bottle.

Ultimately, 'craft' became something of a marketing term for modern-style beers, particularly those with an obvious US influence, easily appropriated by the multinational groups as they began buying up smart new breweries like Beaver-town and Magic Rock (the latter since returned to independent ownership). I and many others continue to talk more inclusively of craft beer as a product made with quality ingredients, skill, experience and imagination, whether following deep-rooted local brewing traditions or innovating with new and experimental recipes and styles. By that definition, pretty much all cask is craft.

The increasing popularity of non-cask craft beers posed a dilemma for CAMRA. Repetitions of Graham Lees's assertion that the Campaign wasn't against keg as such were ignored by some local activists who insisted there was no difference between these newcomers and the 'industrial yellow fizz' of the past. The apparent double standard whereby non-cask draught beers were welcome at GBBF and other CAMRA festivals if they were imported but banned if brewed in the UK became increasingly difficult to justify. Ultimately, as Michael Hardman had recognised, the proof was in the tasting: many of the new beers tasted good, with obvious character and complexity, and many were also well-marketed, attracting new and more demographically diverse drinkers to try good beer, including younger people and women who were underrepresented in the traditional cask market.

Encouraged by the increased availability of beers in membrane kegs (KeyKeg), which, though pressurised, didn't require contact between gas and liquid (as explained in Chapter 3), some smaller CAMRA festivals began introducing craft keg bars in the later 2010s, the better to represent their local breweries, and the GBBF followed in 2019. By then, the Campaign was not only engaging more with beer education but reconsidering some of its long-held tenets, as Gillian Hough explains:

> A single definition of real ale had become unsustainable, so CAMRA's Technical Advisory Group was charged with coming up with one that was fit for purpose in the 21st century. They proposed two things. The first was to separate out cask-conditioned beer for special attention and then go on to define the generic characteristics of all formats of "real ale". The second was to keep the definitions short and sharp, then adding a few "best practice" notes. The old definition of real ale ran to several pages. Today's definition of cask runs to 27 words, with the generic definition of "live beer" taking just 40.

At the same time, it's undoubtedly true that craft keg has abstracted volumes from cask. Overall beer sales have continued to decline in the 21st century, from 56.7 million hl per year in 2000 to 39.5 in 2020. The initially puzzling concurrent explosion in brewery numbers is explained by shifts in market share: much of the decline has been at the expense of the big industrial brands, as customers

Brewery taproom at Track Brewing Co, Manchester

who are increasingly drinking less choose better quality products. In the early years of the craft beer boom, cask benefitted from this trend, rising from 7.3% of overall volumes in 2010 to 8.3% in 2015. Its growth in market share subsequently stalled, declining to 6.6% in 2019 (Fish 2022:9, 13). The biggest slump was in the more traditional amber beers, while 13 million adults now claimed to drink craft beer (Eley 2019:6, 20). Cask once accounted for close to 100% of the production of small breweries: in 2022 it was only 46% (Nodder 2022:11). Fewer pubs were stocking it, others had reduced their ranges, and fewer breweries were brewing it.

In 2021 cask accounted for only 4.3% of overall beer production and 15% of draught sales. That's still quite a lot of beer: about 1.8 million hl, almost 317 million pints, but a tiny proportion of the 52 million hl, or over 9 *billion* pints, produced on the eve of World War I. Just as beer shed its role as an everyday, all-day drink for everyone and became an optional treat, so cask beer has dwindled in its home nation to the extent that it's just another speciality among many, albeit one important enough to write a book about.

8 The future of cask

On 20 March 2020, in response to the growing Covid-19 pandemic, all pubs and bars in Britain were closed in the interests of social distancing. Any hope that this was only a temporary measure soon faded as the pandemic continued to worsen, and normal trading conditions didn't resume until July 2021. The pandemic was, of course, a catastrophe, primarily for the many victims of the disease itself and their loved ones, and its overall negative impacts on society will doubtless be felt for years to come. But it posed particular problems for the brewing and hospitality industries, which depend so much on bringing people together rather than keeping them apart.

Cask beer, with its short shelf life and dependence on communal drinking, was hit particularly badly in the early days. CAMRA chief executive Tom Stainer says the scars of the 'Big Pour' that followed, in which millions of litres of unsaleable cask beer literally went down the drain, have yet to fade, as licensees have reduced or eliminated cask stocks for fear of being forced to repeat the exercise with a short shelf-life product. In retrospect, the lockdowns inadvertently provided a wake-up call in demonstrating what a world without cask might be like and emphasising the value of small businesses embedded in their local communities. While the big groups largely pulled down the shutters and furloughed staff, smaller operators had little choice but to apply flexibility and resourcefulness in adapting as best they could.

If you look after cask, cask looks after you.
MARK HYSON, Stewart Brewing, 2022

I've spoken to countless business owners who were deeply moved and heartened by the way their customers rallied round. Many brewers and retailers found an eager demand for the next best thing to cask in a pub, in the form of freshly filled growlers, bag-in-box and minikeg. Eddie Gadd of Ramsgate brewery recounts:

> Before the pandemic, we were 95% cask, and were left with a warehouse full of beer when the first lockdown started. Then we thought, we know most of the people who drink it, most are within 15 miles of the brewery, they're all on social networking. So we built a new webshop, put out the word, bought an electric van and just worked our way through the stock, decanting into four-pint containers and polypins and delivering it to 50 customers a day, every day. After about four months we had to start brewing again, and we carried on like that for a whole year.

A cask-slanted Surrey brewery told me they were astonished at the length of the socially distanced queue that formed the day they reopened for takeaway. They were ultimately able to maintain volumes, with the additional advantage of direct income, paid immediately, rather than on credit with distributors and retailers taking their cut. Some pubs, bars and micropubs offered similar services, with local customers eagerly awaiting the tweets and Instagram posts about which casks were being decanted next.

The people offering such services soon found that if customers were missing anything even more than good beer it was social contact. 'We were called the fifth emergency service,' says Eddie Gadd. Alison Taffs, of Hornchurch micropub the Hop Inn, remembers having to allow more time on the delivery round for distanced chats with self-isolating customers desperate for social contact. And many businesses rallied to provide more extensive community services, as evident from those nominated for Lockdown Heroes awards by their local CAMRA branches: pubs and breweries that delivered groceries as well as beer, acted as food banks and hot meal hubs, raised substantial sums for other community charities through activities like virtual pub quizzes and many similar initiatives.

The experience made the anticipation of a return to the pub even sweeter. London's Kernel brewery, as recounted in Chapter 8, was one of those new craft arrivals that had attracted widespread admiration in the 2010s despite not producing cask regularly. But its founder Evin O'Riordain was surprised to find himself developing an unexpected thirst:

> Previously, I wouldn't go out of my way to drink cask beer, it wasn't a huge part of my life, but after the lockdowns, it was "Get me to the pub!" You can get great beer at home, but it's not the same thing. London does not have a good reputation for looking after cask but the cask beer I've had since has all been

much better, every pub seems to be cleaning their lines, people have less lines on and they're kept better and turning over faster. That's prompted us to put a few more beers in cask on a regular basis for the first time.

Some reopening breweries even reported they were overwhelmed with pent-up demand in circumstances where they weren't yet quite up to speed and short-staffed due to people leaving during the lockdowns, or, inevitably, off sick or self-isolating with Covid. The uptick is evident in the statistics: overall beer sales fell 14.2% in 2020, with cask's share reduced from 6.6% in 2019 to only 3.5%. Sales increased by 5.9% in 2021 and another 4.9% in 2022, still 4.7% down on pre-Covid levels, but cask recovered to 4.3% of the total in 2021. Contrary to expectations, the percentage of cask sold by small independent brewers who are members of SIBA increased modestly from 46% in 2022 to 53% in 2023, perhaps a sign that they're embracing 'the reopening of the on-trade, the spiritual home of the independent brewer' (Nodder 2023:19).

The long-term reduction in cask sales, though, is dramatic, down from 17% in 1980 to under 5% today, and the figures haven't turned convincingly around quite yet. If SIBA members are a bellwether, 79% of their output was still in cask in 2015, and setting aside the abnormal conditions of 2020 and 2021, today's 53% figure is what you'd expect from a continuing downward trend, as is evident from the graph below. The most recent edition of annual industry survey *The Cask Report*, the year before the pandemic struck, found that while 'there is a huge amount of love and affection on both sides of the bar for cask beer,' this was 'not generally being reflected in sales at the pumps' (Eley 2019:6). Even when the overall decline in pubs and pub visits was considered, cask was still underperforming compared to premium lager and keg pale ales, both of which had shown growth. Did conditions in the lockdowns that followed anticipate a bleak future for cask? And if it can survive, how?

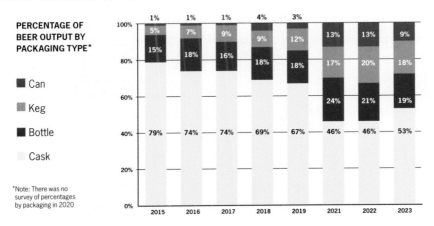

PERCENTAGE OF
BEER OUTPUT BY
PACKAGING TYPE*

■ Can

■ Keg

■ Bottle

Cask

*Note: There was no
survey of percentages
by packaging in 2020

Cask under threat?

Some people in the industry are sanguine about cask's future. Cask has been threatened before and bounced back, they say. In the 1970s it was transformed from an obsolescent beverage for elderly men to the trendsetting choice of young activists, then aged with that generation into grandad's drink again before being rediscovered in the 2000s. Something similar will happen again, at some time. 'As with many things in life, from music to fashion, food and drink go through phases and almost constant re-invention,' says Cask Marque assessor and former brewer Nigel Sadler. 'If we lost cask tomorrow,' says trainer and former licensee Annabel Smith, 'someone else would rediscover it straight away and make a success of it.' And some in the industry, particularly in parts of England that remain cask strongholds, fail to recognise any sense of crisis in their own experience: 'Cask doesn't seem to need rescuing in Yorkshire,' Tom Fozard of Rooster's in Harrogate told me.

I'm not sure this entirely accounts for the historic plummet in consumption, nor the scale of today's challenges. Overall consumption of alcoholic drinks continues to fall: 20% of respondents in a recent SIBA survey said they don't drink alcohol and 29% of today's pub visits don't involve alcohol. Contrary to some assumptions, this isn't just driven by younger people: 20% of over-55s are now abstaining too. As we saw in Chapter 7, reduced consumption can benefit more specialist and characterful products to some extent as drinkers choose to spend their units wisely, but the big volumes of the past are unlikely to return. Tom Stainer offers the insightful observation that 'cask has always been under threat, and the minute you take your attention off it and something more profitable or trendy comes along, it could disappear alarmingly quickly.'

Pub closures have accelerated as the aftermath of the lockdowns, rising energy prices, staffing issues exacerbated by Brexit, and a rocketing cost of living combine to knock many over the edge: from almost 40,000 pubs in 2019, Britain had only just over 36,500 in 2022 (Nodder 2023:20). As I write, the closure rate is estimated at 51 a month, or almost two a day (Brignall 2023). Less remarked upon but no less relevant are reductions in hours. When I first compiled my London pub and beer guide in 2011, nearly all beer outlets were reliably open from lunchtime to late evening every day, but that's no longer the case, with many places shut in the afternoon or even closed completely earlier in the week. Trade body UKHospitality reported early in 2023 that half of its members were planning to restrict winter opening hours further (Middleton and Partridge 2023).

Pub closures have accelerated in the aftermath of the lockdowns

This is all bad news for cask, which depends on communal drinking and thrives on volume and rapid consumption. More and more, the sort of low-turnover, infrequently open venue for which the big brewers originally devised keg beers is becoming the norm, and keg and small pack, with their longer shelf life and less demanding management regime, once again seem better suited to the trading environment. Such beers today, in contrast to the past, are worthy competitors to cask.

Quality

Every regular cask drinker I've ever spoken to has experienced it far more than once. It happened at one of the interviews arranged for this book, ironically enough when drinking with a cellar inspector with whom I was discussing cask quality. The sour, flat, warm pint, presented in a grease-streaked glass, or one still warm and reeking of detergent from the glass washer. There follows the internal debate about whether to complain, weighing up the likely reaction. Will your beer be changed or refunded without question and with profuse apology? Or will you get an indifferent shrug, a sigh, a scowl, a remark like 'nobody else has complained', or 'I don't drink the ales'? Or even, as I overheard on another research trip, 'It's near the end of the barrel and, believe me, people who really know their ales say that's when it's at its best.' Will the offending beer be removed and the line cleaned, or will they carry on selling it to other unfortunates, even if they replace yours? Or will you, like most consumers, simply shrug, leave most of your expensive purchase behind and go somewhere else, perhaps to drink a more reliable keg beer instead?

Beyond the horror story anecdotes, quality problems are borne out by research. Figures in 2020 showed that, although there had been some improvement in recent years, 27% of beer was still being poured through unclean lines and 22% of cask was served at the wrong temperature (Vianet 2020). Over a third of glassware is 'unfit to fill' by industry standards. Temperature problems worsen in the summer: in July 2018 a staggering near–70% of cask was served too warm, with only 26% at the recommended temperature and 2% served above 25°C. This is based on a target range of 11–13°C, but as I found, some brewers and licensees are now pushing towards the lower end and beyond, and there's evidence to show most customers prefer this too, with one survey finding 64% of drinkers would prefer it at below 11°C, including 56% of keen cask drinkers. 'Most cask ale is served far warmer than even devoted cask drinkers would like,' the most recent *Cask Report* concludes (Eley 2019:23).

Nearly all licensees say they recognise cask needs special care and are either aware of cellar advice and follow it or consider themselves expert cellar managers already. But there's clearly a gap between this perception and customer experience. Many guests disappointed with substandard beer, perhaps two-thirds of them, keep their silence, not just because they fear an unsympathetic reaction but because they lack the confidence in their own knowledge and judgement, perhaps assuming it's 'real ale and supposed to be like that', as ignorant or disingenuous bar staff sometimes say. But 40% of people served a poor cask beer will vote with their feet and never return to the offending pub.

Concerns about staff reactions aren't unfounded either. The *Cask Report* found that while 89% of publicans said they'd offer a replacement or refund to a complainant, guests found this happened only 77% of the time. '80% of publicans said they would taste the pint themselves to check it,' the report continues, 'whereas drinkers said this only happened 39% of the time; 59% said they would take the beer off sale, but only 23% of drinkers claim this happened when they complained.'

Good cask, in contrast, creates what quality advocates call a halo effect, rubbing off on the pub's reputation in other areas. Even people who don't drink cask see its presence as the sign of a 'proper' pub. Market research shows that when people drink in groups, it's normally the cask drinker who determines the choice of venue, and sometimes the choice of beer as well, as others in the group trust the 'expert' to order for them. Cask drinkers are more likely to talk about the beer, to other customers as well as bar staff, and make recommendations. They also spend more in pubs, including on food, to the tune of £1,030 a year on average in 2017.

One long-recognised problem is overambitious stocking policies. In the past, pubs typically signalled their beer-friendliness with a forest of handpumps, but falling turnover has made it increasingly difficult to empty casks while still in good condition. While there are signs that ranges are reducing, research suggests the average pub has three taps too many, including non-cask beers, while 26% of pubs still have as many as seven cask lines, including 12% with an income of less than £4,000 a week. Plenty of casks are still not being emptied on time, resulting in either expensive wastage or poor beer. 'We're trying to educate licensees,' says George Young at St Austell, 'that if you've got four handpumps on, all four beers must be in good condition. If they aren't, you shouldn't have four.'

Some 60% of drinkers, it turns out, would rather see a smaller range at a higher quality, and likely offering more of a meaningful choice. A range of six variations of amber bitters at around 4% ABV, most of them well-known brands, isn't doing much to bring in new drinkers who don't particularly like bitter and reinforces the stereotype that all cask tastes the same. 'If I go out drinking with friends after work,' says Great British Beer Festival organiser Catherine Tonry, 'the cask offering in most of the local pubs is the same three beers, all similar in style. Those same pubs have a far wider variety of keg beers.' Contrast this with the well-run micropub that may only offer three or four cask beers at one time but ensures they always include a lower-alcohol session option, a dark beer, something stronger or more exotic, and plenty of local brands, all in top condition of course.

One way of maintaining a wider range with lower turnover is by using smaller casks, thus the recent surge of interest in 4½ gallon (20.5 l) pins which are half the size of the more typical firkins (9 gallons, 40.9 l). Pins are more comparable to the 20 or 30 l, or sometimes even smaller, containers used for speciality keg, a product with a longer shelf life. There are issues for the brewer here: the pins themselves are almost as expensive and involve just as much hassle and expense in filling, delivering, collecting, cleaning and maintaining as firkins, and not all beers behave well in them. Timothy Taylor's Tim Dewey thinks they're an illusory solution. 'You need to think more fundamentally about starting with a smaller range, do that well and build the business up as we get more and more people into cask,' he says. But others are offering more in pins, especially if pubs are prepared to take two of them for every one firkin they previously ordered. In January 2023 major player Greene King announced a 'seven figure' investment in pins for its seasonal beers as a way of increasing variety while 'minimising wastage and maximising profits' (Lloyd 2023).

Another obvious quality gap is in cellar skills, further exacerbated by experienced hospitality staff moving to other jobs during the lockdowns and not coming back. But the lack of mandatory training has been an issue since long before the pandemic, as Annabel Smith points out:

> Anyone can take the keys to a pub not knowing how to clean lines, not knowing how to look after cask. If I went for a job in a pub kitchen, I'd have to have at least a basic food hygiene certificate. And yet we let people with absolutely no skills or knowledge handle beer. Personally, I think it would be fabulous if a basic beer certificate was mandatory but no one in the industry is going to push for that, so we need to encourage voluntary training as best we can. Licensees and pubcos often don't appreciate the importance of training for beer, it falls to the bottom of the pile, even though seven out of 10 alcoholic drinks passing across the bar are beers.

Annabel manages the training programme for Cask Marque (introduced in Chapter 7). Executive director Paul Nunny points to research showing training can increase annual profits by 3% and improve yields of saleable beer by 1.7%,

What is Cask Marque accreditation?

A badge of honour to show that your outlet serves great quality cask ale.

How is the quality measured?

Scores out of 5 for temperature, appearance, aroma and taste on each beer. All beers must score 16/20 to pass. Consistently serve all your cask ales according to best practice, and your pub will definitely qualify!

What's the process?

An inspector calls! You provide free samples of up to 6 cask ales. Each one is tested according to temperature, appearance, aroma and taste. 'Scores on the Cellar Doors' are audited for new applicants. (www.sotcd.co.uk).

Who are the assessors?

Highly qualified, hugely experienced experts from the brewing industry. They introduce themselves – and carry photo ID.

CASK MARQUE BEER

SIGN OF A GREAT PINT

How do we pass?

Serve all your cask ales in perfect condition! Unless they are marketed as cloudy, unpasteurised or un-fined, they should be bright and clear. There shouldn't be any 'off' aromas or flavours. There should be a tingle-on-the-tongue from the naturally-produced carbon dioxide. They should be served at 11 – 13oC. If any are over 15oC, you will fail.

What do we get for passing?

Membership of Cask Marque. A plaque for outside your pub. A framed certificate, drip mats, bar runners and pump clip stickers. Inclusion on the CaskFinder app, which gets 60,000 visits a month. Your pub becoming part of the World's Biggest Ale Trail. The chance to share your success via press releases and social media.

How often do assessors visit?

Twice a year, normally 6 months apart. 10% of Cask Marque pubs get an additional surprise visit.

01206 752212
info@cask-marque.co.uk
www.cask-marque.co.uk

significant figures in an industry where margins are tight. Many of the bigger brewers and pubcos have their own training and quality assurance schemes, sometimes including awards for the best-performing cellars. Yet 30% of licensees aren't happy with the level of training and support they receive with cask, rising to 67% in pubs with the smallest turnover. At the other extreme, everyone involved with improving cask quality has encountered the self-appointed experts who have been institutionalising bad habits for decades and refuse to change.

And it's a particular challenge to raise standards in a sector known for low pay, unsocial hours, high staff turnover and low commitment from staff who are typically young and just starting out on their careers. Bar work, to many who do it, is a casual, temporary job, a bit of extra cash while studying or on a gap year or to keep the wolf from the door until you find something better. Why should workers take the time to train and study, and why should managers and employers invest in people who might move on at any time? Improving the pay and status of such work seems particularly challenging right now, though remains crucial. Meanwhile, Annabel Smith points out that hospitality already offers one of the fastest career paths of any industry, 'from bottle wash to boardroom', for people with a genuine vocation.

Curiously, the specific challenges of cask are also opportunities for keen staff to engage at a more interesting and fulfilling level. Annabel cites her own experience in entering the industry as a way of earning quick money after leaving university and lucking out in a cask-led pub where the landlord inspired her with his own enthusiasm and knowledge. Within six months, she'd become a licensee herself. Mark Hyson, now head of sales at Stewart Brewing, fell in love with cask when his parents ran the Tollbooth Tavern on Edinburgh's famous Royal Mile. For him, as for many other cellar heroes, the challenges were part of the attraction: 'I very much enjoyed looking after it,' he told me, 'making sure it was stored properly, vented properly, poured properly, and seeing it through to the perfect final pint.'

At Theakston in Masham, Simon Theakston expressed similar sentiments:

> Looking after cask ale is complex but not complicated. Once you learn what to do, it becomes routine and is very straightforward. Our challenge is to encourage licensees not to be fearful of cask, and to explain to them that, critically, it gives them a chance to demonstrate their expertise to their customers and to distinguish themselves from the competition. Cask ale allows a licensee to acquire a saleable skill. It's not an entirely precise science, there are variations, every single cellar is different, it depends on the pub and the consumers and what they prefer.

Price

This may well be the point at which I lose some readers, but it must be said: if cask beer is to have a sustainably healthy future, its average price will have to rise in comparison to the pub prices of other drinks. It's a fragile product typically made in small batches at artisanal and labour-intensive breweries and requiring time and skill to serve at its best, yet it's long been cheaper than big brand keg lager, which is longer-lasting, easier to manage and typically made in large batches at giant automated facilities with significant economies of scale. While the average pint of cask bitter cost £3.57 in January 2023, the average pint of standard lager was 18.5% more expensive at £4.23 (Weller 2023).

At prices like these, both brewers and licensees struggle to make a decent living from brewing and selling decent cask beer, further worsening the challenges of improving quality through investment and training. That's one of the reasons many brewers are shifting towards keg, bottled and canned beer as these formats aren't dogged by expectations of low prices. Siren, a much-admired contemporary brewery, put half its beer into cask when it began in 2013. Today, the figure is under 10%. Founder Darron Anley explains:

> I love cask, I love drinking it and making it, but I hate it from a business perspective, it's not treated with the respect that it's due and publicans and consumers expect a price point that has no relation to the product. We know we're not going to get the same value per litre from beer in cask compared to keg. We do it solely because we still like drinking cask and it's useful to have the mix but the impact on the margin is tough to bear. There are pubs used to buying firkins for £50-60 each and then buying three and getting one free: I can't believe you can sell beer at those prices sustainably without cutting corners. Even with the maximum discount we won't sell a cask for less than £80 and we're still taking a hit. If those price expectations don't change, the quality and variety will continue to diminish.

An even more confounding aspect of cask pricing is its lack of differentiation. It's typically determined by alcohol content, reflecting the gradation in duty levels, rather than recipe or provenance. Big pub groups decide what they're prepared to pay based on ABV bands alone. I've even seen similar price scales displayed in pubs. It's hard to think of a comparable product priced this way: nobody would expect to pay the same for, say, an unpretentious blended Pinot Grigio and a vintage premier cru Burgundy just because they're both 13% ABV. The mindset is perpetuated by the media habit of intermittently highlighting

Cloisters Bar, Edinburgh.

BREWERY	BEER	ORIGIN	STYLE	ABV	PRICE
BLACK ISLE	YELLOWHAMMER	MUNLOCHY	PALE	4.0	4.50
STEWART	PENTLAND IPA	EDINBURGH	IPA	3.9	4.30
SWANNAY	THE DUKE	ORKNEY	IPA	5.2	5.20
VERDANT/MENDARIS	EQUIVELENT	LEITH	IPL	4.5	5.00
CROSSBORDERS	HEAVY	DALKEITH	80/-	4.1	3.95
SIREN	UNDERCURRENT	WOKINGHAM	AMERICAN PALE	4.5	5.00
TWO BY TWO	SESSION IPA	WALLSEND	HAZY IPA	4.0	4.60
TEMPEST	PALE ARMADILLO	TWEEDBANK	SESSION IPA	3.8	4.50
TINY REBEL	SLEIGH PUFF... THE PURPLE ONE	NEWPORT	CARAMEL MARSHMALLOW CHOC STOUT	5.2	4.80
WINDSWEPT	APA	LOSSIEMOUTH	AMERICAN PALE ALE	5.0	5.00
KEG BLACK ISLE	ISLE OF DOGS	MUNLOCHY	ORGANIC COFFEE MILK STOUT	8.1	4.00½
KEG PILOT	PEACH MELBA	LEITH	SOUR	4.3	6.30
KEG TEMPEST	MANGO MOON	TWEEDBANK	MANGO + LIME SOUR	4.5	5.20⅔
KEG STEWART	HAZY IPA	EDINBURGH	HAZY IPA	5.0	5.40
KEG ARBOR	MOSAIC	BRISTOL	GF PALE	4.0	5.70

HOUSE KEGS...
BUDVAR - LAGER - CZECHIA
5.0% - £5.40
LUKAS - LAGER - UK - GF
4.2% - £5.00
HOGANS CIDER
WARWICKSHIRE 4.5% - £4.80

...HOUSE KEGS (CONT)
BLONDE - LAGER - 4.5%ABV
- BLACK ISLE - £5.20
PORTER - PORTER - 4.6%
- BLACK ISLE - £5.40

'Britain's most expensive beer' in clickbait headlines, inevitably something strong, rare and imported, and likely at a price that wine enthusiasts would consider a bargain for something of equivalent quality.

When beer was an everyday staple, its price was a question of national import and often subject to government intervention, but even in the 18th century prices varied dramatically between different styles depending on their production cost. World War I legislation formalised a link between price and strength, but for much of the 20th century it was accepted, for example, that bitter would be more expensive than mild. Overall, though, beer was the drink of the labouring classes and there was considerable consumer pressure to keep prices down.

Today's levelled mindset developed following ABV labelling in the 1980s and a race to the bottom in the wake of the Beer Orders in the 1990s, when big pubcos exercised their buying muscle to push down wholesale prices so they could attract customers through discounting. CAMRA once also campaigned for lower prices, and its persistence in promoting discounts as a membership benefit remains controversial: in 2020, 110 brewers signed an open letter urging the campaign to drop the practice. 'A consumer organisation that prices its favoured product out of existence does not make any sense,' commented Phil Saltonstall of Brass Castle, who initiated the action.

Timothy Taylor is much admired within the industry for its hard-nosed approach to selling its beers for what they're worth. Proudly framed on the boardroom wall is an exchange of correspondence from 2005 between a buyer from a major pub group and then-managing director Charles Dent, who in refusing to sell firkins of Landlord at a 40% discount drily states that 'should you ever wish to reconsider your general policy and stock for quality rather than cheapness, I enclose the product description of all our beers'.

Current chief executive Tim Dewey, an American-born outsider with a background in spirits, is baffled by cask pricing practices. He recounts a discussion soon after he joined in 2014 with a licensee who, though he loved Taylor's beer, planned on dropping it as it was too expensive. 'Why don't you just sell it for 40p more per pint?' asked Tim. 'Oh no, I can't do that,' said the licensee. 'All my cask beers have to be the same price.' At his elbow was a small blackboard promoting the pub's gin-and-tonic menu, with a choice of six different gins at numerous price points. 'Why is it that you can charge £4 extra for a premium gin-and-tonic but you can't ask 40p more for a beer?' asked Tim. He didn't get a satisfactory reply. 'I blame the industry,' he tells me, 'for allowing its product to become commoditised, as if all beers are created equal.'

One argument for cheap cask is that it helps drive sufficient turnover to keep the product fresh, but that effect has surely reached its limits when price becomes a barrier to maintaining quality. Of course, nobody wants to pay more, but nobody wants to pay for poor beer either, no matter how cheap. And there's surprising evidence to show drinkers are prepared to dig deeper. In 2022 price was only the second consideration for cask beer drinkers, after flavour, that determined their beer choice; in 2021, it had been in third place, after style. Another survey found that over half of respondents, including over half of committed cask drinkers, didn't even realise that cask was typically cheaper than mainstream lager: 24% thought it was more expensive. Cask Marque concluded in 2018 that up to 67% of cask drinkers would be prepared to pay more for a well-kept beer – so long as they could be confident of brewers and licensees keeping their side of the bargain in delivering quality.

Nonetheless, a CAMRA-sponsored survey in 2022 found that, with the overall cost of living rapidly escalating, over half the wider population now consider draught beer unaffordable (2022c). Price increases are partly driven by cost increases, but a significant component of the price is taxation. Between 2008 and 2013 duty was hiked annually by 2% above inflation under the much-resented 'beer duty escalator' policy, and though it's since decreased in real terms due to inflation, it remains the third highest in Europe. The full rate for a pint of 5% beer in the UK amounts to 54p, lower than only Finland (92p) and Ireland (55p); at the other end of the scale are Germany (4.6p), Luxembourg (4.6p) and Bulgaria (4.5p) (Fish 2022:58). The exchequer takes a further slice as VAT at 20%, amounting to 67p for a £4 pint.

Not everyone pays the full duty: as recounted in Chapter 7, since 2002 smaller brewers have been entitled to up to 50% off thanks to Small Brewers Relief (SBR). This partly explains the accelerated increase in brewery numbers, but it's not been universally welcomed, with some larger operators considering it an unfair distortion of the marketplace. It may even have contributed to lowering cask prices, used in some cases to offer discounts rather than drive quality and growth. In 2017 a group of mainly larger players began actively pressing for the 'reform' of SBR in a way that would greatly reduce entitlement to the full 50% discount. Following several years of industry debates, furious lobbying, mixed messaging and delays, the government finally confirmed in the 2023 budget that it would introduce new rules in August 2023.

Though the fine detail has still to be confirmed at the time of writing, it seems that at least some of the views of organisations like CAMRA and SIBA have been considered and the changes won't be as damaging to small and independent brewers as initially proposed, though some will undoubtedly find themselves with increased duty bills. Concessions will be extended to cider and perry makers and the scheme accordingly renamed Small Producers Relief (SPR), though discounts will be calculated according to the total amount of alcohol produced and not on beer volumes as previously. A lower duty rate will apply below 3.5% ABV, rather than 2.8% as at present, and a higher rate at 8.5% rather than 7.5%. An additional 9.2% duty discount will be granted on drinks supplied in containers of at least 20 l capacity, which includes all traditional cask sizes, even pins, and all but the smallest kegs. This last refinement is potentially good news for cask beer and the hospitality trade, so long as it's invested wisely in improvements rather than used simply to drive down prices further.

Image and awareness

I've spoken to many keen cask drinkers who agree their favourite beverage has an image problem. Some of them even see themselves as part of it, particularly if they're ageing, bearded men with at least a passing resemblance to the 'Real Ale Twats' created by comic artist Davey Jones for the comic *Viz*. As the 2019 *Cask Report* circumspectly puts it, 'cask ale is perceived to be a drink enjoyed mainly by old men. As such, it lacks aspirational intrigue and appears to be a little stuck in the past.' (Eley 2019:16).

But when I spoke to fellow beer writer Pete Brown in his capacity as project manager of a new initiative to improve cask's image, he robustly told me they were ignoring all that, as potential new drinkers don't raise the negative stereotypes unprompted, and research found only 8% of people cite image as a barrier. 'When you ask people why they don't drink it,' he said, 'the most common answer is simply "I don't know". We just need to tell them things about cask that are relevant to them.'

At the time of writing, the Drink Cask Fresh campaign is a pilot project backed by a collective of breweries and trade and consumer bodies that's working in 27 pubs across England through a variety of means, from materials like beermats and posters to staff briefings and information sheets, branded glassware, T-shirts and brightly coloured zip-up sleeves for pump handles to help them stand out on the bar, alongside encouragement to licensees to maintain cellar quality. The target pubs are everyday locals rather than 'cask shrines', and each has been paired with a similar 'control' pub nearby where the intervention isn't happening. The key messages are admirably succinct: cask is a fresh, gently carbonated beer that tastes good, is served at cool cellar temperature, is probably made in small batches by a local or regional brewery, and hasn't travelled far to reach you.

Drink Cask Fresh handpull branding

The results should have been reported by the time you read this, and, if encouraging, the concept will be rolled out further, but the approach is itself fresh. Rather than struggling to make grandad look hip with a superficially trendy makeover, it's focused on the things we know really matter to today's drinkers. Pete says he was initially sceptical about the emphasis on freshness, and it played uncertainly with some of the brewery supporters who were concerned it would suggest their non-cask beers weren't fresh. But having seen evidence that it's the second-most important factor to many drinkers after flavour, and the reactions at focus groups, he's changed his mind. There's certainly room here to challenge drinkers' perceptions: preliminary research found that most of them believed the freshest beer available was bottled lager.

The research found that many of the features cask advocates typically emphasise simply don't resonate with ordinary drinkers and can sometimes even put them off. 'Nobody outside the beer bubble knows anything about secondary fermentation and conditioning,' says Pete. 'Mention live yeast and some people run a mile, particularly women. We showed focus groups the technical definition of real ale and when it got to the bit about a significant reduction in gravity, their response was "what the **** are you talking about?".' Much better, then, to raise awareness of cask's flavour and character and the way it meets contemporary concerns for a generally moderate alcohol content, local hands-on production, and sustainability – part of what marketing experts call a product's 'story', where it comes from and the people who make it. CAMRA's recent increased emphasis on beer education is also particularly timely.

One way cask is taken for granted is that many retailers see little need to boast that they're even selling it. Pub websites and social media pages, increasingly important in helping drinkers plan their night out, typically include extensive information about food, wines, spirits, cocktails, soft drinks and, often, keg, bottled and canned beers. But look for the cask offer and you may well find an unhelpful statement that they also stock 'a selection of real ales' or some out-of-date photos of handpumps. It's often the same on the ground, with cask choices curiously absent from printed menus and the range only obvious from looking at the bar. It's because the cask lines tend to change more frequently than the other drinks, and whoever compiles the information has decided it's not worth making the effort to keep up with them, which sends out a troubling message in itself. And a stand of handpumps with unfamiliar pump clips can make a drinker feel pressured and reluctant to betray their ignorance, making them more likely to default to a familiar keg brand.

That barrier is easily addressed with correct and up-to-date information clearly on display onsite and online, detailing the ABV, colour and style for each available cask brand. Brief tasting notes using familiar and positive terms can help, as can notes on origin, particularly if a beer is local, and highlighting certain beers as 'today's top session choice', 'staff favourite' and so on. There's also strong evidence for 'try before you buy' policies, but only if they're promoted through signs and notices, and staff actively proffer samples when they notice guests deliberating, as asking for one in the absence of such encouragement is daunting. Promoting cask beer with food is another opportunity particularly appealing to new drinkers.

Measures and glassware are another known issue – as mentioned in Chapter 2, traditional glasses don't flatter the product, and many potential drinkers are put off by the perceived need to commit to such a large quantity as a pint, so anything that reassures them smaller measures are available will help. Drink Cask Fresh commissioned elegant, stemmed tulip glasses in both pint and two-thirds sizes, the latter lined for a half-pint: some pubs complained that their regular drinkers didn't like them, for which the simple answer was to offer traditional glasses to the established cask drinkers who aren't the primary targets of the campaign.

One of the most powerful marketing tools is, of course, word of mouth. Licensees and staff who are enthusiastic and knowledgeable about cask are not only more likely to keep it better but to encourage others to drink it. You'll know the type: the person who makes you feel you're being invited to share a positive experience with them rather than simply buying a product.

Bar staff tend to be younger and less likely to drink cask already, so encouraging them to discover it through formal and informal training is vital. In the past, Cask Marque training focused primarily on technical matters like cellar management, but its most recent, and highly accessible, Beer Pro e-learning modules for bar staff also cover beer knowledge and communications, including the need

to taste and learn a little about the beers on sale so you can make confident recommendations and 'upsell' when the opportunity arises. This might help improve on the results of a 2017 survey that found only 10% of drinkers thought bar staff were the most knowledgeable about cask beer. But 50% acknowledged brewers' expertise, giving a rationale for 'meet the brewer' evenings and similar events (Atherton 2017:31).

There are, nonetheless, demographic factors that shape consumption, recognised, among others, by CAMRA, which is currently prioritising diversity and inclusion. Beer in general is stereotypically considered a man's drink: a 2017 survey for Dea Latis, a group which works to encourage women both to drink beer and to work in the industry, found that while 40% of men named it as the alcoholic drink they choose most often, only 9% of women did the same, a figure that hadn't changed significantly since similar research in 2009. A survey for the *Cask Report* the same year found that, while 31% of men said cask was the beer they generally choose, only 16% of women said the same, and 35% had never tried cask, compared to only 15% of men. This confirms what we know anecdotally. 'My other half likes cocktails,' says Annabel Smith, 'and sometimes we go out and I order a beer for me and a Margarita for him. They always put the Margarita in front of me.'

The discrepancies have doubtless been reinforced by many decades of marketing primarily targeted at men, sometimes in the crudest ways. In response to mounting pressure from influential industry figures, CAMRA and SIBA banned beers with sexist names and labelling from their competitions in 2017 and this, together with increasing awareness and changing attitudes, has placed some of the most egregious examples beyond the pale. But there's an argument that some beer marketing continues to favour male audiences in more subtle ways. Research also points to serving quantities, glassware and false beliefs about calorie content (see Chapter 4) as barriers to women.

The Dea Latis survey found, though, that an overwhelming 83% of women who didn't drink beer said this was because that they didn't like the taste. Can taste really be gender-specific, wondered the authors (Smith and Harlow 2018:25)? As mentioned in Chapter 4, women generally have more sensitive palates than men, so may find humans' instinctive wariness of bitter flavours harder to overcome. But that doesn't explain why, while only 13% of beer in Britain is consumed by women, the figures are very different elsewhere: for example, 44% in Spain and 61% in Turkey. Other bitter-tasting foods and drinks, like certain greens and strong black coffee, are enjoyed more readily in those countries too. It's therefore more likely that social factors and marketing in the UK create more barriers to 'acquiring' the taste of beer for women than for men.

The answer is to encourage more people, women and men, to taste more beer, including cask, in a wider range of styles, and to ensure everyone's first experience of beer is as good as it can be. Tasting experts' standard answer to someone who says they don't like beer is that they just haven't found one they like yet, especially as the more mainstream examples, which most of us are first acquainted with, cover only a restricted sample of the full spectrum of flavour. What the industry certainly shouldn't do is to produce a 'beer for women', as several big brewers have attempted: the resulting products have all been withdrawn after disappointing sales and been widely excoriated and ridiculed as patronising and reductionist, as if all women are likely to have the same tastes.

While 33% of people aged 55–64 say they generally choose to drink cask beer, the figure drops to 18% for those aged 18–20, 29% of whom have never sampled it. The need to educate younger bar staff and to offer opportunities to try cask apply here too. But perhaps we should also reconsider the common practice of describing cask as 'traditional', an adjective which came top of the list in a 2018 survey that invited people to distinguish 'craft beer' from 'real ale'. It undoubtedly has positive connotations, like reliability, comfort and familiarity – occasional drinkers are more likely to order cask on leisure visits to rural pubs. 'Cask is a part of history and uniquely British and yet it's still a living, existing, vibrant industry, which is so important,' says Tom Stainer. But tradition is a double-edged sword and perhaps we're leaning a little too much on the fusty, nationalistic and conservative side. 'Tradition isn't a decent enough argument for a younger drinker,' says Annabel Smith. 'Cask isn't a tradition they recognise.'

The ambivalence extends to that widely recognised badge of cask beer, the handpump. Surveys show that even non-beer drinkers see their presence as the sign of a 'proper' pub in the positive sense, and overseas visitors regard them alongside red telephone kiosks and Routemaster buses as British icons. But according to recent *Cask Reports*, they've become 'recessive on the bar', failing to stand out among the ever more eye-catching keg taps. Some breweries have come up with smart ways of redesigning them as more modern and prominent while remaining recognisable, and the Drink Cask Fresh sleeves are a quick fix for the standard models. But there's a balance to be struck in modernising an image without losing the recognition and other positive attributes it already possesses, instead of trying to present cask as something it's not.

One thing cask certainly is, though, by any reasonable definition, is craft beer, and perhaps we should be more robust in challenging the artificial distinction that's arisen between them, taking our cue from Batemans' bold statement that it's been a craft brewer 'since 1874'. 'Cask is our craft,' says Ol Fozard. 'It's the ultimate craft beer,' agrees Sara Barton, and many others echo these sentiments.

'Ask for cask, the original craft beer', runs a slogan on one of the Drink Cask Fresh beermats. I particularly agree with the brewer who describes cask as Britain's lambic, invoking one of the world's most revered styles among connoisseurs. The comparison goes further: lambic, which is also characterised by its unusual fermentation methods, once almost disappeared in its home country because it was taken for granted and insufficiently loved and respected. Andy Slee of SIBA has another pointed comparison: 'Can you imagine the French ever asking if Champagne was worth saving during a period of poor sales?' he asks.

Outside the UK, many brewers regard cask similarly as an international beer treasure and one of the real tests of the brewers' skill: they're concerned about its decline, and bemused by attempts to distinguish it from craft beer. The corollary is that we need to *treat* it as a craft beer, a product made and presented with pride, love and care at a fair price that reflects its quality, something that could be enjoyed by anyone, and which deserves to have its story told.

Cask is truly a thing of beauty.
OWEN OGLETREE, Atlanta Cask Ale Tasting

Niche cask

Just east of Ballyferriter village, a stone's throw from the coast on southwest Ireland's remote and picturesque Dingle peninsula, stands the Tig Bhric ('Bric's House') pub. Surprisingly, given the location, it's a brewpub, home to Beoir Chorcha Dhuibhne (the West Kerry Brewery). Even more surprisingly, its flagship brand is a 3.8% cask dark mild. Owner and brewer Adrienne Heslin explains:

As we're on the Wild Atlantic Way tourist driving route, we regularly had visitors calling in requesting local beer and at that time, in 2008, there was none, so I thought of adding a brewery. I had my own well so that was a good start. But I only had a small budget and by coincidence the kit I bought second-hand was set up to brew cask for handpump dispense, with open fermentation vessels. When I realised, I thought what on earth have I done, as hardly anyone in Ireland was doing cask. But the visitors didn't mind at all, they just wanted a local product. The locals had zero interest at first, but over time the cask has made us a beer destination and when our neighbours in their 60s switched to it from Guinness I was really proud. We went into bottling in 2012 as restaurants nearby wanted a local beer, and added keg in 2015, so compared to most Irish craft breweries we did it all backwards. The mild works best for us, so it's all we do in cask now, particularly as most customers drive here and appreciate the low ABV. It's a very pleasant beer for someone who drives past our door at 11 in the morning after a big breakfast.

Adrienne Heslin

Cask beer was once common in Ireland, but, aside from a few small breweries in the north set up in the wake of CAMRA, it's long been almost entirely displaced by keg and nitrokeg, thanks largely to the stranglehold of big groups, primarily Guinness/Diageo, and one of the most antiquated and restrictive licensing systems in Europe. The craft beer movement has pushed the island's brewery total over 100, and many of them are excellent, but their output is nearly all in keg, bottle and can. Corca Dhuibhne stands out, not only because it makes delicious beer, but because its approach is so unusual, helped by its remarkable location. Adrienne tells me efforts to sell cask outside the pub have largely foundered on a lack of knowledge, skill and turnover in other potential outlets.

The situation is similar in other countries where regular cask brewers and retailers are a tiny minority in a much bigger craft beer community, and where their customers are 'repertoire' drinkers who enjoy cask alongside other beers. The big challenge facing such specialists is the lack of support infrastructure and equipment, and customer familiarity. One of the advantages is that they have no choice but to be dedicated enthusiasts, always striving for quality and constantly proselytising to their customers. Another advantage is that they can promote, and price, cask as an unusual speciality on its own terms alongside other beers without all the baggage it carries in the UK.

'Cask is very much what we are about,' says Mary Beth Keefe, brewmaster at her family's Granite brewpub in Toronto, Canada, a veteran of North American cask brewing that still uses one of pioneer Peter Austin's kits installed in 1990 and a house yeast originally from Ringwood. 'We have many regulars who come here to drink it exclusively.' This isn't surprising given the quality of beers, like the regular best bitter and rare English-style IPA, where 'the lack of forced carbonation allows for the flavours to really shine'. Granite styles itself after the very best traditional English pubs, but Toronto also boasts another small cask producer, Bar Volo, pairing beers like a superb dark mild with Italian-inspired food, because owner Raffaele Morana loves both, in an environment that's more *osteria* than alehouse.

Though casks in the US are sometimes hapless receptacles for one-off specials in inappropriate styles, a handful of brewers strive to offer more sensible core brands, supplying outlets equipped to look after them on a regular basis. Steve Hamburg, the Cask Marque assessor for the whole of the country, tentatively suggests the scene may be growing again after the lockdowns and has a personal list of recommendations that runs into double figures, but admits that some of the venues that approach him back down when they realise they're unlikely to meet the standards. The US craft scene's historic fondness for big flavours and high strengths doesn't favour cask, but an increasing shift towards lower alcohol session beers is helping.

Bluejacket in Washington DC is part of a small chain of East Coast breweries, bars and restaurants where cask always forms part of the offer, thanks to the enthusiasm of those behind it, including co-owner Greg Engert. Greg's outlets sell other people's cask too, and he echoes Steve in noting a modest resurgence of interest as the craze for more extreme beers subsides. He sometimes imports British cask beer – 'it can travel well, and has', he insists – and organises collaborations with breweries like Fyne Ales. The group's best known beer venue is ChurchKey, also in Washington, with three cask lines, typically session styles like golden ales, bitters and porters, particularly appealing to drinkers looking for lower ABVs, alongside 50 kegs and hundreds of bottles and cans. It's not a big money-making thing, especially given the extra cellar care, and they're keen to keep the cask affordable: currently it's around $7 (£5.60) an imperial pint, essentially London prices. Greg comments:

> If I was just concerned with sales, I wouldn't be doing half the things we do. The reason I'm in the business is obviously to make a living, but also to showcase some of the greatest flavours, textures, aromas, tastes in the world, and that's not done simply by responding to what we believe the public wants, otherwise craft beer never would have happened. Cask is a great microcosm of that, that gentle bead and rounded malt character, it's a wonderful opportunity for my staff and myself to talk about beer, to share narratives and histories, to create the singular experience of eating and drinking at our restaurants and bars. I'd like to believe we're creating new fans.

Another cask enthusiast is Dave Blanchard, owner of the celebrated Brick Store in Decatur, a suburb of Atlanta, Georgia, which, since 2021, has boasted a dedicated cask bar with four lines and its own cellar in a previously underused upstairs space. They've worked intensively with local breweries to stock it, but they're also currently the only pub in the world selling a cask version of Sierra Nevada Pale Ale. Dave was advised by local beer enthusiast and tour leader Owen Ogletree, who fell so deeply in love with cask on visits to the UK that he bought his own firkins and persuaded local brewers to fill them, founding the annual Atlanta Cask Beer Tasting event in 2005. 'A perfect pint of proper ale will change your life,' says Dave. 'The only problem is carrying all those firkins up a flight of stairs.'

Hogshead Brewery was set up in 2012 in one of the US's leading craft beer cities, Denver, Colorado, specifically to brew cask, though it now sometimes offers the same beer on cask and keg for comparison in the taproom and does craft lagers too. 'Cask beer is our niche in the otherwise saturated local beer market,' says manager David Liechty, stressing that the theatre is part of the experience: 'The actual pulling of the pint, the cascading of the beer and then the ultimate engagement of taking that first sip.' Head brewer Robert Bell says lack of resources, knowledge and experience are barriers to selling cask more widely in the US. 'For us', he says, 'it's a passion project that has separated us from a slew of other breweries and has, literally, helped sustain us through tough times.'

Interest in cask extends to places like Italy and Scandinavia, and though UK cask exports are miniscule, they're not unknown: you may, for example, find Marble in Finland or Rooster's in Sweden, as options in the broader craft repertoire.

While such initiatives seem at first glance to have little relevance to the UK market, they're not that far from the labours of love at the Kernel or Siren. And UK customers, too, are increasingly repertoire drinkers, or what Tom Stainer calls 'dispense agnostic' – not loyal to any one format. 'We have the advantage that if someone who knows the Kernel sees one of our cask beers on, they'll consider it something special,' says Evin O'Riordain.

Similar considerations apply at Deya Brewing in Cheltenham, founded by Theo Freyne in 2015 after homebrewing, training at Heriot-Watt, and interning at several US breweries. Deya built its reputation on contemporary hoppy and mixed fermentation beers in keg and small pack, but following expansion in 2019, introduced a changing range of cask beers, mainly in more traditional session styles, partly because Theo loves cask for its creamy mouthfeel and elusive hop character, and he and his brewers love working with it. I suggested it was a natural progression given the drinkability of the brewery's flagship Steady Rolling Man

DEYA taproom, Cheltenham

hazy pale ale (5.2%): they do an annual cask version, which works surprisingly well, but the other recipes are specifically devised for the format. Like many others, he finds the margins on cask prohibitively tight and though the format accounts for only 3% of output it is seen as 'massively valuable and a fun part of what we do. Settling into a proper pub with good cask beer, you can't go wrong.'

Then there's the local factor. In its early days, like several comparable businesses in provincial locations, Deya relied on long-distance sales to specialist outlets, but its local identity has becoming increasingly important, and its taproom is now a recognised feature of community life. Cask plays well to this, partly because many pubs in this rugby-oriented area are still cask-focused, partly because, even if cask can be shipped successfully across oceans with effort, it's at its freshest close to home. Local provenance matters to drinkers too. Pete Brown cites two surveys where almost 40% of respondents said they drank cask because it was typically brewed locally.

Even before Covid-19, some brewers had begun to retrench their markets: a decade ago, Batemans was pushing for a regular presence in national pub groups and supermarket chains, but now positions itself primarily as a Lincolnshire brewer supplying its own region. Hook Norton now concentrates on selling direct to pubs and consumers closer to home rather than national distribution. 'We're a historic brewery: we can't brew beer cheaply here,' says managing director James Clarke. 'But we can offer our licensees a good quality service and we've also diversified, with our visitor centre and tours and things like hiring out the brewery as a wedding venue. That's a better focus than trying to cut cask prices.'

Eddie Gadd was reminded of local support during the lockdowns:

When we ran our home delivery service, the customers were so appreciative. Never once did someone say, "I can get it cheaper somewhere else" or "I'll pay you next week". I realised these are the people I make my beer for, not the publicans who only want us every three months because we're on rotation and are constantly bickering about the price. I didn't want to go back to that, so I told the office, I want just 50 likeable, friendly customers within a reasonable distance who buy at least once a fortnight and don't have a history of late payment or being awkward. We got our 50 customers and we bend over backwards for them, spoiling them rotten, but on service, not on prices. We're now a parochial business in East Kent.

Cask's resurgent local identity is masked somewhat by sales of a few big national brands which enjoyed a post-lockdown bounce. Trade paper the *Morning Advertiser* even gave its story announcing the 2022 market leaders the provocative headline 'Who says cask is in decline?':

Best selling UK cask beer brands 2022 *(Morning Advertiser 2022)*

RANK	BRAND	ABV	OWNER	VOLUME hl	VALUE £million
1	Sharp's Doom Bar	4%	Molson Coors	163,281	101.1
2	Timothy Taylor Landlord	4.3%	Independent	103,599	74.4
3	Greene King IPA	3.6%	Greene King	91,884	60
4	Fuller's London Pride	4.1%	Asahi	72,242	54
5	Greene King Abbot Ale	5%	Greene King	50,982	31.3
6	St Austell Tribute	4.2%	St Austell	40,698	28.9
7	Wainwright	4.1%	Carlsberg	40,628	25.5
8	Marston's Pedigree	4.5%	Carlsberg	33,298	20.3
9	Butcombe Original	4%	Liberation	22,351	14.2
10	Young's London Original	3.7%	Carlsberg	17,349	13.6

While most of the brands listed are produced by national and international groups, there are some interesting exceptions. Timothy Taylor's refusal to compromise on both quality and price has clearly paid off, and the presence of Tribute is testament to the inspiration, skill and hard work at St Austell. Both beers are available a long way from home. Butcombe Original, in contrast, is a regional brand, a much-loved must-stock in its heartland of Somerset and surrounding parts of southwest England, but not widely encountered elsewhere. Its debut appearance in the 2022 Top 10 may be a sign of things to come.

One of Titanic's new Bod Bars

Pete Brown suggests the recovery of national brands is a short-lived post-lockdown effect driven less by drinkers and more by nervous licensees reducing ranges and defaulting to the familiar. And the big national and regional groups that still dominate retail continue to insulate many pubs from their local beer culture: the 2016 *Cask Report* found only a quarter of licensees had special relationships with breweries from their own area. But research suggests this might ultimately prove self-defeating. 'The traditional model of chain pubs stocking global brands may be declining,' CAMRA London director Geoff Strawbridge told me in 2021, 'but the real story is the excitement of London's local breweries, its taprooms and its independent pubs.'

Perhaps the time has come (or is already overdue) for the 'premiumisation' of cask, repositioning it as a specialist product like fine wine, artisanal cheese or gourmet chocolate, with a strong sense of place. Consider a return to the days of pubs offering only a bitter, mild and 'old ale/special' on cask, except that these would be locally sourced, top-quality, immaculately kept products in pride of place on the bar. Or even pubs that meet the expectations of the proud brewpub owner Tim Webb encountered in Brazil in 2022, who believed his venue's three handpulls dispensing IPA, porter and imperial stout represented a typically British offer.

Given its current low market share, its weighty reputation, and the fact that 69% of its regular drinkers are in the so-called 'ABC1 demographic' of people in professional and administrative roles, cask is already a niche product in practice. It's just not treated, nor priced, accordingly, and many brewers, licensees and consumer advocates continue to behave as if it's somehow still the everyday drink of the working man. Overcoming that cognitive dissonance would help address many of the challenges cask faces, rendering it more profitable to make and sell, encouraging everyone along the chain to take quality seriously and creating a more positive and aspirational image.

There's evidence to show premiumisation can increase sales, even when times are hard, as people foregoing exotic holidays or new cars turn to more affordable luxuries. And it would intensify the existing halo effect, helping pubs improve their reputation and bringing more non-cask drinkers in. From this reduced but stabilised position it may even be 'discovered by a new generation', as Hogs Back's Rupert Thompson hopes, and grow into a mass-market product again, as those ineffable consumer trends continue to cycle.

This could be a bitter pill to swallow. Evin O'Riordain is concerned for the potential loss of what he calls the 'everydayness' of cask. 'Drinking out is becoming a seriously expensive concern,' he says. 'I can see a strong cask market maintained in places that are more beer-focused, where people are prepared to pay, and we'll lose the experience of cask as an everyday drink that's been part of its appeal until now.' This could be offset by the differential pricing expected of premium products, with a more affordable and sessionable but still good quality beer always on sale alongside more expensive choices.

Or perhaps there are lessons in the business model of smaller traditional brewers like Bathams with their close-knit estates of community pubs selling healthy volumes of quality cask to customers who see it as a badge of local identity. Or the tiny and picturesque Donnington brewery with its estate of 19 mainly rural pubs in the Cotswolds, almost all of them within a 10-mile (16-km) radius. Some newer arrivals also see an estate of their own carefully chosen pubs as an important part of the mix, like Titanic, which is experimenting with a new sub-brand of Bod café-bars, town centre hybrids that happily sell cask alongside craft keg, barista coffee and sandwiches, accommodating daytime laptop tappers as well as evening socialisers.

If you've read thus far, you'll hopefully agree the alternative is unthinkable. I'll leave the last word on the subject to Mark Dorber:

> If we lost cask, we'd lose the myriad flavours that come from the interaction between dry hop and living yeast, the ability to test the ageing potential, to control the subtlety of carbonation, preparing it for particular palates, particular occasions. We'd lose that joy of being in touch with something living that you are actively influencing. Keg and filtered beers are frozen in development at racking. Cask isn't, and for those who are artists in the true sense in the cellar, it would be a huge loss.

Tours and visits

Guided brewery tours, typically coupled with a tutored tasting, are excellent ways to learn more about beer and brewing. The list below covers breweries I visited or consulted while writing this book that also offer regular public tours, as well as a hop farm and a pub cellar. Tours must be booked in advance and there's usually a modest fee. Asterisks (*) indicate breweries on historic sites where there's considerable brewery heritage to admire too. The list is by no means exhaustive: many other breweries offer excellent tours and some that don't advertise public tours accommodate visiting groups by arrangement. For more about my own tours in London, see **desdemoor.co.uk/beer-tours**.

Adnams Brewery, * Southwold, Suffolk IP18 6GB adnams.co.uk
Batemans Brewery, * Wainfleet, Lincolnshire PE24 4JE bateman.co.uk
Beoir Chorcha Dhuibhne (West Kerry Brewery), An Riasc, Kerry westkerrybrewery.ie
Black Sheep Brewery, Masham, North Yorkshire HG4 4EN blacksheepbrewery.com
Bluejacket, Washington DC 20003 bluejacketdc.com
Butcombe Brewing Co, Cox's Green, North Somerset BS40 5PA butcombe.com
Castle Rock Brewery, Nottingham NG2 1NB castlerockbrewery.co.uk
Chiltern Brewery, Terrick, Buckinghamshire HP17 0TQ chilternbrewery.co.uk
Fyne Ales Cairndow, Argyll & Bute PA26 8BJ fyneales.com
Fuller's Griffin Brewery, * London W4 2QB fullersbrewery.co.uk
Gadds' Ramsgate Brewery, Broadstairs, Kent CT10 2YD ramsgatebrewery.co.uk
Greene King, * Bury St Edmunds, Suffolk IP33 1QT greeneking.co.uk
Hand in Hand (pub cellar masterclass), London SW19 4RQ thehandinhandwimbledon.co.uk
Harvey's Brewery, * Lewes, East Sussex BN7 2AH harveys.org.uk
Hogs Back Brewery, Tongham, Surrey GU10 1DE hogsback.co.uk
Hook Norton Brewery, * Hook Norton, Oxfordshire OX15 5NY hooky.co.uk
Hukins Hops, St Michaels, Kent TN30 6TG hukins-hops.co.uk
Marble Beers, Salford M50 2GN marblebeers.com
Moor Beer, Bristol BS2 0QS moorbeer.co.uk
RedWillow Brewery, Macclesfield, Cheshire SK11 7JW redwillowbrewery.com
Sambrook's Brewery* (Ram), London SW18 1UR sambrooksbrewery.co.uk
Siren Craft Brew, Finchampstead, Wokingham RG40 4RF sirencraftbrew.com
Southwark Brewing Company, London SE1 2EZ southwarkbrewing.co.uk
St Austell Brewery, * St Austell, Cornwall PL25 4BY staustellbrewery.co.uk
Stewart Brewing, Loanhead, Midlothian EH20 9LZ stewartbrewing.co.uk
Theakston Brewery, * Masham, North Yorkshire HG4 4YD theakstons.co.uk
Thornbridge Brewery, Bakewell, Derbyshire DE45 1GS thornbridgebrewery.co.uk
Tiny Rebel, Newport (South Wales) NP10 9FQ tinyrebel.co.uk
Titanic Brewery, Burslem, Stoke-on-Trent ST6 1JL titanicbrewery.co.uk
Windsor & Eton Brewery, Windsor SL4 1SE webrew.co.uk
Woodforde's Brewery, Woodbastwick, Norfolk NR13 6SW woodfordes.com

Further reading and sources

1. Making cask

What is beer?

My definition of beer is shared with most modern technical sources: see for example the discussion in Boulton and Quain (2001:1–2). A worthwhile encyclopaedia-style reference is Oliver (2012), though it's not always entirely reliable and hasn't yet been updated to reflect the very latest developments. On sake brewing, Wu (2019) has a good summary. Chicha has been familiar to UK brewers from some time: see Faulkner (1884:126).

Most other beer books aimed at interested drinkers include an outline of the ingredients and brewing process: Bamforth (2003) is succinct and accessible though written by a highly knowledgeable and authoritative brewing scientist. For a more journalistic but entertaining and illuminating exploration of the four main ingredients, see Brown (2017).

If you want to dig even deeper, the four volumes in the Brewing Elements series are the standard texts. These are written for professionals and keen homebrewers but are at least in part accessible and informative for the very curious general reader. Separate volumes cover malt (Mallett 2014), water (Palmer and Kaminski 2013, by far the most forbiddingly technical), hops (Hieronymous 2012, highly recommended) and yeast (White and Zainasheff 2010).

Hops

Barth and others (1994) provide a comprehensive and generously illustrated, though now a little out-of-date, German-language survey of hop cultivation throughout the world, with some historical notes: an English translation, *The Hop Atlas*, was also published but is now very rare. Neve (1991), a former director of research at Wye College, gives a thorough technical account of hop biology, cultivation and processing, and covers the plant's likely origin in China (1991:16). See Bocquet and others (2018) and Cocuzza and Pfeiffer (2021) on the plant's antimicrobial properties. Ben Hughes first explained raw beer to me, and there's much more detail, including its role in traditional northern European brewing, in Garshol (2018a).

Yeast and fermentation

Bamforth (2008) compares the fermentation processes of beer and wine. Jonathan Edger at Castle Rock first showed me yeast through a microscope. On the evolution of alcoholic fermentation, see Dashko and others (2014). Walker (2022) has more on house yeasts. The leading expert on kveik is Garshol (2020): see also the account in Bullen (2019a). Sean Ayling was helpful on its practical advantages. The Milk the Funk wiki (2022) has plenty of technical material on unusual yeasts and bacteria used in brewing, as does Sparrow (2005).

For experimental evidence that closed vessels reduce flavour compounds, see for example Renger and others (1992). Southby (1885:122) describes a slate Yorkshire square. White (1999) has a concise but useful explanation of the fermentation timeline, while there's a classic account in De Clerck (1957: Ch 19) and a more recent, and highly technical, biochemical account in Boulton and Quain (2001:Ch 3). For more on carbon dioxide capture at the Ramsgate Brewery, see Gadd (2022). For more on the National Collection of Yeast Cultures, including the full searchable catalogue of the open collection, see ncyc.co.uk.

Bullen (2019b) describes several brewers' interesting encounters with biotransform-ation, while Aron (2020) has a more technical account of what might be happening. The early study is King and Dickinson (2003). On hop creep, see Stokholm and Shellhammer (2020).

Narziss (1972:Ch 2–3) has a clear and detailed technical account, though in German, of classic lager brewing and ferm-entation. There's more detail about lambic fermentation in Sparrow (2005:156–168), much of it drawing on the classic paper on the subject, Van Oevelen and others (1977). For more about lambic, see Webb and others (2010) and Van den Steen (2011: there's also an English edition).

2. From tank to glass

Casks

There's more on cask history in Cantwell and Bouckaert (2016:Ch 1) and Twede (2005). The original Pliny quote is '*Circa Alpes ligneis vasis condunt*' (1906:Ch 27:132). Partington (2003) has a brief history and much detail on the manufacture of metal casks. O'Neill (2020) includes an overview of cask design and materials, and a useful appendix on wooden casks. The British Beer & Pub Association and others (2019) set out technical standards for steel casks. For more about Keg Watch, see kegwatch.co.uk.

Cellar management

The most comprehensive source on contemporary best practice for managing cask beer on the retail side is O'Neill (2020). It goes into much more detail than the average general reader will require, but is clearly and concisely written and contains much useful background and theory. I've also referred to the excellent internal trade quality manuals issued by Greene King (2018) and St Austell (2022). There are useful resources for practitioners as well as information about training courses on the Cask Marque website, cask-marque.co.uk, under Pubs: Training & Assessment.

Protz (2010) covers the launch of Fast Cask, with a little more detail, and Brown (2010) anticipates many of the objections to it. For a fascinating discussion about the supposed need to introduce oxygen during venting, see Seth (2014), commenting on a post by Razzall (2014).

Dispense

Hadland (2021:106–108) covers the air pressure and cask breather controversies. Protz (1978:81–82) has a fair-minded account of the former written shortly afterwards. For more on air pressure dispense in Scotland see Alexander (2022:203–210) and Slaughter (2007:77); the latter also advises where to find the system today. Boak and Bailey (2018b) outline the history of electric pumps.

Cornell (2015) provides a fascinating history of the beer glass. A proponent of the 'maximising hop character' theory of sparkler distribution is Smith (2022), while Waite (2021) gives a recent account of both pro- and anti-sparkler arguments.

3. Cask compared

Dogfish Head (2017) describes a system for dispensing barrel-aged beer from its own vessel. For an account, now slightly outdated, of how CAMRA came to accept membrane kegs, see O'Donnell (2015). As often, the principle is older than most people think: see De Clerck (1957:486) on 'pressure bag casks'. Robertson (2019) gives a brief but interesting history of bag-in-box; O'Neill (2020:38) explains methods for venting such containers.

4. The flavour of cask

Taste and appreciation
On tasting, Mosher (2009) remains an essential read, though not specific to cask. A more recent, well-illustrated and thoughtful text covering similar ground is Dredge (2022). Holmes (2017) provides a fascinating overview of the science of flavour for the general reader.

It turns out very high temperatures, above 35°C, also suppress taste, though you're unlikely to encounter these while drinking beer, except perhaps for the occasional mulled novelty. There's more technical stuff on the topic from Talavera Pérez and others (2007).

Beer flavours
For another recent reinterpretation of the flavour wheel, see Dredge (2021:39). Bamforth (2003:73–80) has an excellent overview of beer flavour, while Smagalski (2023) has an impressively comprehensive list of tasting terms. The Brewers Association (2014:7–11) describe the effects of ageing on flavour, while there's more on the contribution of Brettanomyces in Licker and others (1998). Off-flavours are covered in many beer and brewing reference books but there's a concise and comprehensive summary by Carr (2016). On the contribution of malt origins to flavour, see de Moor (2014).

Alcohol
Bamforth (2008:Ch 10) gives a very readable summary of the evidence on the health benefits of wine and beer, and the pitfalls of assessing it, though perhaps partisan given

his background. Marcos (2017) has a more recent overview, albeit from a scientific committee backed by the European brewing industry. The same author and others followed this up in a more technical paper in 2021. Official advice for various countries is easily found by searching on health service websites such as nhs.uk.

Styles
For international styles, including British ones, Dredge (2022) and Webb and Beaumont (2020) are a good start. Cornell (2010a) provides a useful and fascinating look at the history of key British styles.

For the Champion Beer of Britain style guide, see CAMRA (2020); there's more about the competition itself at CAMRA (2019), including a downloadable spreadsheet listing all the previous medallists in all the style categories up to 2019 – an excellent source of suggestions for more beers to try. For more granular and technical distinctions, see Strong and England (2021) and Brewers Association (2022). Protz (2015) recalls the history of the original Ind Coope Draught Burton Ale. There's more about Scottish styles and the shilling system in the history section.

Beer with/in food
Although now two decades old, Oliver (2003) remains the essential text on beer and food pairing. A more recent entry, with recipes, is Bullen and Ferguson (2019), while Cole (2018) explores both beer pairing and cooking with beer in another recipe-based book. The basics of pairing are set out in Mosher (2009:Ch 7) and Dredge (2022:84–93).

5. Beer in casks (and other vessels): 7000 BCE–1700 CE

Hornsey (2003) provides a general history of brewing from a brewing scientist's perspective, particularly strong on ancient brewing, though by no means free of unverified claims. Corran (1975) is shorter and more accessible: it's now rather old but still useful. Cornell (2003) could also benefit from updating but remains a useful and entertaining read, while its follow-up (2010a) covers the ground from the point of view of British beer styles and there's much of interest too on the author's website at zythophile.co.uk. On the history of brewing science see Sumner (2016). I've relied on his potted biographies of the major contributors to the discipline (xiii–xviii) for many of their dates as given in the index below.

Ancient and medieval beer

The discovery at Raqefet Cave is reported in Liu and others (2018). On the Chinese discoveries, see McGovern and others (2004) and Wang and others (2021); for Hornstaad-Hörnle, Heiss and others (2020). For Sedgeford, see Hilts (2021) and SHARP (2018).

Unger (2004) gives a comprehensive account of European brewing in the medieval and renaissance periods. I've resisted repeating in the main text the well-known but entirely groundless claim that ale conners discharged their duty by sitting in a pool of beer in leather trousers to see if it stuck, rather than the obvious expedient of smelling and tasting it. There's certainly no reference to the practice in the oath the City of London required them to take (Carpenter and Whitington 1861:274).

The figures from St Paul's are sometimes attributed to the Domesday survey of 1089, but turn out to be from a record book of 1222 known as *The Domesday of St Paul's*, analysed by Maitland (1897:439–440). I've referred to Bennett (1996:62–63), Brewers' Company (2023) and Brown (2012) o n the dates for early brewers' gilds. The rough prose translation of de Bibbesworth (1990:14) is partly my own, partly the one quoted by Cornell (2021); the original passage begins '*Puis serra le brez molu*'. The poem once prompted comment among brewing historians as it didn't appear to mention yeast, although it turns out they were looking at an incomplete Victorian translation.

The ascent of hops

On the spread of hops, I've found Behre (1999), Bennett (1996:79–84), Cornell (2009), Garshol (2022), Hornsey (2003:303–326) and Neve (1991:25–33) useful. Wilson (1975) has much detail on the Graveney Boat and the early spread of hops in England. There's some confusion in the literature about the location of Corvey abbey: Adalard was earlier abbot of Corbie, on the Somme near Amiens in France, but in 822 founded a new abbey with the same name at the German site mentioned, and likely drew up his statutes in the process.

On contemporary farmhouse brewing with stones and boiled mashes, see Garshol (2022:134–139, 142–149). On the displacement of gruit in the Low Countries through exports from the Hanseatic League, I've also referred to Daane (2016:20–41), Meussdoerffer (2009:16–18), Papin (2004) and Verberg (2018).

Pajic (2019) attempts to pin down the arrival of hopped beer in England. Lawrence (1990:1–2) suggests Flemish weavers began cultivating hops in Kent in the 1330s, much earlier than is generally accepted, but assumes they were already used to drinking hopped beer: according to Papin (2004:139), hops weren't established as a brewing ingredient in Flanders itself until the end of the 15th century. Hop growing remained important in Essex and other parts of eastern England for some time: see Hornsey (2021). In modern German, of course, *Bier*, like all nouns, is written with an upper case initial. Protz (2016) has more on the Gruut brewery.

Monks, housewives, alewives and common brewers

Chevallier (2013) has much to say on the beer versus water debate. Monckton notes problems with brewers using water from public conduits in the 14th century (1966:16) and speculates that the Dissolution of the Monasteries may have raised brewing standards overall as former monastic brewers became more widely dispersed through society (96). King (1947:16–20) quotes records of monastic brewhouses.

The brewhouse at Queen's College, Oxford, survived into the 1930s: see Queen's College, Oxford (2017) and the account given by Hind (1938:1–2), who visited while it was still operational.

Sambrook (1996) is an excellent source on country house brewing. Bennett (1996) looks at the changing role of women as brewers in England in medieval and early modern times. Regarding long mashing times with large quantities of malt, John Ham is still recommending three hours in 1829 (7). On Dublin Castle beer, see FoodCult (2021): other reconstructions of early modern beer are described by Robinson (2013), based on Harrison's beer, and Placeway (1998), based on an account in Bennett (1998:18–21). Sambrook (1996:154–165) discusses seasonality in country house brewing. For more on coming-of-age beers, see Cornell (2013).

The list of beer styles available in London in 1715 is from the *Vade Mecum for Malt-worms* (Ward 1866?), an early 18th-century pub guide written in sometimes impenetrable humorous verse: I'm grateful to Cornell (2010) for digging these out of it. Ellis (1759:48) is one of several 18th- and early 19th-century authors to mention white ale: his example is from Plymouth. For an intriguing summary of other accounts, see Cornell (2010a:148–151).

6. Cask beer rising: 1700–1914

Two classic texts on the British industry in the modern period are Mathias (1959), covering 1700–1830, and Gourvish and Wilson (1994), continuing the story from 1830–1980. Both books focus more on the business side and the wider economic and social role of brewing than on what was being brewed. Ron Pattinson's website, barclayperkins.blogspot.com, is a mine of information on historic brewing recipes and techniques.

Porter and pale ale
The much-quoted origin story for porter – that it was 'invented' in 1722 by Ralph Harwood, a Shoreditch publican and brewer, as a convenient all-in-one-cask replacement for a beverage called 'three threads' comprised of three separate beers blended at the point of dispense – turns out to be fanciful. Mathias (1959:Ch 2–3) has much detail on the growth of porter brewing, MacDonagh (1964) gives a more convincing account of how the style evolved, while Cornell (2010:Ch 4) has done much recent work to debunk the myths. Ellis (1759:11–14) provides a clear summary of mid 18th-century malts. Sumner (2016) has more on the early spread of scientific measurement in brewing. Combrune mentions brown stout (1762:164).

On the brewing history of Burton upon Trent, I've consulted Owen (1987) and Webster (2018). Brown (2009) provides an accessible history of India Pale Ale and the British in India, intercut with an entertaining account of his own journey from Burton to Kolkata. Tomlinson (1994) describes IPA's voyage in the days of sail.

Nothing but mild
On blending beer, Berkshire spirit merchant John Adams says in parliamentary evidence that it's common in local pubs 'to see a gentleman's servant come for two pots of strong beer, and one of small, to mix together, the former being too strong to drink by itself.' (1819:508). Pereira (1843:418) has the sulphuric acid suggestion. The sugar statistics are ultimately from Noël Deerr's *History of Sugar* (1949–50) but I've quoted them from Johnson and others (2007:901). Gourvish and Wilson (1994: Ch 1) consider the 1830 Beerhouse Act in detail.

Mathias (1959:107–108) and Monkton (1966:147–148) recount the introduction of the beer engine. Mathias (1959:51) covers 18th-century use of finings; among primary sources are Combrune (1762:7) and Watkins (1758:107). The 1897 edition of *Handy Book for*

Brewers (Wright 1897:42) says finings may be added at the brewery, or by the drayman, or in the cellar; its 1927 successor (Ross-Mackenzie 1927:33) simply says 'finings are now added before the beer is dispatched'. The 'Brewery Cellars Manager' (1923:14) includes instructions on fining if needed.

Cornell (2015) has more on the history of pub glassware. Good sources on the tied house system are Corran (1975:153–157), Gourvish and Wilson (1994:128–137, Ch 7), Mathias (1959:99–138), Vaizey (1958:397–403) and Wilson (1940:Ch 9). Gourvish and Wilson mention the shift from butts to barrels (130). Amsinck (1868) distinguishes running from vatted ales in his recipes. On tower breweries, see Pearson (1997:72–73) and several entries in Protz (2020).

Mild and bitter

Ron Pattinson's blog reproduces and compares numerous historic recipes from brewery archives – see for example Pattinson (2012) on X ales. The recipes in Harrison (1991) have inspired many home and professional brewers' interest in heritage styles. On ale as a pseudonym for mild, see Gorham (2011:99); on AK, Cornell (2014); on mild's trajectory in the 19th and 20th centuries, Pattinson (2011). Priming with unfermented wort in Ireland is mentioned by Baker (1905:116–117) and Southby (1885:366); see Alworth (2016) and Cornell (2010:67–68) on high and low casks. Later sources on priming include Jeffery (1956:244), who recommends all running ales are primed, and the casks rolled frequently, though others disagree: De Clerck (1957:435) believes British brewers prime only rarely as a fix when things have gone wrong, Monckton (1966:22) says only some brewers prime and Miles (1972:14) warns it can cause over-conditioning in warm weather, thus some breweries only resort to it in winter. Moritz (1899:190) is one of those who believed that the character and palate of running ales made with 100% malt 'compare unfavourably with those…brewed with a small amount of [sugar] substitute'. On spiling for storage and transport, see Ellis (1759:64–65), porter/stout recipes 7 and 17 in Amsinck (1868) and Southby (1885:374).

From gods to genomes

The text of the 1516 Bavarian purity law is widely reproduced: see for example Gesley (2016). Garshol (2018b) provides an excellent account of the early development of yeast management in brewing. On the late 18th- and 19th-century developments in the scientific study of fermentation and microorganisms that had such a bearing on brewing, there's an excellent overview in Teich and Needham (1992:Section I) including key extracts from primary sources, and a shorter summary in Holmes (2003). On Pasteur, brewing and medicine, see Anderson (1995); on his contribution to antisepsis, see Institut Pasteur (2022, in French). Casey (1990) provides an account of Hansen's work. The decoding of the yeast genome was reported by the National Human Genome Research Institute (1996) and the National Library of Medicine (2023) now has an extensive set of downloadable genomes.

Lager

Dredge (2019) provides an accessible and entertaining but well-informed history of lager; Dornbusch (1997) and Meussdoerffer (2009) are also useful. On the heritage of Pilsner Urquell, see de Moor (2012b). Thausing (1882) gives a thorough and influential account of what he calls the 'Vienna system' of lager brewing in the period when it was spreading most rapidly. The Dutch examples are from Schippers (1992). Ogle (2007) describes the development of the modern US brewing industry from the viewpoint of an informed historian rather than a beer enthusiast; see also Arnold and Penman (1933:47–57). On the early days of lager in the UK, see Boak and Bailey (2014b).

Bottled beer

Cornell (2010c) provides a short history of bottled beer. Pepys (1893) drank Hull ale on

4 November 1660. Posada (1987:380–381) covers the history of filtration; see also De Clerck (1957:447–468), including on early use of centrifuges in Britain. On force carbonation, see Yates (2006). Arnold and Penman (1933:97) suggest Richard Shannon first came up with the idea. On 20th-century bottling methods, see Baker (1905:124) and Foy (1955).

Scotland
Alexander (2022) offers a short history of Scottish brewing for the general reader. Donnachie (1979) is denser and more academic. On heather ale, see Horvath (2022), who also reproduces the best-known retelling of the story in Robert Louis Stevenson's 1890 poem. On the Scottish shilling system, see Alexander (2022:125–134) and Spake (2005). On modern Scottish hops, see James Hutton Institute (2018). Contrary to widespread assumptions, Edinburgh well water, though good for brewing purposes, has quite a different profile to Burton water: see Alexander (2022:148–151).

Secondary fermentation
Anderson (2012) has a good account of the debate about pure yeast in British brewing, while Shimwell (1947) offers the mid 20th-century hindsight of a yeast expert.

Peak cask
Gourvish and Wilson (1996:286–313) cover industry challenges in the early 20th century. Olsen (1999:228–230) deals with 18th-century attitudes to alcohol, and there's much more about 19th-century temperance-inspired legislation in Wilson (1940:Ch 15).

7. Cask at bay 1914–2020

Beer at war
On World War I alcohol restrictions, see Gourvish and Wilson (1996:317–356), Hornsey (2003:579–588) and Wilson (1940:Ch 13). Bennison (2021) notes the profitability of the industry during the war. Kershaw (2015)

summarises the Carlise Experiment. The data on declining gravities are from Pattinson (2008), based on the Brewers' Almanack. Cornell (2010:Ch 4) covers the downward trajectory of porter. Ross-Mackenzie (1927) devotes an entire chapter to setting up a lab.

On the continued rise of bottled beer, see Cornell (2010c) and Jeffery (1956:Ch 10). Felinfoel's claim to introducing UK canned beer is in the *Brewers' Journal* (1936); see also Jurado (2018). Stack (2003) collates statistics on the rise of small pack in the USA. Farrell (2014) has more on Watney's introduction of keg; see also Gillman (2020). Glover (1995) covers the experiences of Britain's breweries and pubs during World War II in considerable detail.

Merger mania and the rise of keg
Merger mania is covered by Gourvish and Wilson (1996:Ch 11), Hornsey (2003:684–699), Spicer and others (2012:Ch 1) and Vaizey (1958). Vaizey's (1960:154) brief but pithy remarks on low investment levels are notable. Bower (2014) explains the Whitbread umbrella. Barber and others (2012) provide useful data about the various breweries affected. Protz (1978, 2014, 2018) is a compelling, if partisan, source on the rise and fall of the Big Six/Seven.

Boak and Bailey (2019b) re-evaluate the reputation of Red Barrel through modern recreations. On the use of top pressure with cask, see O'Neill (2020:74) and Boston (1976:64-66), though note the discussion in Chapter 2 on the supposed role of oxygen during cask conditioning. On post-war British lager, see Cornell (2010:Ch 16). Baillie (1973) provides a comprehensive guide to the output of British breweries in the early 1970s.

Cask fights back
For a brief but fascinating history of wine connoisseurship, see Gibb (2021). Becky's Dive Bar is covered by Boak and Bailey (2014a:80-83) and Boston (1976:96–98). On homebrewing, see Boak and Bailey (2019a) and the relevant entry in Oliver (2010). Hadland (2021) provides a comprehensive

history of CAMRA based on recent interviews and archival research; see also Boak and Bailey (2014a:Ch 2–3) and Protz (1995:116–125). On the 'famous four' surviving brewpubs in the 1970s, see de Moor (2021a); on the history of the Firkin brewpub chain, particularly in London, see de Moor (2022a).

Protz summarises the origins of the Beer Orders and their aftermath (2018) and provides a comprehensive guide to the old-established family brewers that survived into the 21st century (2020). On beer tasting language, see de Moor (2011). Boak and Bailey (2014a) chronicle the British scene since the 1960s.

The age of craft

The five surviving bottle-conditioned beers in 1971 were Bass Worthington White Shield, Courage Imperial Russian Stout, Eldridge Pope Thomas Hardy's Ale, Gale's Prize Old Ale and Guinness Extra Stout (Evans 2013:15): only White Shield is still in regular production, though is becoming increasingly hard to find. On Anchor, see de Moor (2013); on Hoegaarden, Jackson (1992:111–112); on Boon, de Moor (2020). Ogle (2006:Ch 7–8) covers the emergence of US craft brewing. Boak and Bailey track the emergence of 'palenhoppy' (2015, 2021), 'world' (2012) and 'craft keg' (2016) beer in the UK. On Meantime and the Kernel see de Moor (2021b:241 and 204–206); on the term 'craft beer', de Moor (2012a).

Readers with an interest in beer and brewing history should investigate the Brewery History Society: breweryhistory.com

8. The future of cask

On the impact of the Covid-19 lockdowns on London brewing, see de Moor (2021:23–24). The most recent statistics on cask sales are from Fish (2022:13) and Nodder (2022:8, 2023:19). Many of the market research findings and brewery statistics are taken from the two most recent *Cask Reports* (Davenport and others 2018, Eley 2019) and the latest *Craft Beer Report* (Nodder 2023). For a pithy take on the issues surrounding price, see Brown (2022).

The new duty system should be in place by the time you read this, so any references will be out of date, but there's an outline of the proposals at Masala and others (2023) and a good explanation by Dunkley (2023). If you've never met the Real Ale Twats, see Boak and Bailey (2018a). The market research on women and beer is from the Dea Latis survey (Smith and Harlow 2018) and already cited reports. I'm grateful to Pete Brown for sharing his unpublished compendium of facts and figures.

You may wish to refer to the latest *Good Beer Guide* (Haines 2023) to plan your own participation in the future of cask.

Bibliography

I translated all quotations from languages other than English unless otherwise stated in the bibliography. I've also modernised spellings in quotations from older English texts. Where more than five authors are credited, for reasons of space I've listed an entry only under the first author's name, with an indication of the numbers of others. I haven't given full URLs for online references, as these not only take up space but often change when sites are redesigned: use the search function on a homepage or a search engine like Google. Several of the historic texts are freely available online as scans or transcriptions, through Google Books and similar resources: again, search engines can help.

ACCUM, Friedrich (as Frederick) 1820, *A Treatise on Adulterations of Food and Culinary Poisons*, 2nd edition, London: Longman Hurst Rees Orme and Brown

ADAMS, John 1819, evidence, 'Minutes taken (in 1818) before committee on petition respecting price and quality of beer,' *Parliamentary Papers* 1819 V:503–509

ALEXANDER, John 2022, *The Little History of Scottish Brewing*, Cheltenham: The History Press

ALWORTH, Jeff 2016, 'The man who invented nitro', *All About Beer: The Beer Bible Blog*, allaboutbeer.com

AMSINCK, George Stewart 1868, *Practical Brewings: a series of fifty brewings in extenso*, London: Amsinck

ANDERSON, Ray G 1995, 'Louis Pasteur (1822–1895): An assessment of his impact on the brewing industry', in European Brewery Convention, *Proceedings of the 25th Congress Brussels 1995*: 13–24, Oxford: Oxford University Press

ANDERSON, Ray G 2012, 'One yeast or two? Pure yeast and top fermentation', *Brewery History* 149:30–38

ARNOLD, John P and Frank Penman 1933, *History of the Brewing Industry and Brewing Science in America*, Chicago IL: Peterson

ARON, Pattie 2020, 'Biotransformation', *Brew Your Own* May–June 2020, byo.com

ATHERTON, Sophie 2017, *The Cask Report 2017: How to make money from cask*, Cask Matters, cask-marque.co.uk

BAKER, Julian L 1905, *The Brewing Industry*, London: Methuen

BAILEY, Paul 2013, 'Cellarmanship', *Paul's Beer and Travel Blog* 7 April 2013, baileysbeerblog.blogspot.com

BAILLIE, Frank 1973, *The Beer Drinker's Companion*, Newton Abbot: David and Charles

BAMFORTH, Charles 2003, *Beer: Tap into the art and science of brewing*, 2nd edition, first published 1997, New York NY: Oxford University Press

BAMFORTH, Charles 2008, *Grape vs Grain: A historical, technological and social comparison of wine and beer*, New York, NY: Cambridge University Press

BARBER, Norman and Mike Brown, Ken Smith 2012, *Century Plus Plus of British Brewers 1890 to 2012*, Hebden Bridge: Brewery History Society

BARCLAY, Charles 1819, evidence, 'Minutes taken (in 1818) before committee on petition respecting price and quality of beer,' *Parliamentary Papers* 1819 V:545–550

BARNARD, Alfred 1890, *The Noted Breweries of Great Britain and Ireland Volume III*, London: Joseph Causton and Sons

BARRETT, John 1817, evidence, 'Minute of evidence taken before the committee on the state of the Police of the Metropolis', *Parliamentary Papers* 1817 VII:211–213

BARTH, Heinrich Joh and Christiane Klinke, Claus Schmidt 1994, *Der grosse Hopfenatlas: Gesichte und Geographie einer Kulturpflanze*, Nürnberg: Joh Barth & Sohn

BAVERSTOCK, James 1811, *Practical Observations on the Prejudices against the Brewery*, London: White and Cochrane

BAXTER, E Denise and Daniel Cooper, Gillian M Fisher, Robert E Muller 2007, 'Analysis of isinglass residues in beer', *Journal of the Institute of Brewing* 113:2:130–134

BEHRE, Karl-Ernst 1999, 'The history of beer additives in Europe – a review', *Vegetation History and Archaeobotany* 8:35–48

BENNETT, Judith M 1996, *Ale, Beer, and Brewsters in England: Women's work in a changing world, 1300–1600*, New York NY: Oxford University Press

BENNISON, Brian Robert 2021, 'The brewing trade in North East England, 1869–1939, Part III', *Brewery History* 188:30–70

BETTS, Bryan 2017, 'The secrets of British cask conditioning', *Craft Beer & Brewing* 5 September 2017, beerandbrewing.com

BIRD, Christopher 2012, 'Off-flavors' in Oliver 2012: 623–624

BLACK, William 1849, *A Practical Treatise on Brewing, based on chemical and economical principles*, 4th edition, first published 1835, London: Longman Brown Green and Longman

BOAK, Jessica and Ray Bailey 2012, 'World beer in the UK: A timeline', *Boak & Bailey* 21 November 2012, boakandbailey.com

BOAK, Jessica and Ray Bailey 2014a, *Brew Britannia: The strange rebirth of British beer*, London: Aurum

BOAK, Jessica and Ray Bailey 2014b, *Gambrinus Waltz: German lager beer in Victorian and Edwardian London*, e-book. boakandbailey.com

BOAK, Jessica and Ray Bailey 2015, 'The emergence of "pale'n'hoppy" beers in the UK', *All About Beer*, allaboutbeer.com

BOAK, Jessica and Ray Bailey 2016, 'Q&A: What was the first kegged craft beer?', *Boak & Bailey* 9 September 2016, boakandbailey.com

BOAK, Jessica and Ray Bailey 2018a, 'Davey Jones, the man behind the Real Ale Twats', *Boak & Bailey* 12 June 2018, boakandbailey.com

BOAK, Jessica and Ray Bailey 2018b, 'Q&A: Electric beer pumps', *Boak & Bailey* 27 February 2018, boakandbailey.com

BOAK, Jessica and Ray Bailey 2019a, 'The history of homebrewing in the UK', first published 2018, *Boak & Bailey* 24 February 2019, boakandbailey.com

BOAK, Jessica and Ray Bailey 2019b, 'Watney's Red Barrel – how bad could it have been?', *Boak & Bailey* 20 January 2019, boakandbailey.com

BOAK, Jessica and Ray Bailey 2021, 'A pale'n'hoppy timeline', *Boak & Bailey* 17 May 2021, boakandbailey.com

BOCQUET, Laetitia and Sevser Sahpaz, Céline Rivière 2018, 'An overview of the antimicrobial properties of hop', in Jean-Michel Mérillon and Céline Riviere 2018, *Natural Antimicrobial Agents*, New York NY: Springer: 31–54

BOORDE, Andrewe 1542, *Here Foloweth a Compendyous Regymente of Dyetary of Health*, London: Thomas Colwel

BOOTH, David 1852, *The Art of Brewing on Scientific Principles*, new edition, uncredited and undated, first published 1829, London: James Cornish

BOSTON, Richard 1976, *Beer and Skittles*. Glasgow: Fontana/Collins

BOULTON, Chris and David Quain 2001, *Brewing Yeast and Fermentation*. Oxford: Blackwell

BOWER, Julie 2014, 'What was the Whitbread umbrella protecting? From brewing to coffee via pub retailing', *BAM 2014 Conference Proceedings*, London: British Academy of Management, bam.ac.uk

BRADLEY, Richard 1727, *The Country Housewife and Lady's Director in the Management of a House, and the Delights and Profits of a Farm*, London: Woodman and Lyon

BRAIDWOOD, Robert J and 8 others 1953, 'Did Man once live by beer alone?', *American Anthropologist* 55:515–526

BREWERS ASSOCIATION 2014, *Best Practices Guide to Quality Craft Beer*, Boulder CO: Brewers Association, brewersassociation.org

BREWERS ASSOCIATION 2022, *2023 World Beer Cup Competition Categories: Beer style descriptions and specifications*, worldbeercup.org

BREWERS ASSOCIATION 2023a, 'GABF official numbers', *Great American Beer Festival*, greatamericanbeerfestival.com, accessed March 2023

BREWERS ASSOCIATION 2023b, 'Stats and data: National beer sales & production data', brewersassocation.org, accessed March 2023

BREWERS' COMPANY 2023, 'History of the Company', *History and treasures*, Brewers' Company, brewershall.co.uk, accessed February 2023

BREWERS' JOURNAL 1936, 'Britain's first canned beer', *Brewers' Journal* 15 April 1936, reproduced at breweryhistory.com

BREWERS OF EUROPE 2017, *Beer statistics 2017 edition*, Brussels: Brewers of Europe

'A BREWERY CELLARS MANAGER' 1923, 'Ales and stouts and hints on cellar management', in W Bently Capper (editor) 1923, *Licenced Houses and their Management* volume II, London: Caxton: 11–18

BRIGNALL, Miles 2023, '"We can't carry on": over 150 pubs have shut this year as energy bills soar', *The Guardian* 11 April 2023, theguardian.com

BRITISH BEER AND & PUB ASSOCIATION and BFBi (Brewing, Food & Beverage Industry Suppliers' Association), SIBA (Society of Independent Brewers) 2019, *Standards for the design/manufacture/performance/purchasing of 9 gallon stainless steel cask beer containers*, Wolverhampton: BFBi, bfbi.org.uk

BROWN, Horace T 1916, 'Reminiscences of fifty years' experience of the application of scientific method to brewing practice', *Journal of the Institute of Brewing* 22:5:267–354

BROWN, Mike 2012, 'London brewers: some legal cases and their sources', *Brewery History* 151:48–61

BROWN, Pete 2009, *Hops and Glory: One man's search for the beer that built the British Empire*, Basingstoke: Macmillan

BROWN, Pete 2010, 'Marston's redefines cask ale', *Pete Brown* 16 March 2010, petebrown.net

BROWN, Pete 2017, *Miracle Brew: Hops, barley, water, yeast and the nature of beer*, London: Unbound

BROWN, Pete 2022, 'Six reasons why cask ale-loving publicans should immediately whack the price up', *Pete Brown* 13 October 2022, petebrown.net

BULLEN, Claire 2019a, 'A fire being kindled – The revolutionary story of kveik, Norway's extraordinary farmhouse yeast', *Good Beer Hunting* 31 July 2019, goodbeerhunting.com

BULLEN, Claire 2019b, 'An uncharted wilderness – understanding hop compound biotransformation', *Good Beer Hunting* 2 January 2019, goodbeerhunting.com

BULLEN, Claire and Jen Ferguson 2019, *The Beer Lover's Table: Seasonal recipes and modern beer pairings*, London: Dog 'n' Bone

BUSHNAN, J Stevenson 1853, *Burton and its Bitter Beer*, London: William S Orr

CAMRA (Campaign for Real Ale) 1972, 'The definition of REAL ale', *What's Brewing* November 1972:3

CAMRA (Campaign for Real Ale) Hertfordshire Branches 1982, 'AGM report', *The Hertfordshire Newsletter* 51, May 1982, southherts.camra.org. uk

CAMRA (Campaign for Real Ale) Eastern Region 1999, 'Cask breather trial', cambridge-camra. org.uk

CAMRA (Campaign for Real Ale) 2015, *External Policy Document 2015–2016*, St Albans: CAMRA

CAMRA (Campaign for Real Ale) 2019, 'Champion Beer of Britain', camra.org.uk

CAMRA (Campaign for Real Ale) 2020, *CAMRA's Beer Styles: A guide to the Champion Beer of Britain style categories*, camra.org.uk

CAMRA (Campaign for Real Ale) 2022a, *Campaign Policy Document*, camra.org.uk

CAMRA (Campaign for Real Ale) 2022b, *CAMRA's Definition of Real Ale*, camra.org.uk

CAMRA (Campaign for Real Ale) 2022c, 'CAMRA renews call for government support as new research shows over half of people think the average price of a pint is now unaffordable', press release 3 August 2022, camra.org.uk

CANTWELL, Dick and Peter Bouckaert 2016, *Wood & Beer: a brewer's guide*. Boulder CO: Brewers Publications

CARPENTER, John and Richard Whitington (compilers) 1861, *Liber Albus: The White Book of the City of London*, compiled 1419, translated by Henry Thomas Riley, London: Richard Griffin

CARR, Nick 2016, '18 common "off" flavors in beer (and how they are caused)', *Kegerator Learning Center* 1 July 2016, learn.kegerator.com

CASEY, Gregory Paul 1990, 'Yeast selection in brewing', in Chandra J Panchal, *Yeast Strain Selection*, New York NY: Dekker: Ch 4

CASK MARQUE 2023, 'About Cask Marque', cask-marque.co.uk, accessed March 2023

CHAMBERS, Robert (editor) 1869, *Popular Rhymes of Scotland*, new edition, first published 1841, Edinburgh: W & R Chambers

CHAPMAN, A Chaston 1912, *Brewing*, Cambridge: Cambridge University Press

CHAUCER, Geoffrey c1385, 'The Miller's Prologue', *The Canterbury Tales*, accessed at librarius.com

CHEVALLIER, Jim 2013, 'The great medieval water myth', *Les Leftovers* 16 November 2013, leslefts.blogspot.com

CLARK, Peter 1984, 'The alehouse and social integration in English towns (1500–1700)' in Maurice Garden and Yves Lequin (editors), *Habiter la ville, xve-xxe siècles*, Lyon: Presses universitaires de Lyon: 225–231

CLAUSSEN, N Hjelte 1904, 'On a method of application of Hansen's pure yeast system in the manufacturing of well-conditioned English stock beers', *Journal of the Institute of Brewing* 10:4:308–331

COCUZZA, Sandro and Frank Pfeiffer 2021, *The Antimicrobial Effects of Hops*, technical factsheet, Mainburg: Hopsteiner, hopsteiner.com

COLE, Melissa 2018, *The Beer Kitchen: The art and science of cooking & pairing with beer*, London: Hardie Grant

COMBRUNE, Michael 1762, *The Theory and Practice of Brewing*, London: J Haberkorn

COMMISSION OF ENQUIRY INTO INDUSTRIAL UNREST No 5 Division 1917, *Report of the Commissioners for the London and South-Eastern area* Cd 8666, London: HMSO

COMMITTEE ON PUBLIC BREWERIES 1818, Report, *Parliamentary Papers* 1818 III:295-299

COMMITTEE ON THE STATE OF THE POLICE OF THE METROPOLIS 1817, Report, *Parliamentary Papers* 1817 VII:3-22

COOK, John C H (as John Bickerdyke) 1965, *The Curiosities of Ale and Beer: an entertaining history*, first published 1889, London: Spring Books

COOMBS, James H 1982, *Bar Service*, 2nd edition (1975) reprint, first published 1965, London: Hutchinson

CORNELL, Martyn 2003, *Beer – The Story of the Pint: The history of Britain's most popular drink*, London: Headline

CORNELL, Martyn 2007, 'Myth 2: Hops were forbidden by Henry VI', *Zythophile FAQ – False Ale Quotes*, zythophile.co.uk

CORNELL, Martyn 2010a, *Amber Gold & Black: The history of Britain's great beers*, Cheltenham: History Press

CORNELL, Martyn 2010b, 'The origins of porter (and a bit about three-threads)', *Zythophile* 22 November 2010, zythophile.co.uk

CORNELL, Martyn 2010c, 'A short history of bottled beer', *Zythophile* 15 January 2010, zythophile.co.uk

CORNELL, Martyn 2013, 'A glass of something very treble extra: Coming-of-age ale, a long-forgotten British beer style', *Brewery History* 153:2-10

CORNELL, Martyn 2014, 'Second thoughts on the mysterious origins of AK', *Zythophile* 23 July 2014, zythophile.co.uk

CORNELL, Martyn 2015a, 'More notes towards the history of the beer mug', *Zythophile* 28 March 2015, zythophile.co.uk

CORNELL, Martyn 2015b, 'A short account of the surprisingly long history of putting beer in cellar tanks', *Zythophile* 21 October 2015, zythophile.co.uk

CORNELL, Martyn 2021, 'How to brew like a medieval knight', *Zythophile* 29 April 2021, zythophile.co.uk

CORRAN, H S 1975, *A History of Brewing*, Newton Abbot: David and Charles

COUNTRY BREWERS' SOCIETY 1900, 'Pure single-cell yeast', *Brewing Trade Review* 14:166:77

'A COUNTRY GENTLEMAN' 1724, *A Guide to Gentlemen and Farmers, for Brewing the Finest Malt Liquors, Much Better and Cheaper than hitherto known*, 4th edition, first published 1703, London: S Poppin

DAANE, Marco 2016, *Bier in Nederland: Een biographie*, Amsterdam: Atlas

DASHKO, Sofia and Nerve Zhou, Concetta Compagno, Jure Piškur 2014, 'Why, when and how did yeast evolve alcoholic fermentation?', *FEMS Yeast Research* 14:6:826-832

DAVENPORT, Rosie and Frances Brace, Andrew Lane 2018, *The Cask Report 2017/2018*, Cask Marque, cask-marque.co.uk

de BIBBESWORTH, Walter 1990, *Le tretiz*, written c1250, edited by William Rothwell, London: Anglo-Norman Text Society

De CLERCK, Jean 1957, *A Textbook of Brewing* Volume One, translated by Kathleen Barton-Wright from *Cours de Brasserie* Volume I, first published 1948, London: Chapman and Hall

de MOOR, Des 2010, 'The tastes they are a-changin', *BEER* 10:6-13

de MOOR, Des 2011, 'The language of beer: a long journey', in Roger Protz (editor), *CAMRA at 40*, St Albans: CAMRA Books: 57-68

de MOOR, Des 2012a, 'Is cask craft?', *Beer Culture with Des de Moor* 19 January 2012, desdemoor.co.uk

de MOOR, Des 2012b, 'Pilsner Urquell: an old Czech fairy tale', *Beer Culture with Des de Moor* 20 June 2012, desdemoor.co.uk

de MOOR, Des 2013, 'Anchor and the birth of craft beer', *Beer Culture with Des de Moor* 29 May 2013, desdemoor.co.uk

de MOOR, Des 2014, 'The marvels of malt: tasting single malt beers', *Beer Culture with Des de Moor* 11 May 2014, desdemoor.co.uk

de MOOR, Des 2020, 'Real Ale Heroes Number 32: Frank Boon – How one man saved a beer style', *BEER* 50:24-27

de MOOR, Des 2021a, 'The Famous Four: England's historic brewpubs', *BEER* 51:12-14

de MOOR, Des 2021b, *London's Best Beer, Pubs and Bars*, 3rd edition, first published 2011, St Albans: CAMRA Books

de MOOR, Des 2022a, 'The Firkin Brewery (Bruce's Brewery, Allied)', *Beer Culture with Des de Moor* 22 December 2022, desdemoor.co.uk

de MOOR, Des 2022b, 'London breweries year by year', *Beer Culture with Des de Moor*, updated 22 December 2022, desdemoor.co.uk

DEPARTMENTAL COMMITTEE ON BEER
MATERIALS 1899, *Report of the Departmental
committee on beer materials, minutes of evidence*,
C.9171 C.9172, London: HMSO

DIODORUS SICULUS 1939, *The Library of History
(Bibliotheca historica)*, written c35 BCE, translated
by C H Oldfather, accessed at penelope.
uchicago.edu

DOGFISH HEAD 2017, 'Rack AeriAle provides an
all-new way to enjoy barrel brews', *Dogfish Head
Blog* 14 August 2017, dogfish.com

DONNACHIE, Ian 1979, *A History of the Brewing
Industry in Scotland*, Edinburgh: John Donald

DORNBUSCH, Horst D 1997, *Prost! The story of
German beer*, Boulder CO: Brewers Publications

DREDGE, Mark 2019, *A Brief History of Lager: 500 Years
of the World's Favourite Beer*, London: Kyle Books

DREDGE, Mark 2021, *The New Craft Beer World:
Celebrating over 400 delicious beers*, London:
Dog 'n' Bone

DREDGE, Mark 2022, *Beer: A Tasting Course*,
London: Dorling Kindersley

'A DRINKER' 1933, *A Book About Beer*, London:
Jonathan Cape

DUNKLEY, Steve 2023, 'Small Producers Relief',
Beer Nouveau Blog 17 March 2023, beernouveau.
co.uk

DYE, Geoff 2021, 'Brickwoods: "The Best Beer
Under the Sun". The final years, 1953–1983',
Brewery History 187:23–40

ELEY, Matt (editor) 2019, *The Cask Report 2018/2019:
Cask reconsidered*, Cask Marque, cask-marque.
co.uk

ELLIS, William (as 'a person formerly concerned
in a public brewhouse in London') 1759,
The London and Country Brewer, 7th edition,
first published 1738, London: T Astley

ESCOFFIER, Auguste 1903, *Le guide culinaire:
Aide-mémoire de cuisine practique*, Paris: Escoffier

EVANS, Jeff 2011, 'The World Guide to Beer',
Brewery History 139:6–11

EVANS, Jeff 2013, *CAMRA's Good Bottled Beer Guide:
The best British real ales in a bottle*, 8th edition,
first published 1998, St Albans: CAMRA Books

EXMOOR ALES 2023, 'Exmoor Gold',
exmoorales.co.uk, accessed March 2023

FARRELL, T 2014, 'Over a barrel: a history of
Watney's Red', *Let's Look Again* 14 November
2014, letslookagain.com

FAULKNER, Frank 1884, *The Theory and Practice of
Modern Brewing*, revised and enlarged edition
of *The Art of Brewing*, first published 1876,
London: F W Lyon

FISH, Nick 2022 (editor), *British Beer and Pub
Association Statistical Handbook 2022: A compilation
of drinks industry statistics*, London: Brewing
Publications

FOLEY, Niamh 2021, *Pub Statistics*, Briefing Paper
8591, London: House of Commons Library

FOODCULT 2021, 'Brewing historical beer',
*FoodCult: Food, culture and identity in Ireland
c1550–1650*, foodcult.eu

FOY, C F 1955, *The Principles and Practice of Ale, Beer and
Stout Bottling*, London: Binsted & Sons

FULLER, Thomas 1840, *The History of the Worthies of
England Vol 2*, new edition, first published 1662,
London: Thomas Tegg

GADD, Eddie 2022, 'CO$_2$ capture in a small
brewery – a case study', *Gadds' BREWblog*
9 September 2022, gaddsbeershop.blogspot.
com

GARSHOL, Lars Marius 2018a, 'Raw ale', *Brew Your
Own* May–June 2018, byo.com

GARSHOL, Lars Marius 2018b, 'When did people
start reusing yeast?', *Larsblog* 29 April 2018,
garshol.priv.no/blog

GARSHOL, Lars Marius 2020, *Historical Brewing
Techniques: The lost art of farmhouse brewing*,
Boulder, CO: Brewers Publications

GARSHOL, Lars Marius 2022, 'The early history
of hops', *Larsblog*, 6 December 2022,
garshol.priv.no/blog

GESLEY, Jenny 2016, '500 Year Anniversary of
the Bavarian Beer Purity Law of 1516
("Reinheitsgebot")', *Library of Congress Blogs:
In custodia legis*, 21 April 2016, blogs.loc.gov

GIBB, Rebecca 2021, 'The birth of the wine
connoisseur', *GuildSomm* 16 April 2021,
guildsomm.com

GILLMAN, Gary 2017, 'Origins of the beer sparkler',
Beer et seq 12 November 2017, beeretseq.com

GILLMAN, Gary 2020, 'A UK "keg beer" in 1936. Part I',
Beer et seq 24 July 2020, beeretseq.com

GLOVER, Brian 1995, *Brewing for Victory: Brewers
beers and pubs in World War II*, Cambridge:
Lutterworth Press

GORHAM, Maurice 2011, *Back to the Local*, e-book
reprint, first published 1949, London: Faber
and Faber

GOURVISH T R and R G Wilson 1994, *The British
Brewing Industry 1830–1980*, Cambridge:
Cambridge University Press

GREENE KING and Belhaven 2018, *Cellar
Management Manual*, revision number 7.00,
Bury St Edmunds: Greene King

GREENWAY, Herbert H 1923, 'The beer cellar: its equipment and arrangement', in W Bently Capper (editor) 1923, *Licenced Houses and their Management* volume I, London: Caxton: 61–68

HADLAND, Laura 2021, *50 Years of CAMRA*, St Albans: CAMRA Books

HAINES, Emma (editor) 2023, *The Good Beer Guide 2024*, St Albans: CAMRA Books

HAM, John 1829, *The theory and practice of brewing, from malted and unmalted corn, and from potatos* [sic], London: Simpkin and Marshall

HANSCOMB, John (editor) 1974, *Good Beer Guide*, Leeds: John Waddington

HANSON, Neil 1983 (editor), *Good Beer Guide 1984*, St Albans: CAMRA Books

HARDMAN, Michael 1976a, *Beer Naturally*, London: Bergström + Boyle (no page numbers)

HARDMAN, Michael (editor) 1976b, *Good Beer Guide 1977*, St Albans: CAMRA Books

HARPER, D R 1980, 'Microbial contamination of draught beer in public houses', *Process Biochemistry* 16:1:2–7, 21

HARRISON, John 1991, *Old British Beers and How to Make Them*, 2nd edition, with members of the Durden Park Beer Circle, first published 1976, London: Durden Park Beer Circle

HARRISON, William 1889, *Elizabethan England: from 'A Description of England,' by William Harrison, in 'Holinshed's Chronicles'*, first published 1577, edited by Lothrop Withington, Camelot Series, London: Walter Scott, accessed at gutenberg.org

HEISS, Andreas G and 17 others 2020, 'Mashes to mashes, crust to crust. Presenting a novel microstructural marker for malting in the archaeological record', *PLoS ONE* 15:5:e0231696

HERBERT, James 1872, *The Art of Brewing India Pale Ale and Export Ale, Stock & Mild Ales, Porter & Stout*, 5th edition, first published 1865, Burton upon Trent: Herbert

HERZ, Karl O 1964, 'Tabernaemontanus on sixteenth-century beer', *Wallerstein Laboratories Communications* **27**:93/94:111–13

HIERONYMOUS, Stan 2012, *For the Love of Hops: The practical guide to aroma, bitterness and the culture of hops*, Boulder CO: Brewers Publications

HILDEGARD von Bingen 1998, *Hildegard von Bingen's Physica*, originally written c1158, translated by Priscilla Throop, Rochester VT: Healing Arts Press

HILTS, Carly 2021, 'Brewing up history: unearthing evidence for middle-Saxon malting at Sedgeford', *The Past* 30 August 2021, the-past.com

HIND, Herbert Lloyd 1938, *Brewing, science and practice Volume 1: Brewing materials*, London: Chapman and Hall

HIND, Herbert Lloyd 1940, *Brewing, science and practice Volume 2: Brewing processes*, London: Chapman and Hall

HM Revenue and Customs 2019, 'Alcohol duty rates from 1 February 2019', gov.uk

HM Revenue and Customs 2022, 'Reform of Alcohol Duty and Reliefs', Policy paper 23 September 2022, gov.uk

HM Treasury 2021, *Small Brewers Relief: Technical consultation*, London: HM Treasury, gov.uk

HOLMES, Bob 2017, *Flavor: The science of our most neglected sense*, New York NY: W W Norton

HOLMES, Frederic Lawrence 2003, 'Fermentation', in J L Heilbron (editor), *The Oxford Companion to the History of Modern Science* 297–298, Oxford: Oxford University Press

HORNSEY, Ian S 2003, *A History of Beer and Brewing*. London: Royal Society of Chemistry

HORNSEY, Ian S 2021 'Hop-growing in East Anglia', *Brewery History* 189:14–52

HORVATH, Cristina 2022, 'The secret of heather ale (fíon an fhraoich)', *Gaelic Algorithmic Research Group* 24 August 2022, blogs.ed.ac.uk/garg

HUTT, Christopher 1973, *The Death of the English Pub*, London: Arrow

INSTITUT PASTEUR 2022, 'Hygiène hospitalière: Louis Pasteur prône l'asepsie', *La lettre d'Institut Pasteur* 115:2, pasteur.fr

JACKSON, Michael 1977, *The World Guide to Beer: The brewing styles; the brands; the countries*, London: Quarto

JACKSON, Michael 1992, *The Great Beers of Belgium*, 2nd edition, first published 1991, Antwerpen: Coda

JACKSON, Michael 1993, *Michael Jackson's Beer Companion*, London: Mitchell Beazley

JAMES HUTTON INSTITUTE 2018, *Hops in Scotland: A rough guide for growers*, Aberdeen: James Hutton Institute, hutton.ac.uk

JEFFERY, E J 1956, *Brewing Theory and Practice*, 3rd edition, first published 1936, London: Nicholas Kaye

JENNER, Miles 2019, 'Brewing on the Bridge Wharf: A company history', unpublished manuscript

JOHNSON, Richard J and 8 others 2007, 'Potential role of sugar (fructose) in the epidemic of hypertension, obesity and the metabolic syndrome, diabetes, kidney disease, and cardiovascular disease', *American Journal of Clinical Nutrition* 86:899–906

JURADO, Jamie 2018, 'A brief (and condensed) history of the beer can', *Craft Beer and Brewing* 9 July 2018, beerandbrewing.com

KEG WATCH 2022, kegwatch.co.uk, accessed November 2022

KERSHAW, Roger 2015, 'The Carlisle Experiment – limiting alcohol in wartime', *The National Archives Blog* 15 January 2015, blog.nationalarchives.gov.uk

KING, Andrew J and J Richard Dickinson 2002, 'Biotransformation of hop aroma terpenoids by ale and lager yeasts', *FEMS Yeast Research* 3:1:53–62

KING, Frank A 1947, *Beer has a History*, London: Hutchinson

LAWRENCE, Margaret 1990, *The Encircling Hop: A history of hops and brewing*, Sittingbourne: SAWD

LEVESQUE, John 1854, *The Art of Brewing, and Fermenting, and Making Malt*, 5th edition, London: J Leath

'A LICENSEE' 1950, 'Notes Practical and Useful', in in W Bently Capper (editor) 1950, *Licenced Houses and their Management* volume I, 5th edition, London: Caxton: 28–31

LICKER, Jonathan and Terry Acree, Thomas Henick-Kling 1998, 'What is "Brett" (Brettanomyces) flavor? A preliminary investigation', *ACS Symposium Series* 714:96–115

LIU Li and Wang Jiajing, Danny Rosenberg, Zhao Hao, György Lengyel, Dani Nadel 2018, 'Fermented beverage and food storage in 13,000 y-old stone mortars at Raqefet Cave, Israel: Investigating Natufian ritual feasting', *Journal of Archaeological Science: Reports* 21:783–793

LLOYD, Gary 2023, 'Greene King to launch cask pins', *Morning Advertiser* 10 January 2023, morningadvertiser.co.uk

LOTT, Frank E 1895, 'Notes on the training of a brewer', *Journal of the Institute of Brewing* 1:2:177–194

LOTT, Frank E 1901, "Bottled beers', *Journal of the Institute of Brewing* 7:2:190–211

MACDONAGH, Oliver 1964, 'The origins of porter', *Economic History Review* 16:3:530–535

MAITLAND, Frederic William 1897, *Domesday Book and Beyond: Three essays in the early history of England*, Cambridge: Cambridge University Press

MALLETT, John 2014, *Malt: A practical guide from field to brewhouse*, Boulder CO: Brewers Publications

MARCHANT, W T (editor) 1888, *In Praise of Ale or Songs, ballads, epigrams, & anecdotes relating to beer, malt, and hops*, London: George Redway

MARCOS, Ascensión (editor) 2017, *Beer and Health Scientific Review: Moderate consumption as part of a healthy lifestyle*, 5th edition, updated, Wageningen: Kennisinstituut Bier, beerandhealth.eu

MARCOS, Ascensión and 5 others 2021, 'Moderate consumption of beer and its effects on cardiovascular and metabolic health: An updated review of recent scientific evidence', *Nutrients* 13:3:879

MARKHAM, Gervase 1623, *Countrey Contentments, or The English Huswife, containing the inward and outward vertues which ought to be in a compleate woman*, first published 1615, London: IB

MASALA, Francesco and Antony Seely, Matthew Keep 2023, 'Research briefing: The new alcohol duty system', *House of Commons Library* 4 April 2023, commonslibrary.parliament.uk

MASCALL, Leonard 1572, *A booke of the arte and maner, howe to plant and graffe all sortes of trees howe to set stones, and sowe pepines to make wylde trees to graffe on, as also remedies and medicine*, London: John Wight

MATHIAS, Peter 1959, *The Brewing Industry in England 1700–1830*, Cambridge: Cambridge University Press

McGOVERN, Patrick E and 12 others 2004, 'Fermented beverages of pre- and proto-historic China', *PNAS* 101:51:17593–17598

MEILGAARD, Morton C and C E Dalgliesh, J F Clapperton 1979, 'Beer flavour terminology', *Journal of the Institute of Brewing* 85:1:38–42

MEUSSDOERFFER, Franz G 2009, "A comprehensive history of beer brewing', in Hans Michael Eßlinger (editor), *Handbook of Brewing: Processes, technology, markets*, Weinheim: Wiley-VCH

MEW, James and John Ashton 1892, *Drinks of the World*, London: Leadenhall Press

MIDDLETON, Joe and Joanna Partridge 2023, 'UK pubs and restaurants cut winter hours to weather "perfect storm" in 2023', *The Guardian* 3 January 2023, theguardian.com

MILES, J G (editor) 1972, *Innkeeping: A manual for licensed victuallers*, for the National Trade Development Association, 6th edition, first published 1953, London: Barrie and Jenkins

MILK THE FUNK 2022, 'Brettanomyces', 'Kveik', 'Lactobacillus', 'Pediococcus', *Milk the Funk Wiki*, milkthefunk.com/wiki, accessed November 2022

MOLA Headland 2019, 'Earliest physical evidence of beer making process in Britain discovered on the A14C2H improvement scheme', *MOLA Headland Infrastructure* 30 January 2019, molaheadland.com

MONCKTON, H A 1966, *A History of English Ale and Beer*, London: Bodley Head

MONOPOLIES AND MERGERS COMMISSION (UK) 1989, *The Supply of Beer*, Cm 651, London: HMSO

MONOPOLIES COMMISSION (UK) 1969, *Beer: A report on the supply of beer*, London: HMSO

MORNING ADVERTISER 2022, 'Who says cask is in decline?', 30 November 2022, morningadvertiser.co.uk

MORITZ, Edward R and George H Morris 1891, *A Text-Book of the Science of Brewing*, London: E and F N Spon

MORITZ, Edward R 1899, Evidence, in Departmental Committee of Beer Materials 1899: 190–203

MORRICE, Alexander 1819, *A Practical Treatise on Brewing the Various Sorts of Malt Liquor*, 6th edition, London: Sherwood, Neely and Jones

MOSHER, Randy 2009, *Tasting Beer: An insider's guide to the world's greatest drink*, North Adams MA: Storey

NARZISS, Ludwig 1972, *Abriß der Bierbrauerei*, 3rd edition, Stuttgart: Ferdinand Enke

NATIONAL COLLECTION OF YEAST CULTURES 2022, *Catalogue*, ncyc.co.uk, accessed November 2022

NATIONAL HIGHWAYS 2022, 'Pints from the past', *National Highways* 18 May 2022, nationalhighways.co.uk

NATIONAL HUMAN GENOME RESEARCH INSTITUTE (US) 1996, 'International team completes DNA sequence of yeast', press release 24 April 1996, genome.gov

NATIONAL LIBRARY OF MEDICINE (US): National Center for Biotechnology Information 2023, *Genome*, ncbi.nlm.nih.gov, accessed February 2023

NEVE, R A 1991, *Hops*, London: Chapman and Hall

NHS (National Health Service UK) 2019, 'The risks of drinking too much' and 'Alcohol units', nhs.uk

NHS (National Health Service UK) 2020, 'Calories in alcohol', nhs.uk

NODDER, Caroline 2022, *The SIBA Craft Beer Report 2022*, Ripon: SIBA, siba.co.uk

NODDER, Caroline 2023, *The SIBA Craft Beer Report 2023*, Ripon: SIBA, siba.co.uk

O'BRIEN, Ivar 1992, 'Flowers Original Part 2', *Brewery History* 70:32

O'DONNELL, John 2015, 'When is a keg not a keg? Real ale from key-kegs explained', *Opening Times* November 2015, amended version in *What's Brewing* December 2015, thcamra.org.uk

O'NEILL, Patrick 2020, *Cellarmanship: How to keep and serve real ale*, St Albans: CAMRA Books

OGLE, Maureen 2006, *Ambitious Brew: The story of American Beer*. Orlando FL: Harcourt

OLIVER, Garrett 2003, *The Brewmaster's Table: Discovering the pleasures of real beer with real food*, New York NY: Ecco

OLIVER, Garrett (editor) 2012, *The Oxford Companion to Beer*, New York, NY: Oxford University Press

OLSEN, Kirstin 1999, *Daily Life in 18th-century England*, Westport CT: Greenwood Press

ONE HUNDRED YEARS OF BREWING: A complete history of the progress made in the art, science and industry of brewing in the world, particularly during the last century 1903, authors uncredited, Chicago IL: H S Rich

OWEN, C C 1987, 'The history of brewing in Burton upon Trent', *Journal of the Institute of Brewing* 93:1:37–41

PAJIC, Milan 2019, '"Ale for an Englishman is a natural drink": the Dutch and the origins of beer brewing in late medieval England', *Journal of Medieval History* 45:3:285–300

PALMER, John and Colin Kaminski 2013, *Water: A comprehensive guide for brewers*, Boulder CO: Brewers Publications

PAPIN, Kristof 2004, 'De hophandel tijdens de Middeleeuwen in Noord- en Midden-Europa (13de–16de eeuw)', *Handelingen der Maatschappij voor Geschiedenis en Oudheidkunde te Gent* 58:1:105–146

PARTINGTON, Eric R 2003, 'Barrels: Beer making', in Benjamin Caballero (ed), *Encyclopedia of Food Sciences and Nutrition* Volume 1:383–393, London: Academic Press

PASTEUR, Louis 1865, 'Nouvelles observations au sujet de la conservation des vins', *Comptes rendus hebdomadaires des séances de l'Académie des sciences* 61:274–278

PASTEUR, Louis 1866, *Études sur le vin, ses maladies, causes qui les provoquent, procédés nouveaux pour le conserver et pour le vieillir*, Paris: Victor Masson et fils

PASTEUR, Louis 1879, *Studies on Fermentation: The diseases of beer, their causes, and the means of preventing them*, translated by Frank Faulkner, D Constable Robb from Pasteur 1928 [1876], London: Macmillan and Co

PASTEUR, Louis 1928, *Études sur la bière, ses maladies, causes qui les provoquent, procédé pour la rendre inaltérable, avec une théorie nouvelle de la fermentation, Œuvres de Pasteur 10*, originally published 1876 (see Pasteur 1879 for English translation), Paris: Victor Masson et fils

PATTINSON, Ronald 2008, 'Average OG UK beer 1900–1993', *Shut up about Barclay Perkins* 11 January 2008, barclayperkins.blogspot.com

PATTINSON, Ronald 2009, *1909! Beer style guide*, Amsterdam: Kilderkin

PATTINSON, Ronald 2011, 'A short history of mild', *Beer Advocate* 49 February 2011, beeradvocate.com

PATTINSON, Ronald 2012, 'X ale grists in the 1860's', *Shut Up About Barclay Perkins* 28 November 2012, barclayperkins.blogspot.com

PATTINSON, Ronald 2013, *War!*, Amsterdam: Kilderkin

PATTINSON, Ronald 2021, 'What was AK?', *Shut Up About Barclay Perkins* 8 June 2021, barclayperkins.blogspot.com

PEARSON, Lynn 1999, *British Breweries: An architectural history*, London: Hambledon Press

PEPYS, Samuel 1893, *The Diary of Samuel Pepys MA FRS, Clerk of the Acts and Secretary to the Admiralty*, written 1660–1669, London: George Bell, accessed at pepysdiary.com

PEREIRA, Jonathan 1843, *Treatise on Food and Diet*, London: Longman, Brown, Green and Longmans

PLACEWAY, Paul 1998, 'Recreating medieval English ales: a recreation of late 13th–14th c. unhopped English ales', *Tofi Kerþjalfadsson*, cs.cmu.edu/~pwp/tofi

PLINY THE ELDER (Gaius Plinius Secundus) 1855, *The Natural History*, written c79 CE, translated by John Bostock and H T Riley, accessed at perseus.tufts.edu

PLINY THE ELDER (Gaius Plinius Secundus) 1906, *Naturalis Historia* Volume 14, written c79 CE, edited by Karl Friedrich Theodor Mayhoff, Leipzig: Teubner, accessed at penelope.uchicago.edu

POOLE, Thomas 1781, *A Treatise on Strong Beer, Ale, &c. fully explaining the Art of Brewing, in the best manner*, London: Poole

POSADA, J 1987, 'Filtration of beer', in J R A Pollock (editor) 1987, *Brewing Science* Volume 3, London: Academic Press:380–439

PRATT, Edwin A 1907, *The Licensed Trade: an independent survey*, London: John Murray

PREISS, Richard and Caroline Tyrawa, Kristoffer Krogerus, Lars Marius Garshol, George van der Merwe 2018, 'Traditional Norwegian kveik are a genetically distinct group of domesticated *Saccharomyces cerevisiae* brewing yeasts', *Frontiers in Microbiology* 12 September 2018, frontiersin.org

PROTZ, Roger 1978, *Pulling a Fast One: What the brewers have done to your beer*, London: Pluto

PROTZ, Roger 1995, *The Ale Trail*, Orpington: Eric Dobby

PROTZ, Roger 2010, 'Marston's unveils cask revolution', *Morning Advertiser* 16 March 2010, morningadvertiser.co.uk

PROTZ, Roger 2014, 'Tied hand and foot: the sad and sorry saga of the rise of Britain's giant "pubcos"', *Protz On Beer* 27 December 2014, protzonbeer.co.uk

PROTZ, Roger 2015, 'DBA: Gone for a Burton', *Protz On Beer* 6 January 2015, protzonbeer.co.uk

PROTZ, Roger 2016, 'Annick's gruut beer is the spice of life', *Protz on Beer* 31 January 2016, protzonbeer.co.uk

PROTZ, Roger 2018, '40 years on, Big Beer still rules the roost', *Protz On Beer* 24 August 2018, protzonbeer.co.uk

PROTZ, Roger 2020, *The Family Brewers of Britain: A celebration of British brewing heritage*, St Albans: CAMRA Books

PROTZ, Roger and Graham Lawley 1990, 'AGM 1990', *What's Brewing* May 1990

PUBLIC HEALTH ENGLAND 2016, *Government Dietary Recommendations: Government recommendations for energy and nutrients for males and females aged 1–18 years and 19+ years*, London: Public Health England, gov.uk

QUEEN'S COLLEGE Oxford 2017, 'Queen's College brewhouse history', *Brewery History Wiki*, breweryhistory.com

RAZZALL, Ed 2014, 'A hastily written piece on cellarmanship', *The Beer Thinker* 12 May 2014, thebeerthinker.wordpress.com, archived at web.archive.org

REES, Abraham 1972, 'Porter', *Rees's Manufacturing Industry Volume Four: A selection from The Cyclopaedia; or Universal Dictionary of Arts, Sciences and Literature*, first published 1814, edited by Neil Cossons, London: David and Charles Reprints: 193–201

RENGER R S and S H van Hateren, K Ch A M
Luben 1992, 'The formation of esters and
higher alcohols during brewery fermentation:
The effect of carbon dioxide pressure',
Journal of the Institute of Brewing 98:6:509–513

RICHARDSON, John 1798, *The Philosophical Principles
of the Science of Brewing*, 2nd edition, first
published 1788, Hull: Richardson

ROBERTS, William H 1837, *The Scottish Ale Brewer:
A practical treatise on the art of brewing ales according
to the system practised in Scotland*, Edinburgh:
Oliver and Boyd

ROBERSTON, Luke 2019, 'Goon of fortune –
the enduring shelf life of bag-in-box beer',
Good Beer Hunting 28 August 2019,
goodbeerhunting.com

ROSS-MACKENZIE, John 1927, *A Standard Manual
of Brewing and Malting and Laboratory Companion*,
revised and expanded version of Wright 1897,
London: Technical Press

ROWLAND, Peter 1975, *Lloyd George*, London:
Barrie and Jenkins

SALAMON, Alfred Gordon 1890, Evidence, Select
Committee on the Hop Industry 1890:114–140

SALTONSTALL, Phil 2020, 'Brewers urge CAMRA
rethink over discounting real ale', *Brass Castle
Blog* 28 February 2020, brasscastle.co.uk

SALZMANN, L F 1913, *English Industries in the Middle
Ages: Being an introduction to the industrial history of
Medieval England*, London: Constable, accessed
at gutenberg.org

SAMBROOK, Pamela 1996, *Country House Brewing in
England 1500–1900*, London: Hambledon Press

SCHIPPERS, Hans 1992, 'Bier', in H W Lintsen
(editor) 1992, *Geschiedenis van de techniek in
Nederland: De wording van een moderne samenleving
1800–1890 Vol 1*, Zutphen: Walburg: 170–213

SCHUMACHER, E F 2011, *Small is Beautiful: A study of
economics as if people mattered*, new edition, first
published 1973, London: Vintage

SCOT, Reynolde 1576, *A Perfite Platforme of a Hoppe
Garden, and necessarie instructions for the making
and maytenaunce thereof*, revised edition, first
published 1574, London: Henrie Denham

SEAR, Richard 1971, 'The sobering truth about the
British pint', *Sunday Mirror* 21 March 1971:24–25

SELECT COMMITTEE ON THE HOP INDUSTRY
1890, Report and minutes of evidence,
Parliamentary Papers 1890: 302

SETH, Yvan 2014, 'Three cask ale (semi)fallacies'
and 'Followup: Cask ale fallacies', *Ale.is.Good*
12 and 18 May 2014, ale.gd/blog, archived at
web.archive.org

SHANNON, R 1805, *A Practical Treatise on Brewing,
Distilling, and Rectification*, London: Robert
Scholey

SHARP (Sedgeford Historical and Archaeological
Research Project) 2018, 'Our research', *SHARP*,
sharp.org.uk

SHIMWELL, John L 1947, 'Brettanomyces', *American
Brewer* 80 May 1947:21–22, 56–57

SIBA (Society of Independent Brewers) 2023, *SIBA
UK Brewery Tracker*, siba.co.uk/brewerytracker,
accessed May 2023

SIGSWORTH, E M 1965, 'Science and the brewing
industry 1850–1900', *Economic History Review*
17:3:536–550

SLAUGHTER, Michael (editor) 2007, *Scotland's True
Heritage Pubs: Pub interiors of special historic interest*,
St Albans: CAMRA Books

SMAGALSKI, Carolyn 2023, 'How to interpret the
Meilgaard flavor wheel', *BellaOnline Beer and
Brewing*, bellaonline.com/articles/art62988.asp,
accessed January 2023

SMITH, Annabel 2022, 'Why is there a "north-south"
divide on the way cask ale is served?', *CAMRA
Learn and Discover*, accessed December 2022,
camra.org.uk

SMITH, Annabel and Lisa Harlow 2018, *The Gender
Pint Gap: A study into GB female attitudes and
behaviours towards beer*, Dea Latis, dealatis.org.uk

SOCIETY FOR THE PRESERVATION OF BEERS FROM
THE WOOD (SPBW) 2006, 'History and aims',
SPBW, spbw.beer, accessed March 2023

SOUTHBY, Edmund Richard 1885, *A Systematic
Handbook of Practical Brewing*, 2nd edition,
London: Southby

SPAKE, Neil 2005, 'The Shilling system', *Scottish
Brewing*, scottishbrewing.com

SPARROW, Jeff 2005, *Wild Brews: Beer beyond the
influence of brewer's yeast*, Boulder CO: Brewers
Publications

SPENCE, Charles 2015, 'On the psychological
impact of food colour', *Flavour* 4:21

SPICER, John and Chris Thurman, John Walters,
Simon Ward 2012, *Intervention in the Modern UK
Brewing Industry*, Basingstoke: Palgrave
Macmillan

ST AUSTELL FAMILY GROUP 2022, *Trade Quality
Manual*, St Austell: St Austell

STACK, Martin 2003, 'A concise history of America's
brewing industry', in Robert Whaples (editor),
EH.net Encyclopedia 4 July 2003, eh.net

STEEL, James 1878, *Selection of the Practical Points of
Malting and Brewing and Strictures Thereon, for the
use of brewery proprietors*, Glasgow: Steel

STOKHOLM, Arnbjørn and Thomas H Shellhammer 2020, *Hop creep – Technical brief*, Boulder CO: Brewers Association, brewersassocation.org

STOPES, Henry S 1895, *Brewery Companies*, first published as a series of articles in *The Statist* 1894, London: The Statist

STRABO 1903, *Geography Book V: Italy*, written c25 BCE–20 CE, translated by H C Hamilton and W Falconer, accessed at perseus.tufts.edu

STRONG, Gordon and Kristen England 2021, *Beer Judge Certification Program 2021 Style Guidelines: Beer style guidelines*, BJCP, bjcp.org

SUMNER, James 2016, *Brewing Science, Technology and Print, 1700–1880*, Pittsburgh PA: University of Pittsburgh Press

SYKES, Walter J 1907, *The Principles and Practice of Brewing*, 3rd edition revised with Arthur R Ling, first published 1897, London: Charles Griffin

TABERNAEMONTANUS (Theodor von Bergzabern) 1588, 'Of beer' in *Kräuterbuch*: see Herz 1964

TACITUS, Publius Cornelius 1942, *Germania*, written c98 CE, translated by Alfred John Church and William Jackson Brodribb, accessed at perseus.tufts.edu

TALAVERA PÉREZ, Karel and Yuzo Ninomiya, Chris Winkel, Thomas Voets, B Nilius 2007, 'Influence of temperature on taste perception', *Cellular and Molecular Science* 64:4:377–381

TAYLOR, John 1651, *Ale ale-vated into the ale-titude: or, a learned oration before a civill assembly of ale-drinkers*, London: Taylor, accessed at quod.lib.umich.edu

TEICH, Mikuláš and Dorothy M Needham 1992, *A Documentary History of Biochemistry 1770–1940*, Leicester: Leicester University Press

THAUSING, Julius E 1882, *The Theory and Practice of the Preparation of Malt and the Fabrication of Beer, with special reference to the Vienna system of brewing*, translated by William T Brannt, edited and adapted by A Schwarz and A H Bauer, Philadelphia PA: Henry Carey Baird and Co

THOMAS, Keith 2017, 'Carbonation & oxidation in traditional UK cask ale', *Zymurgy* September/October 2017:31–38

THOMAS OF ECCLESTON 1909, *The Chronicle of Thomas of Eccleston (De adventu fratrum minorum in Angliam)*, written c1258, translated by Father Cuthbert, accessed at archive.org

THOMSON, Thomas (uncredited) 1824, 'Brewing', *Supplement to the Fourth, Fifth and Sixth Editions of the Encyclopædia Britannica* Volume 2:460–492, Edinburgh: Archibald Constable

TIZARD, William L 1857, *The Theory and Practice of Brewing*, 4th edition, first published 1848, London: Tizard

TOMLINSON, Thom 1994, 'India Pale Ale, Part I: IPA and Empire – necessity and enterprise', *Brewing Techniques* **2**.2, accessed at morebeer.com

TRIPP, C Howard 1892, *Brewery Management*, collection of revised versions of articles originally published in *The Brewers" Journal*, London: F W Lyon

TRYON, Thomas 1691, *A New Art of Brewing Beer, Ale, and other Sorts of Liquors*, 3rd edition, first published 1690, London: Salusbury

TUBB, D B 1966, *Kent Pubs*, London: Batsford

TURNER, Robin 2012, 'Beer Here Now: Craft Brewing – 2012 in a Pint Glass', *Huffington Post* 8 January 2012, huffingtonpost.co.uk

TWEDE, Diana 2005, 'The cask age: the technology and history of wooden barrels', *Packaging Technology and Science* 18:5:253–264

UNGER, Richard W 2004, *Beer in the Middle Ages and the Renaissance*, Philadelphia PA: University of Pennsylvania Press

VAIZEY, John 1958, 'The brewing industry' in P Lesley COOK (editor), *Effects of Mergers: Six Studies*, London: George Allen and Unwin: 397–422

VAIZEY, John 1960, *The Brewing Industry 1886–1951: An economic study*, London: Sir Isaac Pitman

VAN DEN STEEN, Jef 2011, *Geuze & Kriek: Het geheim van de lambik*, Tielt: Lannoo

VAN OEVELEN, D and M Spaepen, P Timmermans, H Verachtert 1977, 'Microbiological aspects of spontaneous wort fermentation in the production of lambic and gueuze', *Journal of the Institute of Brewing* 83:6:356–360

VERBERG, Susan 2018, 'The rise and fall of Gruit', *Brewery History* 174:46–79

VIANET 2020, *Beer Insight Report 2019/20: The profit opportunity from every drop*, cask-marque.co.uk

VON BINGEN, Hildegard: see Hildegard von Bingen

WAHL, Robert and Max Henius 1902, *American Handy Book of the Brewing, Malting and Auxiliary Trades*, 2nd edition, Chicago IL: Wahl and Henius

WAITE, Lily 2021, 'In Great Britain, how you serve cask ale is a matter of regional pride', *Wine Enthusiast* 26 March 2021, winemag.com

WALKER, Neil 2022, 'Taming the wildflowers – the beautiful and distinctive house yeasts of British brewing', *Good Beer Hunting*, 22 June 2022, goodbeerhunting.com

WANG Jiajing and Jiang Leping, Sun Hanlong 2021, 'Early evidence for beer drinking in a 9000-year-old platform mound in southern China', *PLoS ONE* 16:8:e0255833, journals.plos.org/plosone

WARD, Edward (uncredited) 1866?, *A Vade Mecum for Malt-Worms: or, a Guide to Good Fellows*, undated reprint, first published c1715, London: T Bickerton

WATKINS, George 1767, *The Compleat English Brewer, or, the Whole Art and Mystery of Brewing in all its various branches*, London: J Cooke

WEBB, Tim 1992, *The Good Beer Guide to Belgium and Holland*, St Albans: Verulam

WEBB, Tim and Chris Pollard, Siobhan McGinn 2010, *LambicLand: a journey round the most unusual beers in the world*, 2nd edition, first published 2004, Cambridge: Cogan & Mater

WEBB, Tim and Stephen Beaumont 2020, *World Atlas of Beer: The essential guide to the beers of the world*, 3rd edition, first published 2012, London: Mitchell Beazley

WEBSTER, Ian 2018, *Brewing in Burton upon Trent*, Stroud: Amberley

WELLER, Rebecca 2023, 'Pint price up 8p in 3 months', *Morning Advertiser* 23 February 2023, morningadvertiser.co.uk

WHITE, Chris 1999, 'Fermentation timeline', *Brew Your Own* January 1999, byo.com

WHITE, Chris and Jamil Zainasheff 2010, *Yeast: the practical guide to beer fermentation*, Boulder CO: Brewers Publications

WILES, A E 1953, 'Identification and significance of yeasts encountered in the brewery', *Journal of the Institute of Brewing* 59:4:265–284

WILMUT, Roger (editor) 1989, *The Complete Monty Python's Flying Circus: Just the Words* Volume 2, London: Methuen

WILSON, D Gay 1975, 'Plant remains from the Graveney boat and the early history of *Humulus lupulus* L in W Europe', *New Phytologist* 75:627–548

WILSON, George B 1940, *Alcohol and the Nation: A contribution to the study of the liquor problem in the United Kingdom from 1800 to 1935*, London: Nicholson and Watson

WRIGHT, Herbert Edwards 1897, *A Handy Book for Brewers, being a practical guide to the art of brewing and malting*, 2nd edition, first published 1892, London: Crosby Lockwood and Son, see also Ross-Mackenzie 1927

WU, Sylvia 2019, 'How is sake made – ask *Decanter*', *Decanter* 15 November 2019, decanter.com

YATES, Donald 2006, 'John Matthews: Father of the Soda Fountain', *Bottles and Extras* Summer 2006:72–75

Author's acknowledgements

Thanks to: Katie Button, formerly of CAMRA Books, for initially expressing interest in this project; her successor, the very patient Alan Murphy, for commissioning and editing it; Dale Tomlinson, not only for designing it but being so enthusiastic about it from the first; Jaega Wise, who got me started leading brewery tours and helped me think about how best to communicate the brewing process; the staff at the British Library, particularly in the Rare Books and Music and Humanities I reading rooms where I did a good deal of the desk work – the first time, though hopefully not the last, that I've made use of their astonishingly helpful and efficient services and facilities; Iain Loe, who once let me into the CAMRA archive to take notes that have since proved their worth many times over; Tim Hampson, particularly for his flexibility with other deadlines; publisher Jo Copestick and *Brewery History* editor Tim Holt for encouraging me when this was just something I talked about a lot; Randy Mosher, for letting us use the latest version of his flavour sprial; Collette Brown, Pete Brown (the Forest Road one), Ryan Gleave, Nick Goodwin, Mateusz Luturek, Nigel Poore, Jamie Price, Jonathan Rogers and Stephen Spencer for supporting my writing; all those authors who set the bar with their big and serious beer books, and particularly Jessica Boak and Ray Bailey, Pete Brown (the beer writer one), Martyn Cornell, Michael Jackson, Maureen Ogle and Tim Webb; all the people I visited, spoke to or corresponded with in connection with this book, both knowingly and unknowingly, who are listed individually at the end; and my family, Adèle de Moor, Sunny Sohanta Singh and, last but by no means least, Ian Harris. Yes, Ian, another bloody book, and this time I've asked if it's cask.

Besides published texts, this book draws on extensive personal conversations and correspondence with a wide variety of individuals, most of them taking place during 2022 and 2023 when I visited numerous breweries and other venues and arranged other conversations specifically with this purpose in mind. Here is the list of the people I spoke to:

Darron Anley, *founder and owner, Siren Craft Brew, Finchampstead, Wokingham*
Bruce Ash, *brewing manager, Woodforde's Brewery, Woodbastwick, Norfolk*
James Atherton, *co-owner, co-founder, Beerblefish Brewery, London*
Sean Ayling, *head brewer, director, Tom's Tap and Brewhouse, Crewe, Cheshire*
Barry Badger, *brewer, Butcombe Brewing, Cox's Green, North Somerset*
Ray Bailey, *beer and pubs historian, blogger, Bristol*
Sara Barton, *founder, head brewer, Brewster's Brewery, Grantham, Lincolnshire*
Stuart Bateman, *managing director, George Bateman and Son, Wainfleet, Lincolnshire*
Alice Batham, *head brewer, Bathams Brewery (Daniel Batham & Son), Brierley Hill, Dudley*
Stephen Beaumont, *beer writer and educator, Toronto, Ontario*
Robert Bell, *head brewer, Hogshead Brewery, Denver, Colorado*
John Bexon, *former head brewer, Greene King, Bury St Edmunds, Suffolk*
Dave Blanchard, *owner, Brick Store Pub, Decatur, Georgia*
Jessica Boak, *beer and pubs historian, blogger, Bristol*
Frank Boon, *founder, owner, Brouwerij Boon, Lembeek, Vlaams-Brabant*
William Bott, *head brewer, Titanic Brewery, Burslem, Stoke-on-Trent*

Colin Brooks, *co-founder, co-owner, Spartan Brewery, London SE16*
Dom Bowcutt, *tour leader, Hukins Hops, St Michaels, Kent*
Pete Brown, *beer writer, consultant, London*
Will Calvert, *co-founder, director, Windsor & Eton Brewery, Windsor*
Mark Carpenter, *former brewmaster, Anchor Brewing, San Francisco, California*
Susan Chisholm, *quality control manager, Greene King, Bury St Edmunds, Suffolk*
James Clarke, *managing director, Hook Norton Brewery, Hook Norton, Oxfordshire*
Ben Collard, *brewery manager, Chiltern Brewery, Terrick, Aylesbury, Buckinghamshire*
Matt Cooper, *assistant brewer, Castle Rock Brewery, Nottingham*
Martyn Cornell, *brewing historian, beer writer, Cromer, Norfolk*
Christine Cryne, *CAMRA tasting panel chair and former director, tasting expert, London*
John Cryne, *secretary, London Brewers Alliance, London*
Brad Cummings, *co-founder, chief executive, Tiny Rebel, Newport/Casnewydd, South Wales*
Gianluca d'Andrea, *head brewer, Southwark Brewing, London SE1*
Yvan De Baets, *head brewer, founder, Brasserie de la Senne/Zennebrouwerij, Brussels*
Jamie Delap, *managing director, Fyne Ales, Cairndow, Argyll and Bute*
Tim Dewey, *chief executive, Timothy Taylor's Brewery, Keighley, Bradford, West Yorkshire*
Bill Dobson, *head brewer, S A Brain & Company, Cardiff*
Mark Dorber, *leaseholder, Anchor, Walberswick, Suffolk*
Malcolm Downie, *head brewer, Fyne Ales, Cairndow, Argyll*
Dominic Driscoll, *production manager, Thornbridge Brewery, Bakewell, Derbyshire*
Steve Dunkley, *founder, brewer, Beer Nouveau, Manchester*
Jonathan Edger, *brewery manager, Castle Rock Brewery, Nottingham*
Greg Engert, *co-owner, Bluejacket Brewery, ChurchKey beer bar, Washington DC*
Euan Findlay, *cooper, T&R Theakston, Masham, North Yorkshire*
Fergus Fitzgerald, *production director, Adnams, Southwold, Suffolk*
Andrew Ford, *general and cellar manager, Hand in Hand, London SW19*
Steve Foster, *brewer, Brewster's Brewery, Grantham, Lincolnshire*
Oliver Fozard, *head brewer, Roosters Brewing Co, Harrogate, North Yorkshire*
Tom Fozard, *commercial director, Roosters Brewing Co, Harrogate, North Yorkshire*
Theo Freyne, *founder, Deya Brewing, Cheltenham, Gloucestershire*
Eddie Gadd, *co-founder, head brewer, Gadds' The Ramsgate Brewery, Broadstairs, Kent*
David Glenwright, *head of marketing, Titanic Brewery, Burslem, Stoke-on-Trent*
Steve Hamburg, *beer writer, cellar consultant, Chicago, Illinois*
John Hatch, *brewer, tour guide, Ram Brewery (Sambrook's), London SW18*
Justin Hawke, *owner, head brewer, Moor Beer, Bristol*
Adrienne Heslin, *owner, head brewer, Beoir Chorcha Dhuibhne/West Kerry brewery, An Riasc, Kerry*
Gillian Hough, *chair, CAMRA Real Ale, Cider and Perry Campaigns Committee, Derby*
Ben Hughes, *founder, head brewer, Jawbone Brewing, Twickenham, London*
Mark Hyson, *head of sales, Stewart Brewing, Loanhead, Midlothian*
Joseph Ince, *head of production, Marble Beers, Salford (Manchester)*
Peter Jackson, *founder, managing director, Southwark Brewing, London SE1*
Phil Janke, *head brewer, Donnington Brewery, Stow-on-the-Wold, Gloucestershire*
Miles Jenner, *head brewer and joint managing director, Harvey's Brewery, Lewes, East Sussex*
Paddy Johnson, *co-founder, director, Windsor & Eton Brewery, Windsor*
Nick Jones, *off trade and export manager, Oakham Ales, Peterborough*
Mike Jordan, *head brewer, Butcombe Brewing, Cox's Green, North Somerset*
Mary Beth Keefe, *brewmaster, co-owner, Granite Brewery, Toronto, Ontario*

John Keeling, *former brewing director, Fuller's Griffin Brewery, London W4*

Andrew Leman, *head brewer, Timothy Taylor's Brewery, Keighley, Bradford, West Yorkshire*

David Liechty, *general manager, Hogshead Brewery, Denver, Colorado*

Rob Lovatt, *production director, Thornbridge Brewery, Bakewell, Derbyshire*

Stu MacLachlan, *stockman, Fyne Ales, Cairndow, Argyll & Bute*

David McGovern, *head brewer, Chiltern Brewery, Terrick, Aylesbury, Buckinghamshire*

Angus McKean, *general and cellar manager, Red Lion, London SW13*

Toby McKenzie, *co-founder, head brewer, Redwillow Brewery, Macclesfield, Cheshire*

Paige Martin, *brand manager, Butcombe Brewing, Cox's Green, North Somerset*

Geoff Mumford, *co-founder, co-owner, Burton Bridge Brewery, Burton upon Trent*

Carmen Nueno-Palop, *yeast specialist, head of collection, National Collection of Yeast Cultures, Norwich*

Paul Nunny, *executive director, Cask Marque, Colchester, Essex*

Owen Ogletree, *founder, Atlanta Cask Ale Tasting, tour leader, Atlanta, Georgia*

Ross O'Hara, *head of brewing, Greene King, Bury St Edmunds, Suffolk*

Evin O'Riordain, *founder, brewer, The Kernel Brewery, London*

Nicky Onorati, *cellar manager, Vat and Fiddle, Nottingham*

Ron Pattinson, *brewing historian, blogger, Amsterdam*

Roger Protz, *beer writer, campaigner, St Albans, Hertfordshire*

Roger Ryman, *former brewing director, St Austell Brewery, St Austell, Cornwall*

Dan Scott Paul, *head brewer, Black Sheep Brewery, Masham, North Yorkshire*

Nigel Sadler, *trainer, Cask Marque assessor, former brewer, Chelmsford, Essex*

Duncan Sambrook, *founder, managing director, Sambrook's Brewery, London SW18*

Craig Scotland, *head brewer, Stewart Brewing, Loanhead, Midlothian*

Rob Shacklock, *chair, Society for the Preservation of Beers from the Wood (SPBW), licensee, master cellarman, Newcastle upon Tyne*

Ed Sharman, *lead brewer, Oakham Ales, Peterborough*

Mark Slater, *head brewer, T&R Theakston, Masham, North Yorkshire*

Andy Slee, *chief executive, SIBA, Ripon, North Yorkshire*

Annabel Smith, *Cask Marque head of training, writer, consultant, Leeds*

Holly Smith, *communications manager, Greene King, Bury St Edmunds, Suffolk*

Mike Smith, *general manager, Bow Bar, Edinburgh*

Tom Stainer, *chief executive, CAMRA (Campaign for Real Ale), St Albans, Hertfordshire*

Jo Stewart, *co-founder, Stewart Brewing, Loanhead, Midlothian*

Geoff Strawbridge, *CAMRA London regional director, London*

Alison Taffs, *tasting expert and trainer, co-owner, the Hop Inn, Hornchurch, London*

Mark Tetlow, *head brewer, Oakham Ales, Peterborough*

Simon Theakston, *joint managing director, T&R Theakston, Masham, North Yorkshire*

Lloyd Thomas, *assistant and cellar manager, Bow Bar, Edinburgh*

Rupert Thompson, *owner, Hogs Back Brewery, Tongham, Surrey*

Catherine Tonry, *Great British Beer Festival organiser, technical director, CAMRA (Campaign for Real Ale), London*

Emma Watts, *trade quality manager, Fuller's Griffin Brewery, London W4*

Tim Webb, *beer writer, campaigner, beer opinionist, Devon*

Yvonne Wernlein, *technical brewer, Fyne Ales, Cairndow, Argyll and Bute*

Robert Wicks, *founder and head brewer, Westerham Brewery, Kent*

Katie Wiles, *senior communications manager, CAMRA (Campaign for Real Ale), St Albans, Hertfordshire*

Bruce Wilkinson, *co-founder, co-owner, Burton Bridge Brewery, Burton upon Trent*

Mike Willetts, *co-founder, co-owner, Spartan Brewery, London SE16*

Gazz Williams, *co-founder, head of beer, Tiny Rebel, Newport/Casnewydd, South Wales*

George Young, *brewing director, St Austell Brewery, St Austell, Cornwall*

Index

Page numbers in **bold** indicate pages where a word is defined or a topic considered in greatest detail.